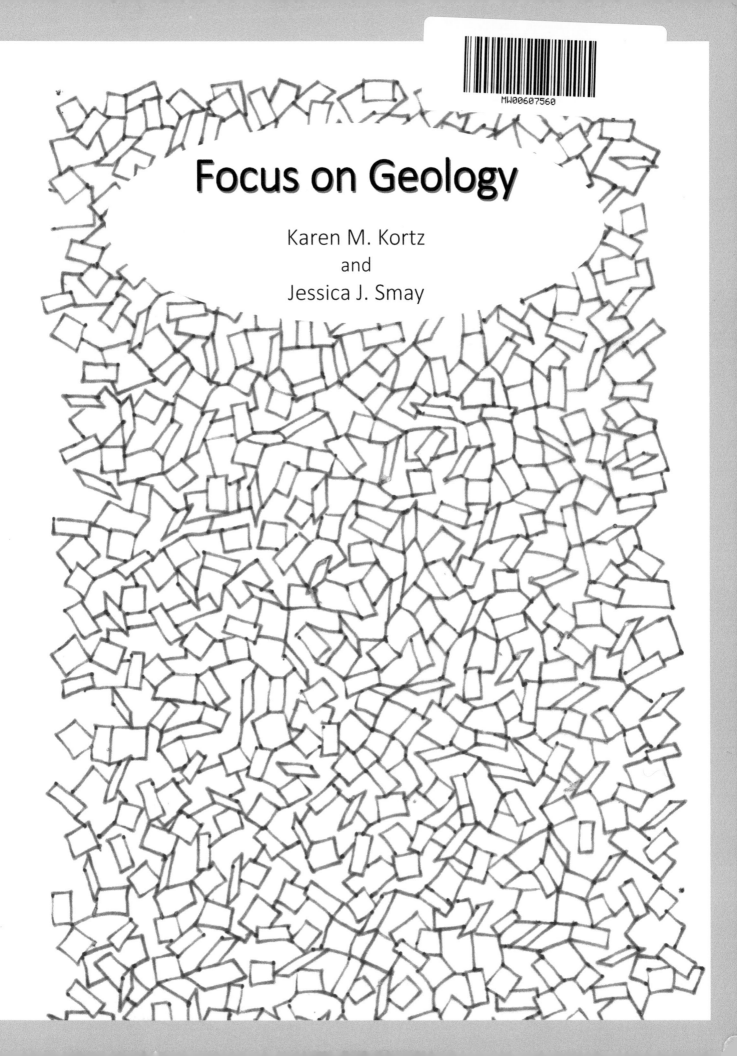

# Focus on Geology

Karen M. Kortz
and
Jessica J. Smay

MW00607560

# Focus on Geology
## Kortz and Smay

### The Authors

We have a history of collaborating together. In particular, we have published *Lecture Tutorials for Geoscience* and *Lecture Tutorials for Earth Science*. Lecture Tutorials are designed to help increase student learning during lecture by making it more interactive and addressing misconceptions. Information about Lecture Tutorials can be found on the SERC website: https://serc.carleton.edu/30439.1298

Karen M. Kortz is a professor of Geology at the Community College of Rhode Island. She received her Ph.D. from the University of Rhode Island, M.S. from Brown University, and B.A. from Pomona College, all in geology.

Jessica J. Smay is a professor of Earth and Space Science at the San Jose City College. She received her M.S. in Geology from the University of California, Santa Barbara, and B.A. in Geology from Pomona College.

### Acknowledgments

We'd like to thank Brian and Gregory for everything you have done to make this book possible. Without your support, we could not have accomplished everything we have done.

We'd also like to thank our Faculty Advisory Board for all your detailed input and encouragement: Jennifer Anderson, Mariela Bao, Joshua Caulkins, Brett Gilley, Kyle Gray, Laura Guertin, Tessa Hill, Kaatje Kraft, Katherine Ryker, Ian Saginor, Cindy Shellito, LeAnne Teruya, Karen Viskupic, Emily Ward, Christine Witkowski, and Tarin Weiss.

We use research-based approaches to increase student learning throughout this textbook. Thank you to the researchers who have done this important work.

Thank you to Dawn Cardace, Sanhita Datta, Eric Grosfils, Ben Jager, Kyle Jager, Sharon Jager, Brian Kortz, Nathan Nelson, Stephanie Pearson, and Beverly Smay for being in or letting us use your awesome photographs.

Thank you, Blythe. This work is so much better because of you.

Partial support for this work was provided by the National Science Foundation's Transforming Undergraduate Education in Science, Technology, Engineering and Mathematics (TUES) program under Award No. 1244881.

© 2019
ISBN 978-1-7326296-1-5

# Focus on Geology
# Kortz and Smay

Brief Table of Contents

# Focus on Geology
## Kortz and Smay
### Detailed Table of Contents

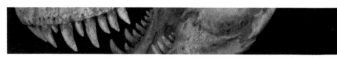

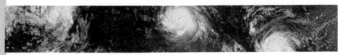

# 12. Climate

# 13. Streams

# 14. Groundwater

# 15. Oceans and Coasts

# 16. Additional Surface Processes

# How to Read This Book

**Key Concept:** **The design of this book is based on how students best learn and guides the reader through the content using the number cues.** Students learn best when they use both diagrams and words but are not overwhelmed **1**. Each page in this book begins with text that places the content on the page in context, and it then guides the reader using number cues like the one at the end of this sentence **2**. When reading any text, it is important to be actively engaged. This book was designed to increase the ability of students to better understand the information presented **3**.

## **1** Overall approach

The design of this textbook is to increase student learning and reduce cognitive load.

### Student learning
This textbook is designed to increase student learning by encouraging dual-coding through words and diagrams. When students learn through both channels of words and pictures, they can combine the information and make stronger connections than if they learned through just one channel.

### Cognitive load
The figures and text are designed to reduce cognitive load. When cognitive load is reduced, then students can focus their mental energy into understanding the concepts instead of being overwhelmed.

## **2** To read this book

Each page or pair of pages is designed to guide you through the content, starting at the beginning.

### 1. Start at the top
As simple as it sounds, it may be tempting to skip to the first numbered title. The Key Concept and the text associated with it help to put the rest of the page in context with the rest of the book.

### 2. Read each header in order
The numbers are there to guide you through the information, which is often building on previous information.

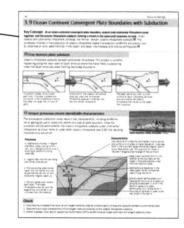

### 3. Study the diagrams
The saying "A picture is worth a thousand words" applies, so don't skip the diagrams and pictures! Go back and forth and link the text and the figures to make sure you understand the concepts presented.

### 4. Actively test your knowledge
As you read, relate the new information to something you already know. Passive reading is not an effective way to study. Therefore, when you're studying, test yourself with the questions

## **3** Based on research

The design of this book was based on a variety research that explores how students learn best. In particular the layout, diagrams and pictures, text, and vocabulary were considered during creation.

### Layout
The text and figures (diagrams and pictures) are near each other and on the same page. A significant amount of text is incorporated into and presented along with the figures. Cognitive principles are incorporated to make the layout clear.

### Diagrams and pictures
Figures are simple with few extraneous details, so they focus on key points rather than pizzazz. Misconceptions and other research inform the design of the figures. For example, the figure above was based on research by Scott Clark, Stephen Thomas, and Julie Libarkin.

### Text
Text is separated into short sections, each focused on a single concept. Essential concepts are included without distracting details. Misconceptions inform the writing of text.

### Vocabulary
Text is focused on concepts, with terminology minimized as appropriate. Terms used were carefully chosen and consistently used.

This list includes examples of scientific papers on which the design of this textbook was based: Busch, 2011; Carney and Levin, 2002; Clark, Libarkin, Kortz, and Jordan, 2011; Cook, 2006; Coyan et al., 2010; Edgcomb et al., 2015; Evans et al., 1987; Groves, 1995; Harp and Mayer, 1997; Harp and Mayer, 1998; Hegarty et al., 2010; Kortz, 2009; Kortz and Caulkins, 2015; Kortz, Grenga, and Smay, 2017; Kosslyn, 1989; Libarkin et al., 2005; Libarkin et al., 2010; Mayer, 1989; Mayer, 2003; Mayer and Gallini, 1990; Mayer and Moreno, 2003; Mayer et al., 1996; Mikkilä-Erdmann, 2001; Novick and Cately, 2007; O'Donnell et al., 2002; Patrick et al., 2005; Reder and Anderson 1980; Reder and Anderson 1982; Schnotz, 2002; Stofer, 2016; Sweller et al., 1998; Tversky, 2004; Van Dyke and White, 2004; Vekiri, 2002; Watkins et al., 2004

# Chapter 1:
# The Science of Geology

## Chapter Objectives

When you are finished reading this chapter, you should be able to …

• describe the study of geology and explain how it is relevant to your daily life (1.1–1.4).

• describe the process of science in detail and identify how geologists apply this process to a variety of projects (1.5–1.8, 1.11–1.12).

• explain themes within geology and why it is unique among the sciences (1.4, 1.9–1.10).

Ch 1: 1<sup>st</sup> Section

# 1.1 – 1.5 Introduction to Geology and Earth

In this section you will learn that geologists study Earth and the geologic processes that change and shape our planet to determine what to expect now and in the future. You will also learn some of the many ways that geology is relevant to your life.

## Frequently Used Terms

The terms listed here are used repeatedly throughout this section, so by learning them before you read this section, you can focus your mental energy on the concepts presented.

**geologic process** A natural occurrence that causes geologic changes; examples include volcanoes erupting, water moving sand, rock melting, and water flowing underground.

**geology** The science that studies Earth and how it works—past, present, and future.

**plate tectonics theory** The scientific theory that describes the movement and interaction of segments of Earth's outer layers, called tectonic plates; this scientific theory explains many seemingly unrelated aspects of Earth's characteristics and processes, such as the locations of volcanoes, earthquakes, and mountains.

**science** The process of answering questions about the natural world using specific guidelines that are often called the process of science or scientific method.

Many cities, such as New York City, were founded next to rivers. This is one example of how human civilization is impacted by geology.

Chapter 1: The Science of Geology    Section 1

# 1.1 What Is Geology?

**Key Concept:** **Geology is the study of Earth and how it works.** Geology is more than just looking at rocks. Geologists learn about the present-day Earth and use those observations and interpretations to figure out Earth's past and make predictions about Earth's future **1**. For example, geologists frequently look at how rock, water and air together influence things like natural disasters, resources, and climate. To do this research, geologists use a variety of ways to collect and analyze a wide range of data.

## **1** Geology is the science that studies Earth

Geologists learn about the present-day Earth, its past, and its potential future by collecting data about many different aspects of Earth and relating them to each other and to people. Some examples of geology in action are given below.

**Glaciers and climate**
Geologists dig ice cores from glaciers to learn about past climates and predict future climates.

**Volcanoes and Earth's interior**
Lava flows contain clues for geologists to learn more about Earth's interior.

**Earthquakes and plate tectonics**
Geologists study plate tectonics and related processes such as earthquakes.

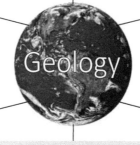

**Minerals and rocks**
Minerals and rocks are located by geologists and mined.

**Oceans, streams, and surface processes**
Geologists study surface processes to understand how they can affect people.

**Fossils and Earth's history**
Geologists learn about Earth's history and past life by studying fossils and rocks.

**Check**   Before you continue, you should be able to answer each check without looking at the page.

☐ List at least four topics that geologists study.
☐ Give two examples of geological topics that you might hear about in the news.

# 1.2 Geology in Our Lives

**Key Concept:** **Many aspects of our daily lives are affected by geology.** Some aspects of geology are fairly noticeable in how they impact our lives, such as the landscape in which we live **1** and the occurrence of natural disasters like earthquakes and landslides **2**. However, you may not have thought about the impact of geology on resources you use daily, such as those needed for buildings **3**, food **4**, energy **5**, and water **6**.

## **1** Landscape

Where cities are built, such as Albuquerque, NM shown, or where farms are plowed depends on how geologic processes, such as building up mountains and wearing them away, have shaped the land. Geology affects the locations of rivers and mountains; the type of rock; the climate; and the shape of the continents, thus affecting where we live.

## **2** Natural disasters

Earthquakes, tsunami, volcanoes, and floods, such as the one shown, are examples of natural geologic processes that dramatically impact people's lives. Geologists study these processes to develop strategies to deal with these events, including preventing the disaster, if possible, and avoiding the area or preparing as necessary.

## **3** Building resources

All metals are mined from Earth. Plastics are created from oil formed in Earth. Rock, gravel, concrete, and asphalt all come from the ground or are made from Earth materials. In short, everything we use for creating buildings and objects, such as those shown in this kitchen, has ties to geology.

## **4** Food resources

Plants grow in soil, which is largely made up of tiny pieces of rock. The location of fertile soil, such as the soil shown here used for farming, is governed by geologic factors such as the type of local rock and the climate.

## **5** Energy resources

Fossil fuels, such as oil and coal, are mined from Earth. For example, the photo shows oil being extracted by a pump jack. Electricity is often produced by burning these fossil fuels but can also be produced by using Earth's water, rock, and air.

## **6** Water resources

The location of water for drinking and farming results from geologic processes, such as water flowing downhill in rivers such as the one in Pittsburgh, Pennsylvania, shown. Oceans, streams, glaciers, and water in the ground all depend on geology.

## Check

☐ State three ways that your life is impacted by geology.
☐ List two examples of building, food, energy, and water resources that you use, and explain how they are related to geology.

# 1.3 Timing of Geologic Processes

**Key Concept:** Geologic processes that affect people can take anywhere from minutes to hundreds of millions of years to happen. As described in the previous section, geology has a major effect on people. Some geologic events, such as landslides, affect people suddenly because they can occur in minutes, but the processes leading up to them, such as the formation of mountain ranges, may build up for millions of years **1**. These very slow processes are often the processes that form geologic resources and landscapes. This geologic time range often takes a little practice to become accustomed to because the breadth of time is difficult to grasp since Earth is 4.56 billion years old.

## **1** Time spans of geologic processes

Each row on this page represents processes that take a similar span of time to occur. Processes at the bottom of the page take many millions of times longer than processes at the top, although all of these processes impact people.

Comparison of lengths of times

### Seconds, minutes, hours to days

**Earthquakes shake the ground**
Movement on a fault caused earthquake shaking that lasted for minutes, destroying someone's home, such as this one in California.

**Rivers flood**
Floods, such as this one near Blanco, TX, can last for days, damaging property and affecting living organisms and ecosystems.

### Months, years to hundreds of years

**Rivers change locations**
The location of streams such as this one has shifted several times over the last hundred years.

**Volcanoes erupt**
The magma beneath this volcano has been periodically erupting for the last several decades.

### Thousands to hundreds of thousands of years

**Magma chambers cool to solid rock**
This rock was liquid rock in a magma chamber, possibly beneath a volcano, that cooled for hundreds of thousands of years.

**Coal and oil forms from living organisms**
Coal and oil take at least hundreds of thousands of years to form from dead plants and tiny organisms.

### Millions to billions of years

**Mountain ranges form**
These mountains were pushed up as faults moved rock during earthquakes over tens of millions of years.

**Living organisms evolve from single-celled to multi-celled**
Multi-celled animals evolved about 3 billion years after single-celled life evolved.

## Check

☐ Give three examples of geologic processes that occur over a short span of time and three that occur over long geologic time ranges.
☐ Explain how short lasting geologic events, such as an earthquake, can be related to processes that take millions of years to occur.

# 1.4 The Uniqueness of Geology

**Key Concept:** Geology requires a unique scientific perspective because of its wide range of time spans and sizes studied, its need to visualize what cannot be seen, and its interdisciplinary approach. Although geologists use the process of science to better understand the world, geology has some characteristics that distinguish it from other sciences. Geologists work with time spans that range from seconds to billions of years **1** and with sizes that range from atoms to entire planets **2**. Because of these time frames and sizes, geologists must frequently visualize things that cannot directly be seen **3**. To study Earth and these processes, the field of geology combines concepts from a variety of other sciences **4**.

## **1** Wide range of time spans

Geologists work with processes that take seconds to millions of years to billions of years. Earth itself is 4.56 billion years old. The lengths of time that geologic processes occur were described in 1.3.

## **2** Wide range of sizes

Geologists work on size scales at the atomic level all the way up through to the size of a planet.

### Angstroms
Atoms are about one angstrom.
1 angstrom = 0.0000000001 m

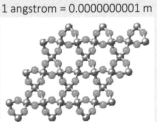

### Millimeters
Atoms form minerals.
1 mm = 0.001 m

### Meters
Minerals form rocks.
1 m (meter, 3.3 feet)

### Kilometers
Rocks form landforms.
10 km = 10,000 m

## **3** Spatial visualization

Geologists visualize things and processes they cannot see, often because they are underground, are too big or small to see, take too long to happen, or happened in the past. These visualizations help geologists think about and understand concepts.

### Maps
Maps represent observations and interpretations from different locations. For example, a map might show the locations of different rocks in North America.

### Simplified representations
Simplified representations illustrate complex processes. For example, a diagram might be used to represent the motions of layers within Earth.

### Models
Physical and computer models illustrate processes that cannot be directly observed. For example, a model might show the movement of contaminated water underground.

## **4** Interdisciplinary

Geologists combine concepts from other scientific disciplines. Four examples are below.

### Geophysics
Geophysicists study physical aspects of Earth, such as how energy from earthquakes travels through Earth.

### Geochemistry
Geochemists study chemical aspects of Earth, such as how atoms bond to form minerals.

### Paleontology
Paleontologists use principles of evolution to study fossils of extinct life forms.

### Astronomy
Planetary astronomers use the study of other planets to inform our study of Earth.

## Check

- ☐ Compare the ranges of time, of distances, and of sizes that geologists work with to what you see on a day to day basis.
- ☐ Explain how geology is related to other scientific disciplines.

# 1.5 Earth's Spheres

**Key Concept:** To model how Earth works, geologists divide it into "spheres" of rock, air, water, and living organisms and consider how each sphere interacts with the others. The previous sections in this chapter discuss what geology is and how it affects people. There are so many interconnected aspects of geology that it is sometimes useful to think about Earth as comprised of independent parts, called spheres, of rock **1**, air **2**, water **3**, and living organisms, including people **4**. This concept of independent spheres helps to create simple models of how Earth works, but these spheres are intimately connected through a variety of geologic processes that are part of an integrated and complex system of Earth. Studying these processes is important because it allows geologists to make connections between the spheres to better understand how they interact, including how they influence how people live and work.

**1 Rock**

The sphere of rock includes the outer layer of rock at Earth's surface as well as the deeper rock layers within Earth.

**Air and rock**

Geologic processes relating spheres:
- Volcanoes emit gas.
- Wind erodes rock and transports sediment.
- Rock stores and releases carbon dioxide.

**Rock and water**

Geologic processes relating spheres:
- Groundwater moves through rock.
- Water helps to break apart rock.
- Streams erode rock and transport sediment.

**People and rock**

Geologic processes relating spheres:
- People mine rock.
- People farm.
- Earthquakes, volcanoes, landslides, and other natural disasters affect life, including people.

**4 Life and people**

People and other living things are part of the biosphere.

**People and air**

Geologic processes relating spheres
- People and animals breathe air.
- People contribute to climate change, which affects life.
- Weather and weather disasters affect life, including people.

**People and water**

Geologic processes relating spheres:
- People use water for farming, drinking, and transporting goods, among other activities.
- Floods affect people.
- People pollute water.

**2 Air**

The sphere of air is the gas surrounding Earth and is called the atmosphere.

**Air and water**

Geologic processes relating spheres:
- Water rains and snows out of the atmosphere.
- Air circulation influences surface ocean currents.
- Oceans absorb and release carbon dioxide.

**3 Water**

The sphere of water includes oceans, rivers, underground water, and frozen water in glaciers and is called the hydrosphere.

## Check

☐ Describe at least six geologic processes that relate Earth's major physical spheres of rock, air, and water to each other.
☐ Summarize how you affect each of Earth's major spheres.
☐ Summarize how you are affected by Earth's major spheres.

Ch 1: 2<sup>nd</sup> Section

# 1.6 – 1.12 Geology as a Science

In this section you will learn that geology has much in common with other sciences, such as using the process of science, being built on well-supported scientific theories, and communicating findings.

## Frequently Used Terms

The terms listed here are used repeatedly throughout this section, so by learning them before you read this section, you can focus your mental energy on the concepts presented.

**process of science**  The guidelines scientists use to do science; they include asking scientific questions; collecting, analyzing, and interpreting data to test scientific hypotheses; reaching consensus; and sharing results; the process of science is flexible and generally requires collaboration and creativity.

**scientific hypothesis**  A proposed explanation to a scientific question based on current knowledge of how nature works.

**scientific question**  A question that is answerable by science because it is testable with evidence, is logical, and can be used to make predictions. It is different than a philosophical or spiritual question.

**scientific theory**  An exceptionally well-supported, overarching explanation of how a part of nature works; a scientific theory is so well supported that it is accepted as the accurate explanation, which is unlike the way "theory" is used in everyday language.

These geologists are collecting data from water in a well to help them answer a scientific question.

Chapter 1: The Science of Geology    Section 2

# 1.6 What Is Science?

**Key Concept:** To study geology we must first recognize that science is both the process used to answer questions about the natural universe as well as the compiled resulting knowledge. Too often people think of science as just a collection of separate pieces of information. However, science comprises much more than independent facts and is instead an ongoing process **1**. Scientists make observations to gather knowledge, but they also organize and build on that knowledge to determine what questions to ask and answer to learn more about the world. Scientific questions must be testable by evidence, be logical, and have predictive power **2**. Other questions such as philosophical or spiritual questions are often important and interesting, but the data collected by scientists cannot be used to answer them **3**. This strategy of asking scientific questions and testing them is part of the process of science.

## **1** Science is an ongoing process

Science is the process of collecting, analyzing, and interpreting evidence to answer questions about what we see in the natural world, and it is the knowledge resulting from those investigations.

Some geologists may run lab experiments to collect data.

Some geologists collect rock samples and make maps based on observations made and data collected outside.

Some geologists create and use computer models to interpret observations of the natural world.

## **2** Scientific questions

Scientific questions (1) are testable with evidence, (2) use logic to find solutions, and (3) have predictive power. If a question does not fit these criteria, then it is not a scientific question. A scientific hypothesis is a proposed explanation answering a scientific question, and includes why it may be the correct explanation. Hypotheses can be tested using the process of science (see 1.7).

### Examples of scientific questions
Were the continents together in the past and then separated?
Why do volcanoes erupt?
How did Earth form?

### These questions are all scientific questions because:

☑ Geologists can make observations and collect data as evidence to test their hypotheses.

☑ Geologists use logic to determine the most reasonable and simplest hypothesis that answers the scientific question.

☑ Geologists can use the answers, or supported hypotheses, to make predictions for the future or for other situations.

## **3** Questions not answerable by science

These are questions that do not fit the criteria of scientific questions and are not answerable by evidence collected in the natural world. For example, philosophical, moral, and spiritual questions are important and interesting, but they are not answerable by science.

### Examples of questions not answerable by science
What is the purpose of the shapes of the continents?
What is the meaning of a volcanic eruption?
Did a divine being create Earth?

### These questions are not scientific questions because:

☒ You cannot make observations and collect evidence to answer the questions.

☒ A logical analysis of data cannot answer the questions.

☒ The answers to the questions cannot be used to predict what might happen in the future or in other situations.

## Check
☐ Explain what makes science more than a collection of facts.
☐ Summarize the three criteria used to define a scientific question.

# 1.7 The Process of Geology

**Key Concept:** To answer scientific questions, geologists use the process of science, often called the scientific method, which involves collecting data, analyzing and interpreting that data, and sharing their findings. Posing scientific questions leads to an informed, researched, and proposed explanation to a scientific question, called a scientific hypothesis **❶**. Geologists collect data to answer scientific questions by making observations, taking measurements, and creating models **❷**. The analysis and interpretation of the data often leads back to asking more questions and collecting more data **❸**. Scientists share their results and conclusions with each other and with the public **❹**. As you can see indicated by the many arrows in the diagram, the process of science is not linear and frequently involves dead ends and sometimes loops back upon itself, requiring creativity and problem solving.

## ❶ Ask scientific questions and develop hypotheses

The questions geologists ask may be guided by other stages of development in a project, including puzzling over surprising observations, talking to other scientists as shown in this photo, and reading published research. Geologists propose hypotheses as explanations of their scientific questions which can be tested by making observations or developing computer or physical models. Testing multiple hypotheses allows geologists to see which hypothesis is most strongly supported.

## ❷ Make observations and collect data

To test multiple hypotheses, geologists may collect evidence in a number of ways. Some geological data must be collected outside, or "in the field", such as collecting water or rock samples as shown in the photo, measuring rock layers, and making maps. Other data are collected remotely, such as GPS data, in a lab by running experiments or creating computer models. The resulting data can come in many forms, such as numerical, descriptive, and maps.

## ❸ Analyze data and develop conclusions

Geologists use various techniques to analyze their collected data. Although some experiments are run as models, or in a lab as shown in the photo, many times what is being studied cannot be reproduced in a lab. Geologists therefore develop creative and logical ways to test hypotheses, such as comparing modern and past environments or relating individual locations to a larger region. Geologists then develop conclusions after analyzing data.

## ❹ Share results and conclusions

Geologists share their findings to continue the process of science. This allows other geologists to learn about their research, ask questions, and give valuable feedback. Sharing can be done informally over coffee or formally by publishing a scientific paper critically reviewed by independent scientists to ensure it is valid or at scientific meetings, as shown in the photo. This process enables geologists to reach a consensus of support for, or require modification to, scientific theories.

## Check

☐ Summarize four actions a scientist must do while completing a scientific project.
☐ Give four examples of how the process of science is not a one-direction, linear process.
☐ Restate in your own words what a scientific hypothesis is, and discuss how it is used in science.

# 1.8 Scientific Theories

**Key Concept:** **Scientific theories are explanations of how nature works that are extremely well supported by numerous studies that use the process of science.** People often say, "I have a theory about . . ." in everyday language. However, what they often mean is that they have an educated guess. Scientific theories, on the other hand, are exceptionally well-supported broad explanations of how nature works **1**. Scientific laws, are different than scientific theories because laws describe a specific single aspect of nature but do not explain why or how **2**.

## **1** Scientific theories are not just guesses

Theories in science are different from theories in everyday life.

**Scientific theories are exceptionally well-supported broad explanations of how nature works.**

| | | |
|---|---|---|
| Scientific theories have been supported time and time again through the process of science, often taking decades or longer to develop. For a theory to be accepted, there can be no findings that directly contradict it. Theories are not the whim of a group of scientists. Rather, the overwhelming evidence supporting scientific theories makes them much stronger than the use of the word "theory" elsewhere. | Because scientific theories are explanations of the how and why of the natural world, scientists use them to make predictions about things that have not yet been observed. These predictions can then be tested through the process of science by asking questions and proposing hypotheses based on the theory as a broad explanation, and findings can be used as further evidence to support the theory or to revise it. Theories are sometimes modified but rarely rejected. | Scientific theories are comprehensive and include a wide range of supported hypotheses that explain observations of and processes in the natural world. They explain why the universe behaves the way it does. Some examples are listed below. |

## **2** Scientific theories compared to scientific laws

Scientific theories are different from scientific laws because laws describe an aspect of nature often as a mathematical relationship, but, unlike theories, they do not explain why there is a relationship. Therefore, scientific theories and scientific laws serve different purposes in science, and a scientific theory will never become a scientific law.

| Scientific theories | Scientific laws |
|---|---|
| Scientific theories explain why there are relationships between aspects of nature. Their purpose is to provide explanations for widespread observations, including those described by scientific laws. | Scientific laws describe an aspect of nature, often as a mathematical relationship, but they do not explain why. Their purpose is to describe single observations. |
| Example<br>The scientific theory of gravity explains why objects are attracted to each other through Einstein's concept of curved space time. This attraction explains why all objects move through space in the way they do. | Example<br>The law of gravity is a mathematical formula that describes the strength of the gravitational pull between two objects, without an explanation of why they are attracted. This mathematical formula describes the movement of objects through space. |
| Example<br>The scientific theory of plate tectonics explains that Earth's outer layer is divided into sections that move and interact at their boundaries. This movement and interaction explains why Earth's geography is the way it is and why earthquakes and volcanoes occur where they do. The plate tectonics theory is further described in 1.9 and explained in Chapter 3. | Example<br>The law of superposition describes the age relationship between sedimentary layers. It states that as long as the sedimentary rock layers have not been disturbed, the layer at the bottom formed first, so it is the oldest layer, and the layer at the top formed last, so it is the youngest layer. The law of superposition is further described in 11.1. |

## Check

☐ Contrast the usage of the term "scientific theory" and the common usage of the word "theory."
☐ Contrast the difference between scientific theories and scientific laws.

# 1.9 Development of the Theory of Plate Tectonics

**Key Concept:** The development of the theory of plate tectonics is an example of how theories can be modified as new information is available. Before the theory of plate tectonics, which explains the relationship between the motion of sections of Earth's outer layer and observed geologic features and events, numerous hypotheses had been proposed to explain the shape of Earth's oceans, the formation of mountains, and the locations of earthquakes **1**. After many additional studies and observations and the advancement of technology, the theory of plate tectonics was proposed, building upon the earlier proposed theory of continental drift and linking these multiple, seemingly unrelated observations **2**. Geologists continue to test hypotheses to refine the theory of plate tectonics and use the theory to make testable predictions about Earth **3**.

## **1** Hypotheses and observations

Observations lead to scientific questions, which in turn lead to hypotheses. In some cases new observations showed that the hypotheses were incorrect. The supported hypotheses can be combined into a larger theory that connects them. Start at the top left arrow on the flow chart.

## **2** Scientific theories

The supported hypotheses may be combined into a theory that explains them. In this example, as new evidence was collected, the proposed theory of continental drift was replaced with the accepted theory of plate tectonics.

## **3** Testing predictions

Testing predictions based on a scientific theory can lead to revisions to a proposed theory, as shown below with continental drift, or to support a theory, as with plate tectonics.

**Observation:** Geologists found matching fossils of the same age in Africa and South America.

**Scientific question:** Why do these ancient fossils match when they are found on distant continents?

**Hypothesis:** Animals migrated on land bridges.

**Hypothesis:** Continents were once together but moved.

**Observation:** No evidence of a land bridge.

hypothesis rejected

hypothesis supports proposed theory

**Observation:** Geologists found evidence of ancient glaciers in currently tropical areas.

**Scientific question:** How could glaciers exist in hot locations?

**Hypothesis:** The entire global climate was colder.

**Hypothesis:** Continents were once together in hot climates but moved.

**Observation:** Evidence of tropical plants at that time.

hypothesis rejected

hypothesis supports proposed theory

**Proposed Theory: Continental Drift:** Earth's continents slowly move, plowing through the rock forming Earth's ocean floors.

**Prediction:** Continents are strong enough to move through the full thickness of the rock that makes up the ocean floor, called oceanic lithosphere.

**Observation:** Laboratory experiments on rock and computer models show that continents are not strong enough. The proposed theory needs to be revised.

**Observation:** The youngest rock that makes up the ocean floor is in the middle of oceans.

proposed theory needs revision

**Scientific question:** Why does new ocean floor form in the middle of oceans?

**Hypothesis:** New rock making up ocean floor forms in the middles of oceans because this is where oceans spread apart.

hypothesis supports proposed theory

**Observation:** Earthquakes deep underground happen next to the long depressions in the seafloor called oceanic trenches.

**Scientific question:** What happens to create oceanic trenches?

**Hypothesis:** Oceanic lithosphere forming the ocean floor bends down and sinks beneath continents.

hypothesis supports proposed theory

**Proposed Theory: Plate Tectonics:** Earth's outer layer, the lithosphere, is divided into moving sections, causing oceanic lithosphere to form, move and sink below other lithosphere, carrying continental lithosphere with it.

theory is supported

**Prediction:** Africa and South America are moving away from each other.

**Observation:** GPS stations confirm earlier observations that Africa and South America are moving apart, supporting the theory of plate tectonics.

## Check

☐ Describe how and why the theory of plate tectonics developed and changed over time.
☐ Summarize five examples of steps in the process of science in developing the theory of plate tectonics.

# 1.10 Themes in Geology

**Key Concept:** Three major themes that weave through this book are the theory of plate tectonics, the rock cycle, and the water cycle. Geologists use scientific theories and scientific models to help make sense of diverse processes. Scientific theories broadly explain how nature works and scientific models represent reality to better understand and visualize specific Earth processes. The theory of plate tectonics explains why Earth's outer layer, broken into tectonic plates, moves creating identifiable features and causing major geologic events **1**. The rock cycle model represents the processes by which rock in a new environment can change to become a new type of rock **2**. The water cycle model follows water in different environments as it changes between liquid, solid, and gas forms **3**. Although they may sound separate from each other, these three themes are often related, such as when a stream of water flows down a mountain, carrying pieces of rock **4**.

## **1** Plate tectonics

The scientific theory of plate tectonics explains that the outer layer of Earth is divided into sections called tectonic plates that move and interact (see Chapter 3).

Tectonic plates are created in some locations and destroyed in others, thereby explaining the formation of major features and geologic events on Earth. The energy that drives plate tectonics comes from the heat in Earth's interior, with motion caused by the pull of gravity on layers with different densities. Plate tectonics is important because it explains why many natural disasters affect people in particular locations around the world.

## **2** The rock cycle

The rock cycle is a scientific model representing the processes that change rock (see 5.2).

The processes that change rock cause bonds to break and form between atoms that make up rock. Different rock types are defined by the processes that form them which are determined by the environment around the rock. These processes may take days, such as when molten rock cools, or they may take thousands of years, such as when water wears a mountain away. The energy that drives the rock cycle comes from a combination of the heat in Earth's interior and the Sun. The rock cycle is important because it explains how many of the resources people use form.

## **3** The water cycle

The water cycle is a scientific model representing the processes by which water moves through different locations above, along, and within Earth's surface (see 13.1).

Water moves between locations by geologic processes such as flowing and evaporating, and the different locations include the ocean, glaciers, rivers, and underground. The energy that drives the water cycle comes from the Sun evaporating water which eventually falls and flows downward again because of gravity. The water cycle is important because it explains why at times there is too much or not enough water for people.

## **4** Interactions between themes

A volcanic environment, like this one near Mount Rainier in Washington, illustrates some ways plate tectonics, the rock cycle, and the water cycle are interrelated.

The rock cycle processes that formed this rock affect the water cycle by influencing where water flows along the surface and how easily it can flow underground.

The plate tectonic processes that formed these mountains affect the rock cycle by changing the environment that rock is in which changes the rock.

The water cycle processes that formed this river affect the rock cycle by eroding and transporting rock.

The plate tectonic processes that formed these mountains affect the water cycle by creating locations for water to gather and flow.

## Check

☐ Describe three themes in the study of geology.
☐ Explain three ways that these three themes relate to each other in a particular environment such as near a volcano.

# 1.11 Using Diagrams to Communicate Science

Key Concept: **Diagrams show information in a way that text cannot, and scientists have strategies to effectively design and read diagrams to communicate scientific results and conclusions.** After scientists collect data, they will frequently turn the data, concepts, models and interpretations, into a diagram to help answer their research question **1**. Diagrams such as graphs often support more effective communication of results and conclusions to peers and colleagues. Many scientific theories and models in geology include complex ideas that are difficult to describe in words alone. The sections titled "Data and Diagrams," are designed to guide you through developing the skills of reading diagrams like scientists, so be sure to answer the questions on each page associated with the diagram. To ensure you are comfortable with necessary terminology for diagram reading, the diagram below guides you through strategies for reading an example graph **2**.

## 1 Being able to read diagrams is a fundamental skill

Diagrams are used in all aspects of life, not just in science. Graphs like the one below are a type of diagram that shows relationships between data. Scientists frequently share information through diagrams such as this graph because they help to convey information visually that cannot easily be seen, such as the meaning of a sequence of numbers or what is happening beneath Earth's surface. Diagrams are effective tools for conveying data and concepts, but they are only effective if the reader can extract the relevant information.

## 2 Parts of a Graph

Although some diagrams can be fairly complex, the example shown below is labeled to ensure you know necessary terminology for reading a simple graph, a common type of diagram. You can use the skills you develop here to read more complex graphs and diagrams.

**Title**
Scientists usually read the title first, because it indicates the main focus that is being conveyed. Next, they read the axes and the key.

**Key**
The key indicates what data the different lines and colors of the graph represent.

**Vertical axis (y-axis) and units**
The vertical axis is usually labeled along the left side of a graph, although it is sometimes labeled along the right. Scientists read the label to know what is being graphed and then look at the units to figure out when or how much of something is being graphed.

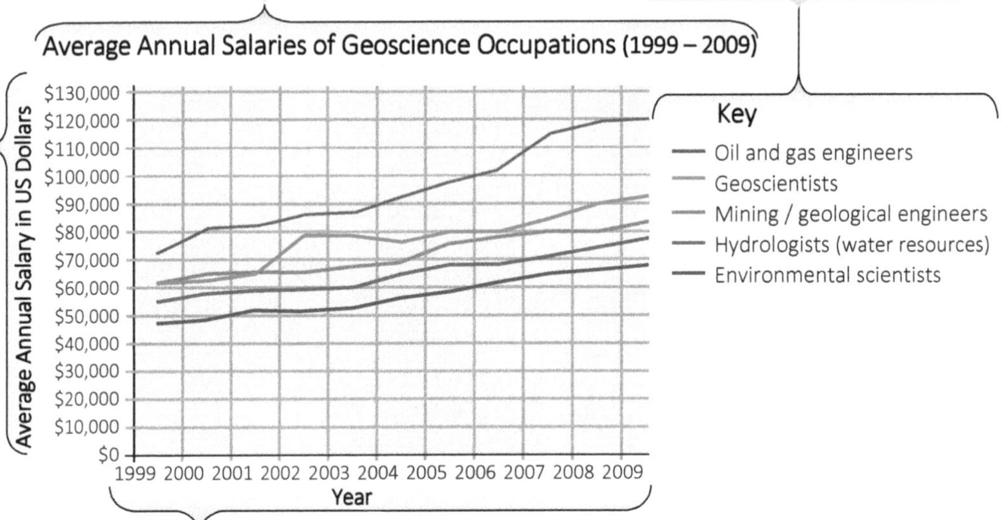
Average Annual Salaries of Geoscience Occupations (1999 – 2009)
Average Annual Salary in US Dollars
$130,000
$120,000
$110,000
$100,000
$90,000
$80,000
$70,000
$60,000
$50,000
$40,000
$30,000
$20,000
$10,000
$0
1999 2000 2001 2002 2003 2004 2005 2006 2007 2008 2009
Year
Key
Oil and gas engineers
Geoscientists
Mining / geological engineers
Hydrologists (water resources)
Environmental scientists

**Horizontal axis (x-axis) and units**
As with the vertical axis, scientists first read the label to know what is being graphed, and then look at the units to determine how much of something is being graphed.

**Data and trends**
After examining the axes and the key, scientists look at the data itself. Although it is tempting to first focus on this part of the graph, it is not very meaningful if you do not know what is being graphed. Scientists tend to look back and forth between the data, the axes, and the key as they begin to make meaning of a graph. The general trend is the overall tendency of the graph. For example, are lines generally rising or falling?

**Meaning**
Finally, scientists try to find meaning in the graph. They examine the graph and ask questions such as: What is the overall trend and why might that be the case? Are there any exceptions to the general trend? What are possible reasons for any exceptions? Is it possible to figure out what might happen by using knowledge beyond what is being graphed?

## Check

- ☐ Describe why it is important for you to be able to read graphs.
- ☐ Put in order the steps scientists follow when analyzing a graph.

# 1.12 DATA AND DIAGRAMS: Geology Salaries

**Key Concept:** Line graphs can show how several factors compare and change over time. This diagram shows the relationship between how the salaries of different professions within the geosciences compare and change over time **1**. To create a graph like this, geologists compiled information of geoscience salaries. Tips on how to read this graph are below **2**. Use the questions to practice interpreting simple graphs **3**.

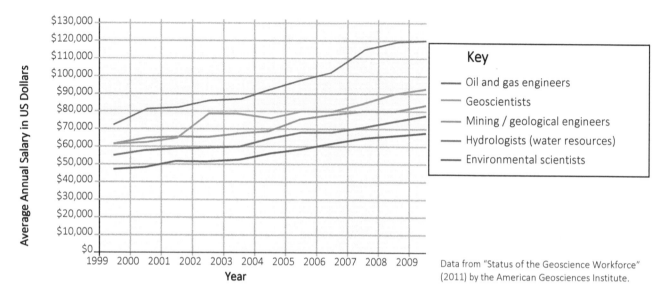

Average Annual Salaries of Geoscience Occupations (1999 – 2009)

**Key**
— Oil and gas engineers
— Geoscientists
— Mining / geological engineers
— Hydrologists (water resources)
— Environmental scientists

Data from "Status of the Geoscience Workforce" (2011) by the American Geosciences Institute.

## 1 How to read the diagram

Determine what is changing on the two axes of the graph, called the variables, by looking at the labels of the graph's axes. In this case, the vertical axis on the left is salary (in dollars), and the horizontal axis on the bottom is time (in years). The key shows that each colored line indicates a different profession related to the geosciences.

## 2 An example of what you might interpret

If you look at the "Geoscientists" line in 2008, geoscientists earned an average salary of about $90,000. This salary increased from the previous years, and it was more than the salaries of mining and geological engineers.

## 3 Questions

**1. What does the graph show?**
a. The annual salary of different geoscience occupations for each year from 1999 to 2009
b. How long it takes for geoscientists in different occupations to earn $120,000
c. How many years it takes a geoscientist to work up to the top salary in their particular occupation

**2. What is the overall trend in average annual salaries for all geoscience occupations over the 10 years shown?**
a. Increasing salaries
b. Fairly level salaries
c. Decreasing salaries
d. It depends on the field within the geosciences

**3. Assuming the trends continue, what is the most likely projection for the mean annual salary for an environmental scientist in 2019?**
a. $45,000/year
b. $65,000/year
c. $85,000/year

**4. How were salaries in the geoscience occupations affected by the recession starting in 2008?**
a. Salaries decreased from what geoscientists were earning before the recession
b. Salaries stayed the same as what geoscientists were earning before the recession
c. Salaries increased from what geoscientists were earning before the recession

**5. What is the main point of this graph?**
a. What the different types of occupations in the geosciences are
b. How salaries for different geosciences occupations have generally increased over 10 years
c. How the number of jobs in different occupations in the geosciences changed over 10 years

## Chapter 1

### End of Chapter Questions: Student Debates

For each of the following questions, determine which student you agree with and explain.why.

1. Two students are discussing whether or not geology is the study of rocks.

   **Student 1:** Geology is the study of rocks because geologists study rocks through the process of making observations in order to describe them and identify them.

   **Student 2:** Geology is more than that, because geologists use information learned from rocks, air, water, fossils, and landscapes to learn how things change over time.

2. Two students are discussing how Earth affects them.

   **Student 1:** Earth affects me because the buildings, technology, and energy I use all come from Earth.

   **Student 2:** Earth may directly impact some people, like those that are hurt by natural disasters, but it doesn't directly affect me.

3. Two students are discussing if science can be done without running experiments.

   **Student 1:** The process of science requires testing hypotheses, so you need to run experiments to test hypotheses.

   **Student 2:** No, you can test hypotheses in other ways, such as making observations of what happened in the natural world, so you don't need to run experiments to do science.

4. Two students are discussing the role of memorizing in science.

   **Student 1:** Being smart requires solving problems by thinking critically and creatively. Although there are facts that you need to know, memorizing is not the focus.

   **Student 2:** Being smart in science requires memorizing information and recalling facts. These facts and terms can be used to answer scientific questions.

5. Two students are discussing if a single scientists can come up with a theory.

   **Student 1:** Theories involve many ideas that come together, which is more than what one individual can do independently.

   **Student 2:** Theories involve an educated guess by a knowledgeable person, so one scientist can independently come up with many theories.

### End of Chapter Questions: Short Answer

Using your own words or sketching and labeling a diagram, answer the following questions.

6. Consider the different topics you might learn in a geology class and explain five different ways that a friend of yours might impact Earth.

7. Identify and explain at least five ways in which geology affected you yesterday.

8. Create a diagram or write a paragraph that illustrates three connections between volcanoes and people.

9. Using geologists studying current and ancient volcanoes as an example, explain how geology is different from other sciences (e.g. physics, chemistry, and biology).

10. Discuss how it is beneficial to the process of science for scientists to work together.

11. Compare similarities between geology and other sciences (e.g. physics, chemistry, and biology).

12. Imagine the scenario where you ask the scientific question, "Why doesn't my phone make calls?" Create a flow chart with three hypotheses and describe how you would test each hypothesis. Add invented observations and use those observations to answer your scientific question.

13. Use the development of the theory of plate tectonics to explain the difference between scientific theories, scientific hypotheses, and scientific questions.

**Hints:** For each question, see the sections listed here for information relevant to answering it.

**1.** (1.1, 1.2) **2.** (1.2, 1.5) **3.** (1.7) **4.** (1.6, 1.7, 1.9) **5.** (1.7, 1.8, 1.9) **6.** (1.1, 1.2, 1.5) **7.** (1.1, 1.2, 1.3, 1.5) **8.** (1.2, 1.5, 1.10) **9.** (1.3, 1.4, 1.5) **10.** (1.7, 1.8, 1.9) **11.** (1.6, 1.7, 1.8, 1.9, 1.11) **12.** (1.7, 1.9) **13.** (1.6, 1.7, 1.8, 1.9)

Chapter 1: The Science of Geology    End of Chapter Questions

# Chapter 2:
# Earth's Formation and Structure

## Chapter Objectives

When you are finished reading this chapter, you should be able to …

• summarize how the universe, solar system, and planets formed and changed over time (2.1–2.4).

• distinguish and explain how we know about the many layers of Earth (2.5–2.6).

• compare and contrast the rocky inner planets and connect reasons for their similarities and differences (2.7–2.12).

Ch 2: 1<sup>st</sup> Section

# 2.1 – 2.6 Planet Formation and Interior

In this section you will learn how Earth and the planets formed and how their interiors became layered. You will also learn how geologists determine what Earth's interior layers are like.

## Frequently Used Terms

The terms listed here are used repeatedly throughout this section, so by learning them before you read this section, you can focus your mental energy on the concepts presented.

**atom** The smallest particle into which elements, such as hydrogen or oxygen, can be divided, while still retaining their basic characteristics.

**brittle and ductile deformation** Brittle deformation breaks an object under stress, such as shattering a glass; ductile deformation changes the shape of an object under stress but does not break it, such as squeezing playdoh.

**density** The mass per volume, or the amount of something compared to how much space it fills; for example, a cotton ball takes up a certain amount of space, but if you squish it, the same amount of cotton takes up less space, so it is more dense.

**differentiation** The process during planetary formation when gravity pulled heavier elements in the melted interior of Earth and other large planetary objects toward the center, and light elements rose toward the outside because of differences in density; this process formed layers with different densities and compositions.

**gravity** The force that pulls objects toward each other's centers; for example, it is the force that pulls you toward Earth's center.

**light and heavier elements** Elements are made up of one type of atom; atoms of light elements, such as hydrogen (H) and helium (He), have few protons, while atoms of heavier elements, such as oxygen (O), carbon (C), silicon (Si) and iron (Fe), have many protons.

**lithosphere** The solid, rigid outer layer of Earth based on how layers behave under stress, made up of the crust and the top of the mantle.

**nebula** In space, a cloud made of mostly hydrogen and helium atoms with some space dust that may eventually collapse to form new stars.

**planetary objects** Objects in the solar system that revolve around the Sun, including planets, their moons, and asteroids.

**planetesimals** Objects roughly the size of a mountain range that once orbited the Sun and collided to form the planets.

Planets orbiting around other stars in the Milky Way Galaxy formed in the same way as Earth formed orbiting around the Sun.

# 2.1 Forming the Universe

**Key Concept:** **The Big Bang formed the universe and all the atoms in it.** The universe began expanding from a single point about 14 billion years ago, in an event called the Big Bang **1**. As the universe expanded and cooled, hydrogen and helium atoms formed **2**. Gravity eventually pulled these atoms together to form stars and galaxies, such as our Milky Way galaxy, as the universe continued to expand **3**. Heavier elements, such as carbon and silicon, formed in the cores of early stars. When those stars died, they exploded, sending the heavier atoms out into space as space dust **4**. As you will see in the next section, these heavier elements are important because they are the elements that form Earth.

## **1** The Big Bang                                                       14 billion years ago

The Big Bang theory states that approximately 14 billion years ago the universe began as a huge amount of energy that suddenly expanded at unimaginable speeds from a single point to create everything that currently exists. Like all scientific theories, this theory has been supported time and time again by observations and experimentation. For example, scientists have evidence the universe is continually expanding because they have observed that all galaxies in the universe move away from each other.

## **2** Forming hydrogen and helium atoms        14 billion years ago

The Big Bang theory explains that as temperatures cooled, some of the energy in the newly formed universe became mass in the form of hydrogen atoms. As the universe expanded, some of those hydrogen atoms combined to form helium atoms. Scientists have made the observation that most atoms in the universe are hydrogen and helium, which supports the Big Bang theory.

## **3** Forming galaxies and stars          13 billion years ago

Gravity eventually pulled together the hydrogen and helium atoms, forming billions of galaxies within the expanding universe. Within each galaxy, the hydrogen and helium atoms formed billions of clouds called nebulae, and some nebulae collapsed due to gravity to form stars. Our Sun is one of the billions of stars in the Milky Way galaxy, which is an example of a galaxy that formed less than a billion years after the Big Bang.

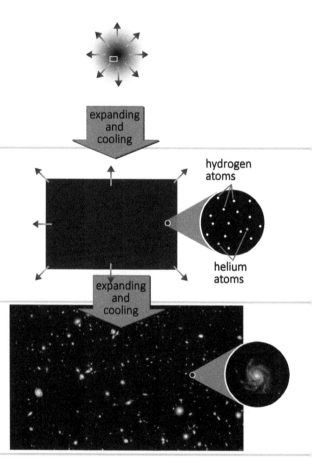

## **4** Forming heavier elements

Heavier elements, such as silicon, iron, and carbon, make up the majority of atoms in rocky planets, like Earth. They formed after the Big Bang, when massive stars fused hydrogen and helium into heavier elements within their cores. When those stars die as supernova explosions, the heavier elements are flung into space as space dust that may enrich a nearby nebula. If that nebula collapses to become a new star, it may have rocky planets, like Earth.

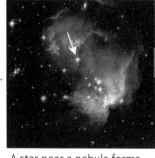
A star near a nebula forms heavier elements.

star explodes — When the star explodes, space dust is scattered.

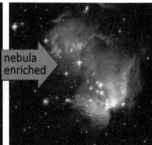
nebula enriched — The nebula now has heavier elements.

**Check**   Before you continue, you should be able to answer each check without looking at the page.

☐ Explain how the hydrogen and helium atoms in the universe formed.
☐ Describe where the heavier elements that make up Earth and other rocky planets came from.

# 2.2 Forming the Solar System and Earth

**Key Concept:** A compacting nebula comprised of gas and space dust formed our solar system, including Earth.

Scientists have determined that the solar system formed 4.6 billion years ago from a nebula enriched in heavy elements, described on the previous page **1**. This cloud of gas and space dust slowly contracted because gravity pulled the atoms together **2**. Almost all of the atoms collapsed into the center to become the Sun, but gravity pulled some of the remaining atoms of gas and space dust together to form planetary objects that orbit the Sun **3**. These objects together with the Sun are our solar system **4**.

## 1 Initial nebula of gas and space dust

The solar system formed between existing stars in the Milky Way galaxy from a contracting nebula made up mostly of hydrogen and helium gas atoms. Nearby exploding massive stars had enriched it with heavier elements, such as carbon, silicon, oxygen, and iron. Gravity is the force that pulls objects together. As gravity pulled gas and space dust toward the center of the nebula, the nebula contracted.

force of gravity

nebula

contraction of nebula

## 2 Contraction of nebula

Gravity continued to pull the gas and space dust toward the center of the nebula, contracting the cloud. Because of its rotation, the spherical nebula became more disk-shaped, like a dinner plate. The inward motion due to contraction caused the atoms to move closer together and collide with each other more, which increased the temperature at the center of the nebula to eventually form the Sun.

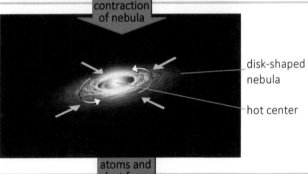

disk-shaped nebula

hot center

atoms and dust form chunks

## 3 Beginnings of planets

Atoms and space dust grouped together to form larger and larger pieces in the disk away from the center, forming planetesimals, which are roughly the size of a mountain range and have internal layers. The process in which gravity pulled atoms and dust together to form planetesimals is called accretion. Planetary objects, such as planets and asteroids, formed through the accretion of planetesimals.

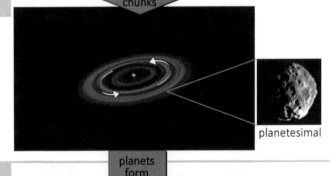

planetesimal

planets form

## 4 Formation of the Solar System

The atoms at the center of the nebula became the Sun, which became hot enough to fuse hydrogen in its core, generating light and heat. Most of the planetesimals in the disk orbiting the Sun combined to form planets, with some remaining as asteroids. The explanation on this page that the solar system formed from a collapsing nebula is the solar nebula theory. Evidence that supports this scientific theory includes observations of other solar systems forming in the same way.

Sun

rocky inner planet

gaseous outer planet

## Check

☐ Explain how the solar system formed from a cloud of gas and heavier elements.
☐ Summarize the steps in the formation of Earth, a rocky inner planet.

# 2.3 DATA AND DIAGRAMS: The Planets

**Key Concept:** Graphs can show the relationship between two variables and how those variables affect a dependent **characteristic.** This diagram shows the distance of each planet from the Sun and the planet's resulting temperature at formation **1**. This temperature affected the types of atom bonded to form each planet. To create a graph like this, geologists observe the planets using telescopes and spacecraft and create models on computers of how the Solar System formed. Tips on how to read this graph are below **2**. Use the questions to practice interpreting this type of graph **3**.

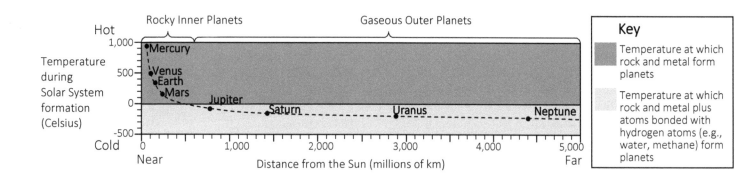

## 1 How to read the diagram

Determine what the variables are. In this case, the horizontal axis is distance from the Sun measured in millions of kilometers, and the vertical axis is temperature when the solar system formed, measured in degrees Celsius. Therefore, based on where the planets are plotted, it is possible to determine the temperature at which each planet formed. The types of atoms that can bond to form planets is a characteristic dependent on the temperature and is shown by background color that transitions from dark to light brown at 0°C.

## 2 An example of what you might interpret

If you look at the conditions at the distance of the planet Jupiter, you would see that it is on a light brown background, so it is composed of rock, metal, and atoms bonded with hydrogen.

## 3 Questions

**1. What does this graph show?**
a. How atoms bond together to form planets.
b. How the rock and metals in the solar nebula changed with distance from the Sun.
c. How temperature and distance from the Sun affected planet compositions.

**2. What is the relationship between temperature and distance from the Sun shown by the dashed black line?**
a. As distance increases, temperature increases.
b. As distance increases, temperature remains the same.
c. As distance increases, temperature decreases.

**3. Based on the graph, which type of planet formed where it was cold?**
a. Rocky inner planets
b. Gaseous outer planets
c. Different planets did not form in specific environments.

**4. What is the significance of the point where the black line crosses the boundary between the background colors?**
a. The composition of the atoms bonding together changed.
b. The distance from the Sun changed.
c. The composition of the solar nebula changed.

**5. If the Sun had been much cooler when it formed, how would Earth's composition have been affected?**
a. Earth would be made up of more metal and rock.
b. Earth would be made up of more hydrogen.
c. Earth's composition would be the same.

**6. What is the relationship between distance from the Sun and composition of the planets?**
a. Planets further from the Sun have more hydrogen compared to the rocky, inner planets because the temperature was colder than the freezing temperature of water.
b. Planets further from the Sun have more hydrogen compared to the rocky, inner planets because the temperature was hotter than the freezing temperature of water.
c. Planets further from the Sun have less hydrogen compared to the rocky, inner planets because the temperature was colder than the freezing temperature of water.
d. Planets further from the Sun have less hydrogen compared to the rocky, inner planets because the temperature was hotter than the freezing temperature of water.

# 2.4 Forming Planet Layers

**Key Concept:** Layers formed within Earth because of differences in density. As discussed earlier, Earth and other planets first formed from planetesimals colliding, so the composition of their interiors were initially uniform **1**. Soon after Earth formed, its interior heated up and melted, allowing the atoms to flow and move. Gravity played a big role in shaping the interior of planets, with dense iron sinking to the center and forming the core, and the lowest density rock rising to the outer part and forming the crust, the outermost layer of Earth. Water and gas are low density, so they rose and escaped out of the rock at Earth's surface, forming the oceans and atmosphere. As a result of this process of separation due to density, Earth has layers **2**, and these layers have distinct compositions and densities **3**.

## **1** Earth had an initially uniform composition

Earth was initially uniform throughout because it formed from planetesimals with similar compositions colliding together. These planetesimals were mostly made of rock and iron, but some included frozen water and gas. Soon after Earth formed, radioactive atoms began breaking apart, Earth continued to be impacted by planetesimals, and gravity compressed the newly formed planet, all of which together heated up Earth's interior enough to melt it. Once it was molten, the atoms were able to flow and separate based on their density, just as oil and water shaken together in a jar separate

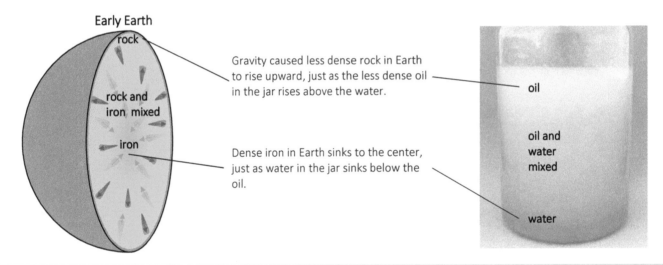

**Early Earth**

rock

rock and iron mixed

iron

Gravity caused less dense rock in Earth to rise upward, just as the less dense oil in the jar rises above the water.

Dense iron in Earth sinks to the center, just as water in the jar sinks below the oil.

oil

oil and water mixed

water

## **2** Differentiation led to a layered Earth

The process of denser elements sinking toward the middle and lighter elements rising toward the surface resulted in distinct layers. This process is called differentiation.

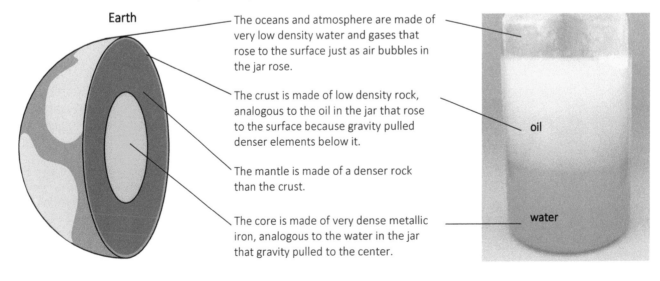

**Earth**

The oceans and atmosphere are made of very low density water and gases that rose to the surface just as air bubbles in the jar rose.

The crust is made of low density rock, analogous to the oil in the jar that rose to the surface because gravity pulled denser elements below it.

The mantle is made of a denser rock than the crust.

The core is made of very dense metallic iron, analogous to the water in the jar that gravity pulled to the center.

oil

water

## 3 Earth's layers are related to density

A complete listing of Earth's layers includes not only the rock layers but also the water and air layers, because these layers continually influence and interact with each other, as described in 1.4. In the diagram below showing layers from the top of the atmosphere to the center of Earth you can see that through differentiation, the less dense layers are above the denser layers. Additional details about layers within Earth are given in 2.5.

### Atmosphere
The atmosphere is air made of nitrogen and oxygen gas, which has a very low density. The density varies because the top of the atmosphere ends where there are no atoms, so there is no density.

### Hydrosphere
The hydrosphere is Earth's water. Water is less dense than rock, so it mostly sits on top of it, making up oceans, rivers, lakes, groundwater, and ice.

### Crust
The crust is made of rock with slightly varying compositions, resulting in different types of rock. It is these different rocks that result in a range of densities.

### Mantle
The mantle has an intermediate density between the rocky crust and the metallic core because it is made of iron-rich rock. The range in densities is because pressure increases with depth inside Earth. Therefore, the bottom of the mantle is under more pressure than the top, so the atoms are squeezed closer together, making the bottom rock more dense.

### Core
The core is the densest layer in Earth, made of metallic iron. As with the mantle, the range in densities is due to a range in pressures, with increasing pressures and therefore densities deeper within Earth.

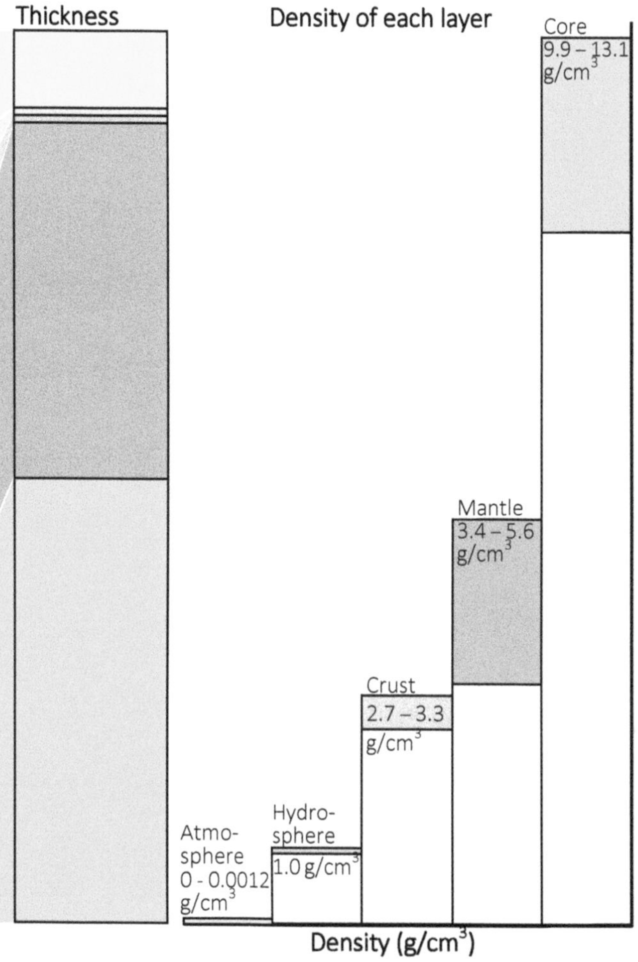

**Thickness**

**Density of each layer**

Core 9.9 – 13.1 g/cm$^3$

Mantle 3.4 – 5.6 g/cm$^3$

Crust 2.7 – 3.3 g/cm$^3$

Atmosphere 0 – 0.0012 g/cm$^3$

Hydro-sphere 1.0 g/cm$^3$

Density (g/cm$^3$)

### Comparing density and weight

Density is not the same as weight. Both density and weight involve the mass of an object, or how much there is. However, density is dependent on how much space the mass fills, called the volume, and weight is dependent on the amount gravity is pulling on the mass of the object. The example illustrates differences between density and weight using the example of a bucket of rock.

|  | Density | Weight |
|---|---|---|
| A bucket filled with rock | The density is dependent on the mass of the rock and the volume of the bucket. | The weight is dependent on the mass of the rock and the amount of gravity pulling on the rock. |
| The same bucket filled with iron | The density is higher because the mass is larger, but the volume is the same. | The weight is higher because the mass is larger, so the pull of gravity is higher. |
| The bucket of rock but compressed to be smaller | The density is higher because the mass has stayed the same, but the volume has decreased. | The weight is the same because neither the mass nor the gravity has changed. |
| The bucket of rock on the Moon | The density is the same because neither the mass nor the volume has changed. | The weight is lower because the mass has stayed the same, but the pull of gravity is lower. |

## Check

☐ Describe the processes that gave Earth its layers.
☐ Explain the relationship between the density of rock, metal, water, and air to the order in which their layers occur on Earth.
☐ Explain the relationship between density, weight, and mass.

# 2.5 Earth's Layers

**Key Concept:** The layers within Earth may be described by their composition or their behavior. Remember that Earth's interior is made up of a series of layers. The layers can be drawn differently depending on if Earth is divided on the basis of composition or behavior. Described by composition, Earth's layers are the crust (rock), mantle (iron-rich rock), and core (metallic iron) **1**. The other criterion used to divide Earth into layers is how each layer behaves when it is stressed. Described by behavior, Earth's layers include the lithosphere (solid that is brittle), asthenosphere (solid that deforms), outer core (liquid), and inner core (solid) **2**. As you read through the diagram below, note that the layers of Earth when divided based on composition (left) do not always line up with the layers of Earth when divided based on behavior (right), as shown with the specific example of the crust and lithosphere **3**.

## **1** Layers based on composition

Earth can be divided into layers based on their composition, specifically which elements are present, as described below. These are the layers described on the previous page as having formed by differentiation because their different compositions have different densities.

| Layer | Depth in kilometers (miles) | Composition |
|---|---|---|
| crust | 0–70 km (0–40 mi) (continental crust) 0–8 km (0–5 mi) (oceanic crust) | rock, made up of mostly oxygen (46%) and silicon (28%) |
| mantle | 8–2,900 km (40–1,802 mi) | iron-rich rock, made up of oxygen (44%), silicon (21%), magnesium (23%), and iron (6%) |
| core | 2,900–6,380 km (1,802–3,964 mi) | metallic iron (86%) |

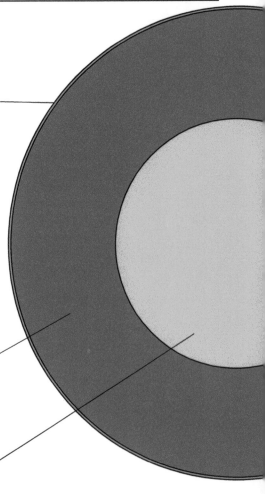

### Crust

The crust is the relatively thin, outer layer of Earth that we see, dig in, and live on. It is primarily made up of rock and includes soil at the surface. Crust in different locations falls into one of two categories. These depend on slightly different compositions based on the relative amounts of silica, which is silicon bonded with oxygen. The continental crust is relatively thick and low density. It makes up land and is primarily the rock granite which has very little iron and about 70% silica. In comparison, the oceanic crust is much thinner and is slightly denser, so it is lower in elevation and forms most of the seafloor. It is primarily the rock basalt which has some iron and about 50% silica.

granite

basalt

### Mantle

The mantle makes up the majority of Earth's interior. It is composed of the iron-rich rock peridotite which has about 40% silica.

peridotite

### Core

The core is the densest and hottest layer in the very center of Earth. It is made up of metal, mostly iron and some nickel, and no silica.

iron

## 2 Layers based on behavior

Earth can also be divided into layers based on their behavior, rather than by composition, as shown below. For example, brittle behavior is when solid rock breaks, and ductile behavior is when solid rock bends or flows. Earth's interior is separated into layers that behave differently because different compositions react differently under different pressures and temperatures, and both temperature and pressure increase toward the center of Earth. This way of dividing Earth's interiors into layers is important when discussing plate tectonics, the scientific theory that is the focus of Chapter 3.

| Layer | Depth in km (mi) | Behavior |
|---|---|---|
| lithosphere | 0 – 100 km (0 – 62 mi) | solid, brittle under stress |
| asthenosphere | 100 – 400 km (62 – 249 mi) | solid, ductile under stress |
| deep mantle | 400 – 2,900 km (249 – 1,802 mi) | solid, ductile under stress |
| outer core | 2,900 – 5,400 km (1,802 – 3,355 mi) | liquid |
| inner core | 5,400 – 6,380 km (3,355 – 3964 mi) | solid |

## 3 Comparing the crust and lithosphere

The outermost layer of Earth that we live on is called both the crust and the lithosphere. These two layers are not the same, since mantle rock is part of the lithosphere but not the crust. A comparison to a layer cake helps to make the distinction more clear.

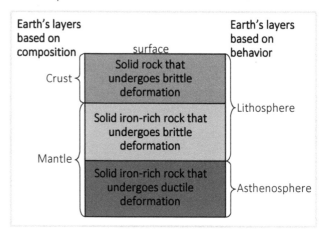

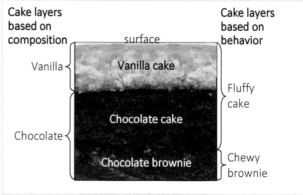

### Lithosphere

The lithosphere includes the crust (the layer we live on) plus the outer part of the mantle. It is solid and brittle, breaking under stress, resulting in earthquakes. As with the crust, the lithosphere can be divided into two categories: the relatively thick continental lithosphere and the thinner, denser oceanic lithosphere. Tectonic plates are the thickness of the lithosphere.

### Asthenosphere

The asthenosphere deforms because it is ductile and flows very slowly, even though it is solid rock. The solid asthenosphere moves only a few centimeters or inches a year.

### Deep mantle

The deep mantle is also solid rock, and moves very slowly, although it is stiffer and stronger than the asthenosphere.

### Outer core

The outer core is the only liquid layer within Earth. It is very hot, but the pressure is not high enough to keep the atoms bonded together as a solid.

### Inner core

The inner core is solid. Although it is hotter than the outer core, the very high pressure locks the atoms in place as a solid.

## Check

☐ Describe the characteristics of the different layers of Earth based on both composition and behavior.
☐ Compare and contrast the crust and the lithosphere.

# 2.6 Techniques that Reveal Earth's Layers

**Key Concept:** Geologists determine the characteristics of Earth's layers by using many different methods. Earth is so big that even the deepest drill holes barely scratch the surface and cannot give information about Earth's interior below the crust or lithosphere. Geologists must therefore use indirect evidence to learn about Earth's interior, just as you might shake a cereal box to determine how much is left without opening the box. Three lines of indirect evidence that geologists use are: interpreting seismic or earthquake waves to detect the boundaries of layers and layer characteristics **1**; comparing the density of Earth and rocks to learn about the composition of Earth's layers **2**; and using the composition of meteorites from space to determine what elements are present in various layers **3**. For each line of evidence, note how observations lead to interpretations about Earth's layers.

## **1** Seismic or earthquake waves

When an earthquake occurs, the energy released travels through Earth in waves, called seismic waves, that shake the ground. Geologists can measure the speed, strength, and motion of these waves using seismometers (see 10.2). Surface seismic waves travel along the surface of the ground, which is what we feel as an earthquake. Body seismic waves travel into and through Earth, so they are useful tools for learning about Earth's interior. Body seismic waves have two types: P waves and S waves.

|  | P waves | S waves |
|---|---|---|
| Name | Primary or pressure waves | Secondary or shear waves |
| Motion | Matter compresses in the same direction the wave is traveling.<br><br>Wave direction →<br><br>← Motion of atoms →<br><br>In comparison, the motion is similar if there is a line of people, and the person at the end of the lines is pushed.<br><br>Wave direction →<br><br>← Motion of people → | Matter wiggles perpendicular to the direction the wave is traveling.<br><br>Wave direction →<br><br>↕ Motion of atoms<br><br>In comparison, the motion is similar if there is a line of people, and the people take turns raising their arms in order to do "the wave."<br><br>Wave direction →<br><br>↕ Motion of people |
| Travels through | Travels through all matter in any phase, including liquid phases. | Travels through solid matter only. Does NOT travel through liquid. |
| Speed | Fastest. A typical speed is 6 km/s or 13,000 miles per hour. | Second fastest. A typical speed is 4 km/s or 9,000 miles per hour. |

## What observations do geologists make about seismic waves?

Geologists observe the seismic waves that travel through Earth to distant seismometers to determine characteristics of Earth's interior, such as its phase (solid or liquid). The speed and angle of seismic waves vary, depending on the density, temperature, and phase of the rock or metal they travel through. By observing and measuring whether and when P and S waves arrive at different seismic stations around Earth, geologists can make interpretations about what the seismic waves traveled through.

## How do geologists interpret observations about seismic waves?

Geologists use observations of seismic waves to make interpretations about the locations and characteristics of layers in Earth, creating the diagrams of Earth's interior seen in the previous few sections. These observations of seismic waves help geologists interpret that Earth's layers have different compositions and densities, with higher densities for deeper layers due to differentiation (see 2.4). Seismic waves have also told geologists that all layers of Earth are solid, except the outer core, which is liquid.

A single, large earthquake generates seismic waves, including both P waves and S waves.

By examining the arrival times of P waves and S waves at seismometers around the world, geologists can make interpretations about the interior of the Earth. See details below.

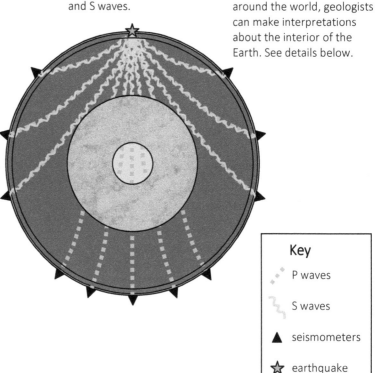

### Key

- ⋯ P waves
- 〜 S waves
- ▲ seismometers
- ☆ earthquake

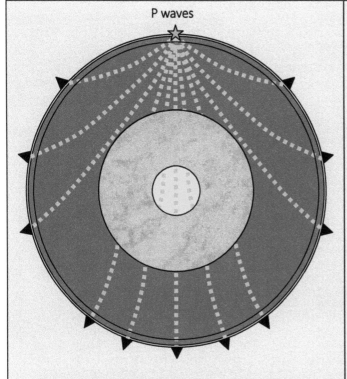

**P waves**

All seismic stations around Earth detect P waves from the large earthquake. Seismic waves may reflect at boundaries or bend slightly where they pass through a boundary, and this bend can be measured. Therefore, geologists can determine the depths to various layers.

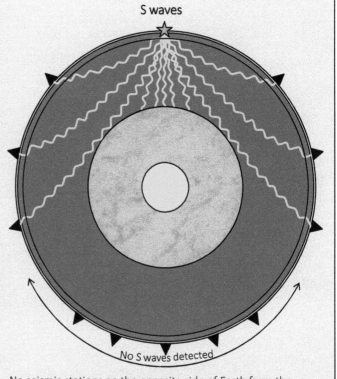

**S waves**

No S waves detected

No seismic stations on the opposite side of Earth from the earthquake detect S waves; therefore geologists conclude there is liquid inside Earth, since S waves do not travel through liquid. By measuring angles from the initial earthquake, they can calculate the size of the liquid iron outer core.

## 2 Density

As we saw in 2.4, different components of Earth have different densities. For example, if you compare two cubes measuring 1 cm on each side (about the size of a dice), the cube made of iron has a mass of 7.9 grams, which has nearly three times the mass as the same size cube of granite rock with a mass of 2.7 grams. Below are comparisons of densities using the units grams per cubic centimeter.

### What <u>observations</u> do geologists make about density?

Geologists have measured the densities of different rocks and metals in a lab and compared them to the density of the whole Earth. Earth's density of 5.5 g/cm³ indicates that it is too high to be made up of typical rocks such as granite and basalt throughout.

### How do geologists <u>interpret</u> observations about density?

The interior of Earth is denser than the rock we measure at the surface. This higher density leads geologists to interpret that the inner layers of Earth are made up of dense metals, and it supports interpretations from other studies that it is part iron (the core) and part peridotite (iron-rich rock making up the mantle).

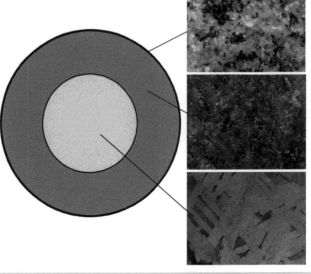

Granite, rock in the crust, has a density of about 2.7 g/cm³.

Peridotite, iron-rich rock in the mantle, has a density of about 3.3 g/cm³.

Iron, metal in the core, has a density of about 7.9 g/cm³.

## 3 Meteorites

Meteorites are planetary objects or pieces of planetary objects that did not become part of a planet during the formation of the solar system and have since fallen to Earth. If they were large enough, the planetary object differentiated into a crust, mantle, and core. When these differentiated planetesimals collided and smashed into small pieces, those pieces represent different parts of the planetesimal.

### What <u>observations</u> have geologists made about meteorites?

Geologists have analyzed the composition of meteorites and observed that they have different compositions, such as rock and iron.

### How do geologists <u>interpret</u> observations about meteorites?

Geologists interpret the different compositions of meteorites to be related to the different layers in the planetesimal that they came from. Because differentiation of layers likely occurred the same way in the planetary object as it did in Earth, geologists interpret the compositions of the meteorites to be the same as the composition of layers within Earth. Geologists used these observations to determine that the composition of elements in Earth's core is mostly iron with some nickel, and a common mineral in Earth's mantle is olivine.

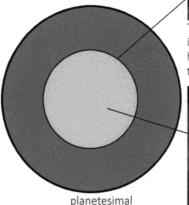

This meteorite is composed of iron and the iron-rich mineral olivine; it is interpreted to have once been on the boundary between the core and mantle of a large planetesimal.

planetesimal

This meteorite is composed primarily of iron; it is interpreted to have once been part of the core of a large planetesimal.

## Check

☐ List three methods used to learn about the composition and behavior of layers inside Earth, and explain how each method works.
☐ Describe what each of the three methods tells about the composition and/or behavior of layers inside Earth.

# 2.7 – 2.10 Comparing Rocky Inner Planets

In this section you will learn that there are geologic processes that affect all inner planets similarly. However, their different internal temperatures, atmospheres, and surface temperatures make each planet unique.

## Frequently Used Terms

The terms listed here are used repeatedly throughout this section, so by learning them before you read this section, you can focus your mental energy on the concepts presented.

**atmosphere** The gases that form a layer above a planet's surface; the atmosphere is also called air on Earth, and is held next to the surface by the planet's gravity.

**lava** Molten rock that has erupted on a planet's surface; when molten rock is still underground, it is called magma.

**rocky inner planets** The planets closest to the Sun that have a surface made up of rock, as opposed to those further away from the Sun that have a "surface" made of gas.

**surface process** The way that the surface of a planet is changed, such as lava flowing, impacts forming, or sediment being moved by wind or water; different surface processes create unique landforms, such as lava flows or impact craters.

This selfie was taken by NASA's Curiosity rover on Mars.

# 2.7 Rocky Inner Planet Similarities

**Key Concept:** The rocky inner planets all have interior layers that formed by differentiation, had flowing lava on the surface, and have impact craters. The rocky inner planets, including Earth, are the relatively small planets close to the Sun that share a similar history of formation. The planets were all once hot enough for their interiors to melt, so they all have layered interiors **1** and cooled lava flows on the surface **2**. They also all have impact craters because they were hit by planetary objects from space **3**. A planet's visible surface may be modified by a variety of surface processes, such as flowing lava, that give the surface a younger age than the interior of the planet **4**. Similarities between the rocky inner planets are described below, and the following sections describe their differences.

## **1** Internal layers

Differentiation during the formation of the planets caused layers with different densities to form. The rocky inner planets all have a crust, mantle, and core, although the layers are different thicknesses.

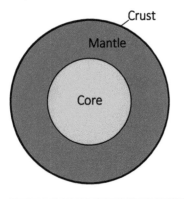

## **2** Lava flows

The term lava flow refers either to lava actively moving across a surface or to the solid rock formation resulting from cooled lava. Only planets with interiors hot enough for rock to melt can have lava flowing on their surfaces, as shown below in the photo of an active lava flow on Hawaii. When the interior of a planet cools, new lava flows cannot form. All rocky inner planets, including Earth, had lava flows in the past, and Earth and Venus have lava flows actively forming.

## **3** Impact craters

When a planetary object from space, such as an asteroid, hits the surface of a planet, a hole, called an impact crater, is formed. Although most impact craters formed billions of years ago when there were many leftover planetary objects, impact craters continue to form on planets today. For example, Meteor Crater in Arizona, shown below, was formed by a meteorite 50,000 years ago.

## **4** How lava flows and impact craters change a surface

Impact craters accumulate on a planet's surface over millions and billions of years. However, surface processes like lava flowing can bury the craters on the surface. The buried planet surface cannot be seen or easily studied, so it can be described as "erased." The older a planet's surface, the more impact craters have accumulated. A planet's surface that has many, many impact craters can be interpreted to be billions of years old and not modified by more recent surface processes. This series of images show how a surface can be modified by surface processes like craters forming and lava flowing.

 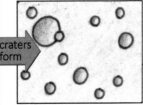 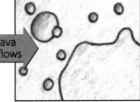 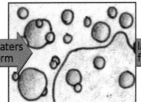 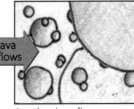

The original surface of the planet.

Impact craters accumulate over time.

A lava flow buries some of the surface, erasing some of the impact craters and creating a new surface.

Impact craters continue to accumulate.

Another lava flow occurs. The oldest surface has the most impact craters.

## Check

☐ Summarize two surface processes that occur on all rocky inner planets.

☐ Explain why all rocky inner planets share some characteristics.

☐ Discuss why the number of impact craters on the surface of a planet shows the age of the planet's surface.

# 2.8 Differences Due to Internal Temperature

**Key Concept:** Billions of years after their formation, the internal temperatures of large rocky inner planets are still hot, while smaller rocky inner planets have cooled. As discussed, the rocky inner planets have many similarities, but they also differ from each other in significant ways. When the planets first formed, they all had hot interiors. However, the smaller planets cooled faster, and larger planets retained their heat **1**. As long as a planet has a hot interior, landforms related to that hot interior can form and create a young surface **2**. In contrast, small rocky planets do not have an interior hot enough for lava flows to occur, and their exposed surfaces are very old.

## **1** Planet size affects internal temperature

As you may have experienced with hot foods and drinks, things that are smaller lose their heat faster than things that are larger. This phenomenon also applies to planets. All planets formed at the same time and started hot. However, small planets such as Mercury, represented by the small tea cup, lost their internal heat quickly. The larger planets, such as Earth and Venus, represented by the large mug, are more slowly losing their heat, so they are still internally hot.

The small and large cups are filled with hot tea.

The small cup is cool, but the large cup is still hot.

## **2** Internal temperature affects landforms

When they first formed, all planets had a hot enough interior to result in lava flows on the surface. Small planets cooled quickly, so the lava flows that we see on their surfaces are nearly as old as the planet itself. Large planets like Earth are cooling more slowly and still have a hot interior, so lava flows still form, creating a new, young surface. Earth also has plate tectonics, which results in a variety of additional landforms discussed in Chapter 3.

### Small planet
Mercury (and the Moon) is small, so it has lost a large amount of its internal heat. Therefore, all the lava flows are very old.

### Medium planet
Mars had active lava flows more recently than Mercury, but the planet interior is likely too cool for abundant new lava flows to form.

### Large planets
Venus and Earth are the largest of the rocky inner planets, so their interiors are still hot enough for lava to continue to erupt on the surface.

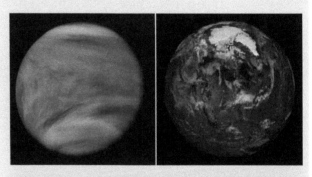

Geologists determined the lava flows on Mercury are very old because of the abundant accumulated impact craters.

Geologists determined the lava flows on Venus are young because they are relatively crater-free.

## Check
- Describe how a planet's size affects its internal temperature.
- Explain how the internal temperature of a planet affects the number of impact craters on its surface.

# 2.9 Differences Due to an Atmosphere

**Key Concept:** Compared to smaller planets, larger planets retain more of an atmosphere, which creates landforms through the movement of wind. As you might expect, larger planets have a stronger gravitational pull because they have a greater mass. This stronger pull prevents gases from escaping into space, so the gases stay near the surface and make up the atmosphere, or air **1**. On these larger planets, wind, which is the movement of the atmosphere, transports and deposits sediments, creating landforms such as sand dunes. Therefore, larger planets have surfaces that are changed by wind, while smaller planets do not **2**.

## **1** Planet size affects the presence of an atmosphere

Much of the gas that makes up planets' atmospheres is derived from gases erupted by volcanoes early in planets' histories as they differentiated. Larger planets have more gravity, so they are able to hold on to their atmosphere, and the gases do not escape into space like they do for small planets.

The diagram shows the amount of gas in the atmosphere compared to Earth's atmosphere for each of the rocky inner planets. Earth and Venus are approximately the same size. However, Venus has 9,200 times the atmospheric pressure as Earth. This difference is primarily because some gas has been removed from Earth's atmosphere through dissolving in the oceans.

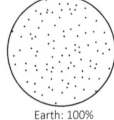

KEY
Each dot represents 1% of Earth's atmospheric pressure

Mercury: no atmosphere

Mars: 0.6%     Venus: 9,200%     Earth: 100%

## **2** The presence of an atmosphere affects landforms

The movement of the atmosphere is wind. Wind transports and deposits sediments, such as dust or sand, on planets' surfaces. Therefore, without an atmosphere, there are no surface processes that can create sand dunes or other landforms formed by the wind.

**No atmosphere**
Mercury and the Moon have no atmosphere, so they do not have landforms formed by wind.

The Moon has no atmosphere because it is a small planetary object. Footprints left by astronauts on the surface of the Moon still have sharp edges because there is no wind to move Moon dust.

**With atmosphere**
Mars, Earth, and Venus all have an atmosphere, so the wind has created landforms.

The atmosphere is visible in this view of Earth from space. Sand dunes, like the ones shown on Mars, were formed by the atmosphere transporting and depositing sand and dust sediments.

## Check

- ☐ Describe how a planet's size affects the presence of an atmosphere.
- ☐ Explain how the presence of an atmosphere affects the landforms present on a planet's surface.

# 2.10 Differences Due to Surface Temperature

**Key Concept:** **The surface temperature of a planet determines whether or not there is liquid water.** Planets closer to the Sun receive more of the Sun's light energy, which makes the surface warmer because more energy reaches the surface. In addition, carbon dioxide in a planet's atmosphere traps light energy, affecting how much heat is retained at the surface **1**. This is important because a surface temperature in the right range, not too hot or too cold, will allow a planet to have liquid water on its surface **2**. In our solar system, Earth is currently the only planet with liquid water and life.

## **1** Distance from the Sun and atmosphere affect surface temperature

Two factors affect a planet's surface temperature: the distance from the Sun and the presence and the composition of the atmosphere. Planets closer to the Sun receive more of the Sun's light energy and therefore will generally have a warmer surface.

The colored arrows below show how the distance between a planet and the Sun affects the relative surface temperatures if there was no atmosphere. However, the composition of the atmosphere also affects surface temperatures. For example, carbon dioxide in the atmosphere traps light energy in the atmosphere, a process called the greenhouse effect, which causes the temperature of the atmosphere to be warmer (discussed in Chapter 12). Therefore, as seen in the table below, planets with carbon dioxide in the atmosphere have higher surface temperatures, independent of distance from the Sun.

| | Surface temperatures can be so hot that liquid water boils. | | The surface temperature is in the range in which liquid water can exist. | The maximum surface temperature is so cold that liquid water freezes. |
|---|---|---|---|---|
| **Sun** | **Mercury** ○ | **Venus** ◯ | **Earth** ◯ | **Mars** ○ |
| Amount of carbon dioxide in the atmosphere | none | 460,000 trillion metric tons | 3 trillion metric tons | 24 trillion metric tons |
| Average surface temperature | The close proximity to the Sun causes Mercury to have temperatures that average 167 °C (333 °F). | The close proximity to the Sun and extreme greenhouse effect cause Venus to have a very hot average temperature of 464 °C (867 °F). | The distance from the Sun and minor greenhouse effect give Earth an average temperature of 15 °C (59 °F). | The large distance from the Sun and minor greenhouse effect mean that Mars' average temperature is -65 °C (-85 °F). |

## **2** Surface temperature affects the presence of water and landforms

Since surface temperature is affected by a combination of the planet's distance from the Sun and the composition of its atmosphere, these factors also affect the presence of water. Water can only exist on a planet if its surface is not too hot or too cold, and it plays an essential role in supporting life on Earth. Liquid water can create a variety of unique and identifiable landforms, such as river valleys and ocean shorelines, and frozen water can create glacial features (see Chapters 13–16).

| | Mercury | Venus | Earth | Mars |
|---|---|---|---|---|
| Surface water and landforms | There is no water because it is too hot. | There is no water because it is too hot. | Water is present as a liquid, solid (ice), and gas (vapor). It dramatically alters the landscape, creating abundant landforms. | Water is present primarily as a solid (ice). It currently does not produce many landforms, but liquid water during a warmer past created abundant ones. |

## Check

☐ Summarize factors that control the surface temperature of a planet.
☐ Explain how the atmosphere and distance from the Sun affect the presence and phase of water (liquid, solid, or gas) on a planet.

## End of Chapter Questions: Student Debates

For each of the following questions, determine which student you agree with and explain why.

1. **Two students are discussing the timing between the formation of the universe and the formation of the solar system.**

   **Student 1:** The universe formed billions of years before the solar system.

   **Student 2:** The universe and solar system formed at the same time by the Big Bang.

2. **Three students are discussing whether the mantle is primarily liquid or solid.**

   **Student 1:** The mantle is solid rock, although it can flow slowly. It must be solid because S waves travel through it.

   **Student 2:** The mantle is liquid magma and flows slowly. It must be liquid because it is very hot and flows.

   **Student 3:** The mantle is layers of liquid magma and solid rock. That way it can flow, but also be a solid.

3. **Two students are discussing which planetary object Earth is most similar to.**

   **Student 1:** Earth is most similar to the Moon because they are so close in space that they formed from the same part of the nebula that formed the planets.

   **Student 2:** Earth is most similar to Venus and Mars because the size of the planet and presence of an atmosphere plays a large role in how they are today.

4. **Three students are discussing how geologists have learned about the layers of Earth.**

   **Student 1:** Geologists drill into the different layers giving us direct evidence for each layer.

   **Student 2:** We can't drill that far, so we know about the different layers through indirect evidence.

   **Student 3:** We actually aren't sure about Earth's layers because evidence is from computer models based on physics.

5. **Three students are discussing the relationship between the lithosphere and crust.**

   **Student 1:** The lithosphere and crust are both layers at Earth's surface, so the term lithosphere is a more scientific name for crust.

   **Student 2:** The terms lithosphere and crust are different ways of describing Earth's layers, so the terms have different meanings.

   **Student 3:** The lithosphere is a layer that is beneath the crust, so they are different layers in Earth.

## End of Chapter Questions: Short Answer

Using your own words or sketching and labeling a diagram, answer the following questions.

6. Draw a table to compare at least four separate aspects of the formation of the solar system and the formation of Earth. Things to consider include the role of gravity, the role of density, composition, and how composition changes with distance to the center.

7. Based on what you know about Earth's layers, write a hypothesis explaining what the layers of Mars are like and why you think so. To test your hypothesis, describe one experiment or observation that could be made by visiting Mars and what it would tell you about your hypothesis.

8. Imagine a solar system formed around the first star, before any other stars existed. Explain how and why the planets in that solar system would be different from the planets in our solar system.

9. Imagine a planet forms from rock, liquid water, and water ice. Sketch a labeled diagram showing the layers based on composition and the layers based on behavior.

10. Describe the composition and behavior of the outer core, and explain how we know.

11. Identify the following layers in the cross sections of the two planets below: crust, mantle, outer core, inner core. A third planetary body did not differentiate. For each, mark the location of an earthquake, and sketch the resulting seismic waves traveling through the cross-section. Clearly distinguish P and S waves using a key.

12. Draw a table to compare and contrast at least four separate aspects of Earth, Mercury and Venus. Things to consider include formation of the planet, differentiation, internal temperature, surface temperature, and processes that affect the surface.

13. Billions of years ago, Mars had a hot interior and a thicker atmosphere of carbon dioxide. If you could time travel and visit Mars in the distant past, explain whether or not you could walk along sand dunes at a beach near an active volcano.

**Hints:** For each question, see the sections listed here for information relevant to answering it.

**1.** (2.1, 2.2) **2.** (2.5,2.6) **3.** (2.8,1.9,2.10) **4.** (2.6) **5.** (2.5) **6.** (2.2,2.3,2.4,2.5) **7.** (2.4,2.5,2.6,2.7,2.8) **8.** (2.1,2.2,2.3,2.4) **9.** (2.4,2.5) **10.** (2.5,2.6) **11.** (2.2,2.4,2.7,2.8,2.9,2.10) **12.** (2.2,2.4,2.7,2.8,2.9,2.10) **13.** (2.8,2.9,2.10)

# Chapter 3:
# Plate Tectonics

## Chapter Objectives

When you are finished reading this chapter, you should be able to ...

• describe what tectonic plates are, and explain why they move (3.1–3.2, 3.5–3.6).

• compare and contrast the direction of motion and locations of the three different types of plate boundaries (3.3–3.4).

• connect the processes that happen at different types of plate boundaries with the resulting characteristics and locations (3.7–3.14).

• summarize evidence that supports the theory of plate tectonics (3.14–3.18).

# 3.1 – 3.6 Tectonic Plate Boundaries

In this section you will learn that in geology, the theory of plate tectonics is a fundamental concept and helps us to understand and explain many of the characteristic landforms and processes that occur on Earth.

## Frequently Used Terms

The terms listed here are used repeatedly throughout this section, so by learning them before you read this section, you can focus your mental energy on the concepts presented.

**asthenosphere** The solid rock layer of Earth that moves and deforms because it is ductile (it bends rather than breaks); the asthenosphere is located under the lithosphere and includes part of the mantle.

**convergent plate boundary** A plate boundary where two tectonic plates are moving towards each other (converging); subduction occurs at convergent plate boundaries.

**density** The mass per volume, or the amount of something compared to the space it fills.

**divergent plate boundary** A plate boundary where two tectonic plates are moving apart (diverging).

**earthquake** The shaking felt when the bedrock making up Earth's crust on either side of a fault suddenly moves and releases energy; most earthquakes happen in the rigid lithosphere at plate boundaries.

**lithosphere** The solid, rigid outer layer of Earth, made up of the crust and the top of the mantle; tectonic plates are composed of lithosphere.

**plate boundary** The edge of tectonic plates where two plates touch each other; there are three types— convergent, divergent, and transform—defined by the motion of the two tectonic plates on either side of the boundary, each resulting in key geologic processes.

**plate tectonics theory** The scientific theory that describes the movement and interaction of segments of Earth's outer layers, called tectonic plates; this scientific theory explains many seemingly unrelated aspects of Earth's characteristics and processes, such as the locations of volcanoes, earthquakes, and mountains.

**subduction** The process by which ocean lithosphere descends into the solid but slowly moving mantle beneath the lithosphere at a convergent plate boundary.

**tectonic plate** A large segment of Earth's lithosphere that slowly moves as one large piece; each tectonic plate touches other plates at its edges, called plate boundaries.

**transform plate boundary** A plate boundary where two tectonic plates on either side slide past each other.

Mount Rainier is a volcano on a plate boundary in Washington State. When it erupts again, it will impact the lives of millions of people.

Chapter 3: Plate Tectonics   Section 1

# 3.1 Tectonic Plates

**Key Concept:** Earth's tectonic plates are segments of the lithosphere, and they cover Earth's entire surface. The lithosphere is Earth's layer that includes both the crust and the uppermost part of the mantle **1**. Thinner lithosphere that is generally covered by oceans is called oceanic lithosphere, and the lithosphere that makes up the continents is called continental lithosphere. The lithosphere is divided into segments called tectonic plates. Continents and tectonic plates are not the same thing. Continents are the large areas of land made up of continental lithosphere, while tectonic plates are the entire layer of lithosphere and are generally made up of both oceanic lithosphere and continental lithosphere **2**.

## **1** Tectonic plates are lithosphere

Recall from Chapter 2 that the lithosphere is Earth's outermost rigid, brittle layer (see 2.5), and its thickness defines the thickness of a tectonic plate. The top part of the lithosphere, called the crust, is composed of rock, while the bottom part is part of the mantle, so it is composed of iron-rich rock. The lithosphere sits on top of the asthenosphere, like a cracker would sit on jello. The asthenosphere is part of the mantle and is solid, but unlike the rigid lithosphere, it undergoes deformation by bending very slowly instead of breaking. Throughout this chapter there are many cross sections, such as the one to the right, in which you can see the lithosphere (the tectonic plate) and the underlying asthenosphere.

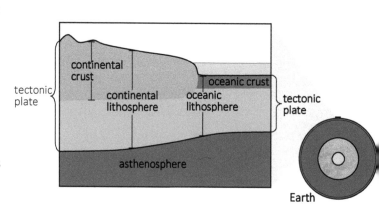

## **2** Tectonic plates include continents

Tectonic plates often include both oceanic lithosphere and continental lithosphere. In contrast, continents are large landmasses that are exclusively comprised of continental lithosphere. Continents are smaller than the tectonics plates they are a part of. Each tectonic plate ends where it meets another tectonic plate at a plate boundary. In comparison, continents end at a continental margin, which is the edge of the continental lithosphere that is covered by ocean water and is next to oceanic lithosphere.

### Continental margins are not always plate boundaries
Tectonic plates and continents are not the same, so tectonic plate boundaries and continental margins frequently do not line up. In the cases where the margin of a continent is the same as the edge of a tectonic plate, it is called an active continental margin. In contrast, where the continental margin is not a plate boundary, but is instead where the continental lithosphere meets the oceanic lithosphere within the tectonic plate, it is called a passive continental margin. As illustrated in the nearby figure, the North American Plate is an example of a plate that is made up of both oceanic and continental lithosphere and has both active and passive continental margins. Continental margins are described in more detail in 8.14 and 15.3.

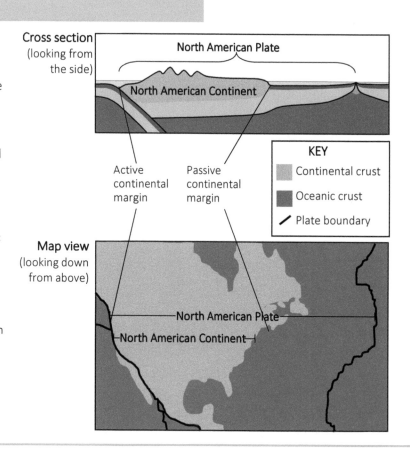

## Check   Before you continue, you should be able to answer each check without looking at the page.

☐ Describe what a tectonic plate is made up of and explain how a tectonic plate differs from a continent.
☐ Explain how continental margins are different from tectonic plate boundaries.

# 3.2 Tectonic Plates and Plate Boundaries

**Key Concept:** Earth's lithosphere is divided into about a dozen major tectonic plates with plate boundaries in **between them.** The theory of plate tectonics asserts that Earth's surface is divided into individual tectonic plates that move. These tectonic plates are pieces of Earth's lithosphere that fit together like puzzle pieces; there are no gaps **1**. The plates meet and move relative to each other at plate boundaries **2**. There are three different types of plate boundaries, and the plates move differently at each one. The behavior of the tectonic plates at these boundaries is a key element in the fundamental concept of plate tectonics and is related to nearly all topics in geology.

## 1 Tectonic plates

The dozen tectonic plates making up the lithosphere sit on top of the asthenosphere. The continental lithosphere that makes up parts of tectonic plates is thicker and less dense than oceanic lithosphere that makes up other parts of tectonic plates, and this difference affects how plates with different types of lithosphere interact with each other as they move relative to each other at plate boundaries.

## 2 Plate boundaries separate plates

A plate boundary is the line between two tectonic plates, where they meet at Earth's surface. There are three types of plate boundaries that are defined by the motion of the plates. Plates move toward each other at convergent plate boundaries; plates move apart at divergent plate boundaries; and plates slide along the boundary in opposite directions at transform plate boundaries.

### Tectonic plates in map view
Plates 1 and 2 are moving apart, which is called diverging. Plates 2 and 3 are moving together, or converging.

| Key | |
|---|---|
| 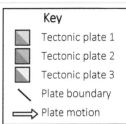 | Tectonic plate 1 |
| | Tectonic plate 2 |
| | Tectonic plate 3 |
| ↘ | Plate boundary |
| ⇒ | Plate motion |

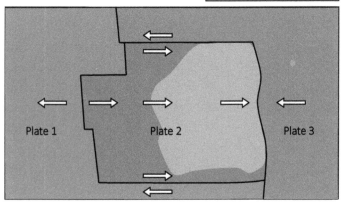

Plate 1          Plate 2          Plate 3

### Plate boundaries in map view
Plate 2 is separated from Plate 1 by divergent and transform plate boundaries, and it is separated from Plate 3 by convergent and transform plate boundaries.

| Key | |
|---|---|
| 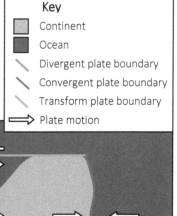 | Continent |
| | Ocean |
| ╲ | Divergent plate boundary |
| ╲ | Convergent plate boundary |
| ╲ | Transform plate boundary |
| ⇒ | Plate motion |

Plate 1          Plate 2          Plate 3

### Tectonic plates in cross section
Plates 1 and 2 are moving apart, and Plates 2 and 3 are moving together so that Plate 3 goes under Plate 2.

| Key | |
|---|---|
|  | Lithosphere |
| | Mantle |

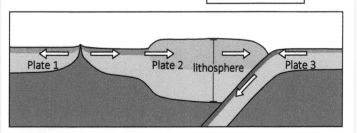

Plate 1          Plate 2   lithosphere   Plate 3

### Plate boundaries in cross section
A divergent boundary is between Plates 1 and 2, and a convergent plate boundary is between Plates 2 and 3.

| Key | |
|---|---|
|  | Lithosphere |
| | Mantle |

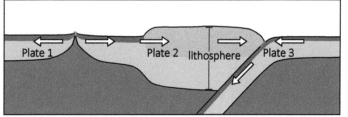

Plate 1          Plate 2   lithosphere   Plate 3

## Check

☐ Draw and label a simple cross section showing two tectonic plates and one plate boundary.
☐ List the three types of tectonic plate boundaries and the motion that occurs at each.

# 3.3 Types of Plate Boundaries

**Key Concept:** The types of plate boundaries are defined by how the tectonic plates at each plate boundary move. At divergent plate boundaries, two tectonic plates move apart and create new oceanic lithosphere **1**. At convergent plate boundaries, tectonic plates move together **2**. At convergent plate boundaries involving oceanic lithosphere, the oceanic lithosphere sinks beneath other lithosphere, allowing the two plates to continue moving towards each other. At transform plate boundaries, two tectonic plates slide past each other **3**.

## **1** Divergent plate boundaries

Where two tectonic plates move apart (diverge) from each other, the mantle underneath the plates rises upwards, and molten rock called magma fills in between the plates and cools to create new seafloor. Instead of forming a gap at the plate boundary, the new seafloor is elevated to form a range of undersea mountains on the floor of the ocean called an ocean ridge that are associated with divergent boundaries. The processes that occur at divergent boundaries and the resulting landforms are described in 3.7 and 3.8.

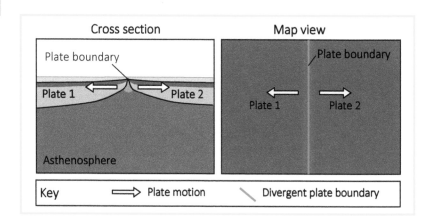

## **2** Convergent plate boundaries

Where two tectonic plates move toward (converge on) each other, volcanoes form and mountains rise where they collide. If at least one plate at the plate boundary is thin, dense oceanic lithosphere, that oceanic lithosphere sinks beneath the other lithosphere, a process called subduction. However, if both plates at the plate boundary are continental lithosphere, the lithosphere does not subduct and only a mountain range forms. The processes that occur at convergent plate boundaries and the resulting landforms are described in 3.9–3.11.

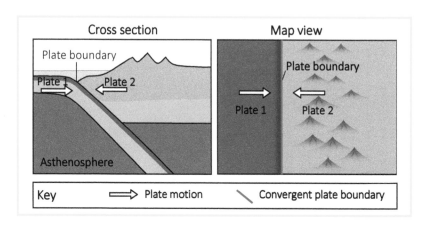

## **3** Transform plate boundaries

Where two tectonic plates slide past each other along the plate boundary, lithosphere is neither created nor subducted, and there are no resulting universal, characteristic landforms. Transform plate boundaries may occur between any two plates. Transform plate boundaries are described in more detail in 3.12 and 3.13.

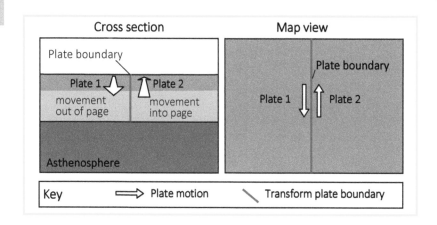

## Check

☐ Describe the motion of plates at divergent, convergent, and transform plate boundaries.
☐ Draw and label three sketches showing the relationship between the cross-sectional view and map view at each type of plate boundary.

# 3.4 Locations of Plate Boundaries

**Key Concept:** Plate boundaries tend to be located in particular geographic locations that relate to the processes that occur at them. For example, if geologists want to locate a divergent plate boundary, they would typically search in the ocean because divergent plate boundaries create new oceanic lithosphere **1**. Similarly, convergent plate boundaries are often located along the edge of a continent where oceanic lithosphere is subducting **2**. Transform plate boundaries tend to be short and connect other plate boundaries to each other **3**.

## **1** Divergent plate boundary locations

Divergent plate boundaries are where two tectonic plates separate, and molten rock called magma comes up and cools, creating new oceanic lithosphere. The oceanic lithosphere is thin and dense, so it has a low elevation and fills with water, creating oceans. Some divergent plate boundaries initially separate two plates of continental lithosphere, but there, too, the magma eventually creates new oceanic lithosphere, and therefore, oceans. The Mid-Atlantic Ridge is a divergent plate boundary currently in an ocean, and the East African Rift is a divergent plate boundary currently separating continental lithosphere.

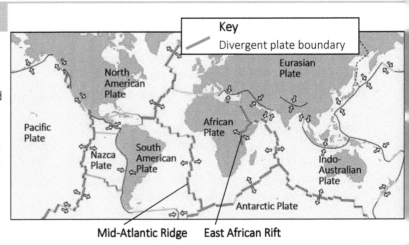

Mid-Atlantic Ridge    East African Rift

## **2** Convergent plate boundary locations

Many convergent plate boundaries are located along the edges of the ocean because oceanic lithosphere subducts beneath continental lithosphere there. For example oceanic lithosphere is subducting along the western side of South America, forming the Andes Mountains, and it is subducting near Alaska, forming the Aleutian Islands. The Himalayan Mountains are an example of a convergent plate boundary in the middle of a continent. These mountains are forming as the two plates of continental lithosphere collide.

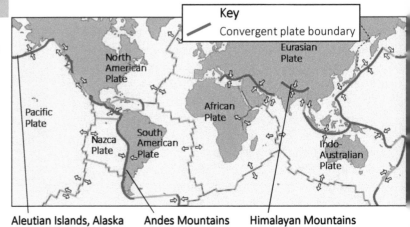

Aleutian Islands, Alaska    Andes Mountains    Himalayan Mountains

## **3** Transform plate boundary locations

There are many transform plate boundaries that create small lateral, or sideways, jumps in divergent plate boundaries in the ocean, such as along the Mid-Atlantic Ridge. These transform plate boundaries allow plates curved along Earth's surface to move apart from each other along relatively straight divergent plate boundaries. Some transform plate boundaries connect plate boundaries on land as well, such as along the San Andreas Fault in California.

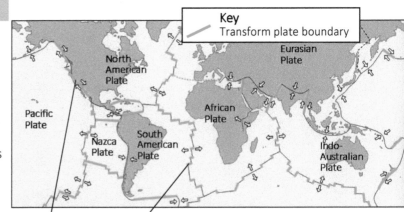

San Andreas Fault    Mid-Atlantic Ridge

## Check

☐ List where each type of tectonic plate boundary is typically found, and explain why each occurs in these locations.
☐ Give one example of each type of tectonic plate boundary, and label it on a map of the world.

# 3.5 DATA AND DIAGRAMS: World Map of Tectonic Plates

**Key Concept:** **Maps can show interpretations about Earth's surface.** This map shows the location of Earth's tectonic plates in relation to the location of the continents **1**. To create a map like this, geologists locate characteristics and features related to plate boundaries. Tips on how to read this map are below **2**. Use the questions to practice interpreting maps **3**.

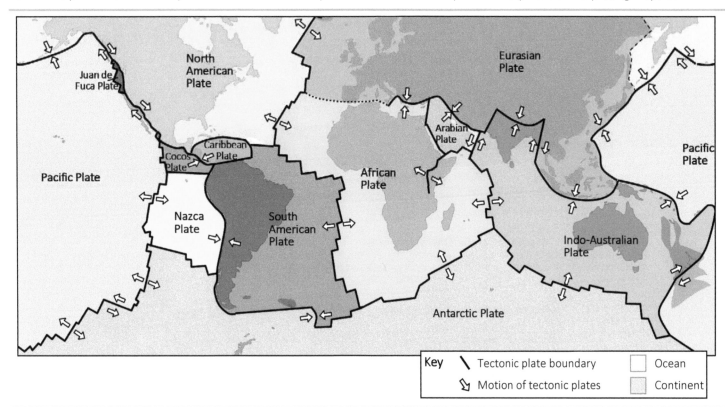

## **1** How to read the diagram

Figure out what data or information the map was created to communicate. Here, information about the shapes and sizes of tectonic plates is mapped onto a diagram of the entire Earth with the continents drawn in as darker shades. The tectonic plates are the colored shapes that are outlined with bold black lines.

## **2** An example of what you might interpret

The North American tectonic plate is shown in yellow-green with bold black boundaries. It includes the North American continent as well as some of the Atlantic Ocean.

## **3** Questions

1. What does the map show?
a. the size and shape of tectonic plates compared to continents
b. the locations where two tectonic plates touch each other
c. the composition of the mantle beneath the tectonic plates
d. both a and b
e. a, b, and c

2. What do the colors represent?
a. types of crust, such as continental and oceanic
b. tectonic plates
c. tectonic plate boundaries

3. Which plate does not have significant amounts of both oceanic lithosphere and continental lithosphere?
a. Pacific Plate
b. African Plate
c. North American Plate
d. South American Plate

4. How can you distinguish different types of plate boundaries on the map?
a. They are indicated with different colored lines
b. They are indicated by the way the arrows point
c. Some are located on land and some are located in the ocean

5. What relationship between continents and tectonic plates does this map illustrate?
a. Tectonic plates are the same shape as continents, because they are continents.
b. Tectonic plates are a similar shape to continents, because continental lithosphere is more important than oceanic lithosphere in plate shape.
c. Tectonic plates are a different shape from continents, because they include continents and ocean.

# 3.6 Tectonic Plate Movement

**Key Concept:** Tectonic plates move because gravity pulls oceanic lithosphere away from high ocean ridges and downward into Earth where it subducts into the mantle. Below tectonic plates, the solid mantle slowly convects because the pull of gravity causes denser, cooler areas of the mantle to sink and less dense areas to rise **1**. However, it is not this motion of the mantle that directly moves the tectonic plates; instead it is the force of gravity, that ultimately pulls the tectonic plates **2**. At divergent plate boundaries, gravity causes the tectonic plates to "slide" downwards, away from the high seafloor at the boundary, pushing the rest of the tectonic plate. At convergent plate boundaries with subduction, gravity pulls the cold, dense oceanic lithosphere downward into the mantle, pulling the rest of the tectonic plate.

## **1** Convection in the mantle does not move plates

The solid layer of mantle rock beneath the lithosphere moves several centimeters (inches) per year in a circulation pattern because of density differences within the mantle and gravity, the force that attracts everything towards the center of the planet. The resulting circulation pattern, called convection, slowly moves the entire solid mantle. However, this mantle convection does not directly drag the tectonic plates due to friction between the convecting mantle and lithosphere.

2. Hotter, less dense, solid mantle rock rises.

3. Near Earth's surface the heat from the solid mantle rock radiates away, and the rock cools. The cooler atoms in the rock pack more closely together, resulting in denser rock.

4. Cooler rock is denser, so the solid mantle rock sinks.

5. As it sinks, the cooled, dense mantle heats up again because of Earth's interior heat, and it eventually moves upwards again, continuing the convection pattern.

1. Earth's interior is very hot and heats up the mantle rock. As rock heats, the atoms that make up the rock spread out and take up more room, resulting in less dense rock.

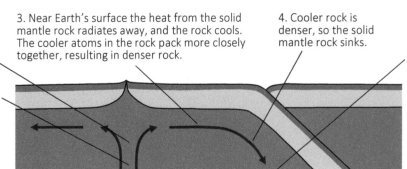

**Key**
→ Motion of mantle
▬ Lithosphere

## **2** Gravity pushes and pulls tectonic plates

Plate motion is primarily caused by gravity pulling tectonic plates downward. The rock that makes up tectonic plates has a lower density than mantle rock, so the plates sit on top of the mantle just as a low-density cracker would sit on top of jello. As the plate cools, it becomes denser and sinks, just as a dense rock would sink into jello. As explained in these diagrams, gravity is the primary cause of motion.

**Key**
⇨ Motion of plate

### Divergent plate boundary

2. The newly formed lithosphere is warm and sits higher than the cooler surrounding lithosphere because it has a lower density. This high area is called the ocean ridge.

1. Hot, solid mantle rock rises and forms new lithosphere, which is the rock that makes up a tectonic plate.

3. The higher part of the tectonic plate near the ocean ridge pushes downward due to gravity.

4. The tectonic plate near the ocean ridge pushes the rest of the tectonic plate in front of it horizontally away from the ridge.

### Convergent plate boundary

1. Old lithosphere cools off. It therefore becomes denser, so it sinks, moving down through the solid mantle.

2. The downward motion of the tectonic plate, or slab, pulls the rest of the tectonic plate behind it.

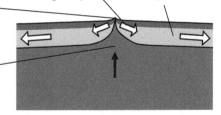

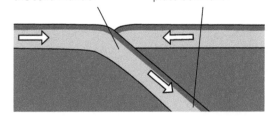

## Check

□ Describe the roles of gravity, temperature, and density in the motion of tectonic plates.
□ Summarize why tectonic plates move.

# 3.7 – 3.13 Types of Plate Boundaries

In this section, you will learn about the tremendous range of features that form at plate boundaries. The different types of plate boundaries are linked to characteristic processes that occur. The landforms that result from these processes are identifiable and help geologists interpret what is happening.

## Frequently Used Terms

The terms listed here are used repeatedly throughout this section, so by learning them before you read this section, you can focus your mental energy on the concepts presented.

**landforms** Natural features with a distinctive shape on Earth's surface, such as mountains, volcanoes, valleys, ridges, and trenches.

**magma** Molten rock that is below Earth's surface; after it erupts at the surface, it is called lava.

**ocean ridge** A range of undersea mountains; ocean ridges form in oceans at divergent plate boundaries.

**ocean trench** A long, deep depression on the ocean floor; ocean trenches form at convergent plate boundaries where subduction occurs.

**volcano** The location from which lava, pyroclasts, and gases erupt and accumulate; the resulting mountain-like formation from the buildup of lava and pyroclasts is also called a volcano; most form at plate boundaries.

Large mountain ranges, such as the Himalayan Mountains, are created by plate tectonic processes.

# 3.7 Divergent Plate Boundaries on Land

**Key Concept:** Some divergent plate boundaries on land develop where continental lithosphere splits into two new tectonic plates. Where continental lithosphere stretches, a single tectonic plate may become two separate tectonic plates **❶**. As the plates move apart over the course of millions of years, the lithosphere thins, resulting in a low-lying area called a rift valley. The separation continues and the plates break apart. New lithosphere forms as magma fills in the cracks **❷**. The new lithosphere is oceanic lithosphere. Therefore, as the rift valley slowly splits further, the divergent plate boundary is surrounded by thin, dense ocean lithosphere, and eventually a new ocean is created.

## ❶ A continental plate splits into two plates that move apart

At a divergent plate boundary on land, a continental plate splits apart into two diverging tectonic plates. This is currently happening in the East African Rift, where the African plate is splitting into two new plates. If the two plates continue to diverge, a new ocean will form.

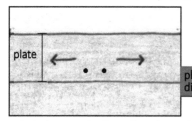 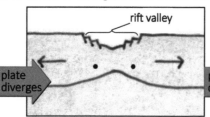 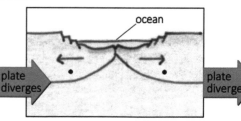

Becomes a divergent plate boundary in the ocean.

A single tectonic plate of continental lithosphere (continental crust plus the top of the mantle) starts to stretch. The dots illustrate how two points move over millions of years.

The continental lithosphere stretches so much that it thins, forming a rift valley. Lava begins to erupt to form new lithosphere.

Magma between the plates cools to become new thin, dense oceanic lithosphere. As this process continues, the low-lying rift valley slowly floods with ocean water and becomes a narrow sea.

## ❷ Unique processes create identifiable characteristics

The processes at divergent plate boundaries create specific characteristics, including landforms, that geologists use to identify the location of this type of plate boundary.

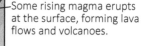

East African Rift Zone

### Processes

3. The magma cools and solidifies to form new rock at the plate boundary. This rock begins to form oceanic lithosphere and may, over millions of years, become a narrow sea and eventually an ocean.

2. The continental lithosphere begins to break apart into two tectonic plates. Magma generated below moves upwards, fills in the cracks, and erupts at the surface.

1. In Earth's interior, pressure increases with depth. Hot mantle rock that moves upwards begins to experience lower pressure. Decreasing pressure on the very hot, solid mantle rock causes some of it to melt to become magma (see why in 6.10).

### Characteristics

The rift valley is a landform that forms on the continent along the plate boundary where a broad region of continental lithosphere is pulling apart and thinning. Rift valleys often contain lakes and rivers because they are low areas, and water collects in low areas.

Some rising magma erupts at the surface, forming lava flows and volcanoes.

Sediments erode from the surrounding land and are deposited downhill in the rift valley.

Shallow-depth earthquakes occur along faults as the thin lithosphere breaks. A fault is a crack in bedrock along which movement occurs, often during an earthquake.

## Check

☐ Describe two characteristics of divergent plate boundaries in continental lithosphere and the processes that create them.
☐ Explain why divergent plate boundaries on land become divergent plate boundaries in the ocean.
☐ Sketch a labeled cross section explaining the formation of landforms at a divergent plate boundary on land.

# 3.8 Divergent Plate Boundaries in the Ocean

**Key Concept:** At a divergent plate boundary in the ocean two tectonic plates move apart, creating new oceanic lithosphere at an ocean ridge. Most divergent plate boundaries are in the ocean. As the two plates move apart, the mantle beneath the plate boundary melts. The magma rises and cools to form new oceanic lithosphere between the separating plates **1**. Oceanic lithosphere forms new ocean floor. The processes at a divergent plate boundary in the ocean result in landforms such as ocean ridges (the long, high regions of the ocean floor) and other characteristics, such as shallow earthquakes and oceanic lithosphere that gets older farther from the plate boundary **2**.

## **1** Two tectonic plates move apart

At a divergent plate boundary in the ocean, two tectonic plates of oceanic lithosphere move apart. This process is currently happening along the Mid-Atlantic Ridge in the Atlantic Ocean.

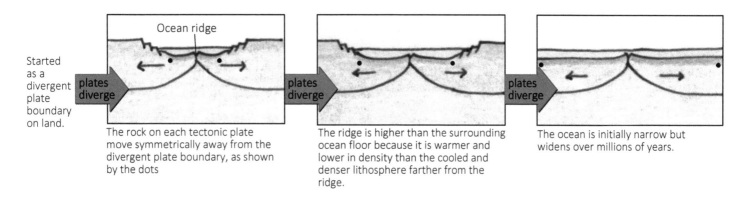

Started as a divergent plate boundary on land.

**plates diverge**

Ocean ridge

The rock on each tectonic plate move symmetrically away from the divergent plate boundary, as shown by the dots

**plates diverge**

The ridge is higher than the surrounding ocean floor because it is warmer and lower in density than the cooled and denser lithosphere farther from the ridge.

**plates diverge**

The ocean is initially narrow but widens over millions of years.

## **2** Unique processes create identifiable characteristics

Just as they do on continents, the processes at divergent plate boundaries in oceans create specific characteristic landforms. These landforms identify the locations of this type of plate boundary. The resulting landforms are somewhat different for divergent plate boundaries in the ocean, although the internal processes are similar.

Juan de Fuca Ridge

### Processes

3. New rock forms at the plate boundary where magma cools and solidifies.

2. Gravity pulls the two tectonic plates down away from the ridge, and magma generated below fills in the resulting cracks.

1. Similar to divergent plate boundaries on land, the decreasing pressure on rising hot mantle melts some of the mantle into magma (see 6.10).

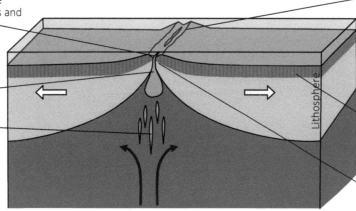

### Characteristics

The ocean ridge is a high line of underwater mountains in the ocean. This landform is composed of newly formed lithosphere, which is still warm, so it has a lower density and therefore rests higher on the underlying mantle it is sitting on. As a result, the ocean ridge is at a higher elevation than its surroundings.

The crust farthest away from the divergent boundary formed first. The farther the oceanic crust is from the divergent plate boundary, the older, cooler, and denser it is.

Shallow-depth earthquakes happen along faults in the thin lithosphere as it breaks along the plate boundary.

## Check

☐ Explain why most divergent plate boundaries are located in the ocean.
☐ Describe two characteristics of divergent plate boundaries in the ocean and the processes that create them.
☐ Sketch a labeled cross section explaining the formation of the landforms at a divergent plate boundary in the ocean.

# 3.9 Ocean-Continent Convergent Plate Boundaries with Subduction

**Key Concept:** At an ocean-continent convergent plate boundary, oceanic and continental lithosphere come together, and the oceanic lithosphere subducts, forming a trench in the ocean and volcanoes on land. When oceanic and continental lithosphere converge, the thinner, denser, oceanic lithosphere subducts **1**. The processes involved in the subduction of oceanic lithosphere create characteristic landforms and events, such as volcanoes on land; deep trenches in the ocean; and deep, intermediate, and shallow earthquakes **2**.

## **1** One tectonic plate subducts

Oceanic lithosphere subducts beneath continental lithosphere. This process is currently happening along the west coast of South America where the Nazca Plate is subducting under the South American plate, forming the Andes Mountains.

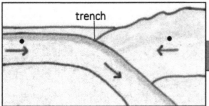 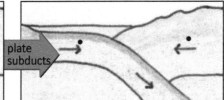 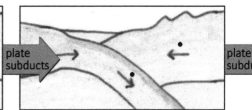

The tectonic plates move toward each other. The dots illustrate how two points in the lithosphere move as the plates converge over millions of years.

At the trench, the oceanic lithosphere subducts under the continental lithosphere because it is denser than the continental lithosphere.

The ocean starts out wide, but over millions of years it becomes narrower and narrower as the oceanic lithosphere that makes up the ocean floor subducts.

## **2** Unique processes create identifiable characteristics

The processes at subduction zones result in key characteristics, including landforms, which geologists use to locate and identify this type of plate boundary. Since the processes are the same whether the oceanic lithosphere subducts under continental lithosphere (as shown here) or under other oceanic lithosphere (see 3.10), the resulting characteristics are similar.

South American Andes Volcanoes

### Processes

4. Magma accumulates in magma chambers, some cooling to form new rock underground and some erupting as lava and building volcanoes.

3. Magma rises into the overriding continental plate above.

2. The subducting plate moves water into hot mantle rock and causes the mantle rock to melt to become magma (see 6.11).

1. The two plates push toward each other. The ocean lithosphere subducts, and the edge of the continental crust crumples from the pressure.

### Characteristics

Mountains form where the continental crust crumples and uplifts to form areas of higher elevation. Volcanoes form in the mountain range where the magma rises to the surface and erupts. This accounts for volcanic mountain ranges along the edge of the continent.

Deep ocean trenches form on the seafloor at the boundary as the oceanic lithosphere bends under the other tectonic plate.

Sediments are deposited in the deep ocean trench, sometimes nearly filling the trench.

Shallow-depth earthquakes occur because of the build-up of pressure along faults between or within the tectonic plates, and deep earthquakes occur along faults in the subducting tectonic plate under the volcanic mountains.

 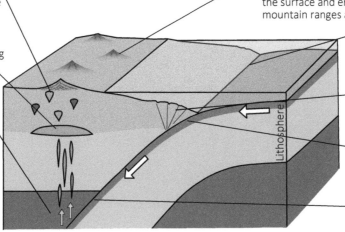

## Check

☐ Describe the processes that occur at convergent plate boundaries where oceanic lithosphere subducts beneath a continental plate.
☐ Describe the unique characteristics of convergent plate boundaries where oceanic lithosphere subducts.
☐ Sketch a labeled cross section explaining the formation of the landforms at an ocean-continent convergent plate boundary.

# 3.10 Ocean-Ocean Convergent Plate Boundaries with Subduction

**Key Concept:** At an ocean-ocean convergent plate boundary, two tectonic plates of oceanic lithosphere come together, and one plate subducts beneath the other plate, forming a trench next to volcanic islands. When two plates of oceanic lithosphere converge, the oceanic lithosphere from one plate subducts beneath the other **1**. The processes of ocean–continent subduction and ocean–ocean subduction are similar. Both result in characteristics such as an ocean trench and deep and shallow earthquakes. However, an arced line of volcanic islands in the ocean results from ocean-ocean convergence instead of a line of volcanic mountains along the edge of the continent **2**.

## **1** One tectonic plate subducts

Oceanic lithosphere subducts beneath oceanic lithosphere. This process is currently happening in the Aleutian Islands in Alaska, where the Pacific Plate is subducting under the North American plate.

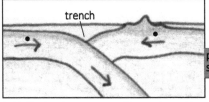 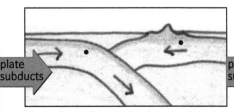 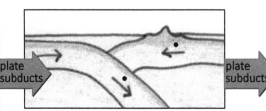

Initially the dots representing rocks on the tectonic plates move toward each other.

The tectonic plate that is denser subducts. The subducting plate is often made up of the older oceanic lithosphere, because it is cooler and therefore denser.

The plate boundary is the trench where the plates meet at the surface.

## **2** Unique processes create identifiable characteristics

The processes at subduction zones result in characteristics, including landforms, which geologists use to identify ocean–ocean convergent plate boundaries. Since the processes that occur at ocean–ocean plate boundaries are the same as those that occur at ocean–continent plate boundaries (see 3.9), the characteristic landforms and events are similar.

Aleutian Islands, Alaska

### Processes

3. Magma accumulates in magma chambers, some cooling to form new rock underground and some erupting as lava and building volcanoes.

2. Magma is less dense than the surrounding rock and rises into the overriding oceanic plate.

1. The subducting plate moves water into hot mantle rock and causes the mantle rock to melt to become magma (see 6.11).

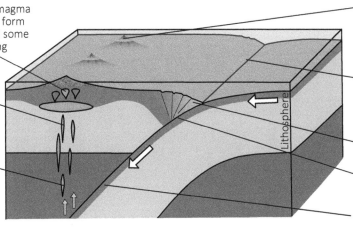

### Characteristics

Volcanoes form on the ocean floor where magma rises to the surface and erupts. If the volcanoes get large enough and their tops rise above sea level, they create a slightly curved line of volcanic islands.

Deep ocean trenches form on the seafloor at the boundary as the oceanic lithosphere bends under the other overriding tectonic plate.

Sediments from the volcanic islands are deposited in the deep ocean trench.

Shallow-depth earthquakes occur because of the build-up of pressure along faults between or within the tectonic plates, and deep earthquakes occur along faults in the subducting tectonic plate under the volcanoes and mountains.

## Check

☐ Describe the processes that occur at convergent plate boundaries when oceanic lithosphere subducts beneath another oceanic plate.
☐ Describe the unique characteristics of convergent plate boundaries where oceanic lithosphere subducts.
☐ Sketch a labeled cross section explaining the formation of the landforms at an ocean-ocean convergent plate boundary.

# 3.11 Continent-Continent Convergent Plate Boundaries

**Key Concept:** At a continent-continent convergent plate boundary, two tectonic plates of continental lithosphere come together, and neither plate subducts forming a large mountain range. After the oceanic lithosphere at a convergent ocean-continent plate boundary is completely subducted, the boundary becomes a continent-continent convergent plate boundary. Subduction slows then stops because the continental lithosphere is not dense enough to descend into the mantle **1**. However, the plates are still moving towards each other, and the processes and characteristics are different from those that occur when one plate subducts. These processes result in large mountain ranges, large amounts of eroded sediments, and many shallow to medium depth earthquakes spread over a wide region **2**.

## **1** Two tectonic plates collide

At a convergent plate boundary where two tectonic plates of continental lithosphere come together, neither is dense enough to subduct. This process is currently happening in the Himalayan Mountains, where the Indian Plate is crashing into the Eurasian Plate.

Starts as a convergent plate boundary with subduction.

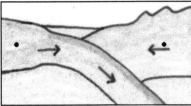 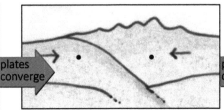 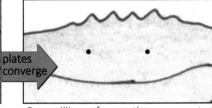

| The tectonic plates move toward each other. The oceanic lithosphere subducts underneath the continental lithosphere completely. | The portions of the plate composed of continental lithosphere run into each other, but neither plate is dense enough to subduct. Large mountain ranges form as one plate overrides the other, and they crumple. | Over millions of years, the movement of the continents slows then stops because the thick continental lithospheres block each other's paths. The two plates merge into one. The mountains no longer grow, and they slowly erode away. |

## **2** Unique processes create identifiable characteristics

The processes at continent-continent convergent plate boundaries result in specific characteristics, including landforms, which geologists use to identify the locations of this type of plate boundary. Subduction does not play a role at this type of boundary, so many of the processes and resulting characteristics are different than those at convergent plate boundaries that involve subduction.

Himalayan Mountains

### Processes

3. There is no subduction to cause mantle melting, so volcanoes are not abundant.

2. A large, broad mountain range forms, the lithosphere thickens as one tectonic plate overrides the other, and the tectonic plates crumple together.

1. Two plates meet and neither continental lithosphere subducts deep into the mantle because neither is dense enough.

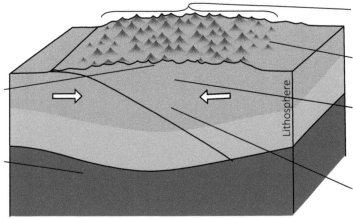

### Characteristics

One side of the large, broad mountain range in the middle of a continent marks the plate boundary.

Sediments erode from the mountains and are deposited downhill next to the mountains.

Shallow- to medium-depth earthquakes occur across a wide region, on faults along the plate boundary and faults that formed throughout the lithosphere both near to and far from the plate boundary.

Immense pressure and high temperatures cause rock that is already there to change into new rock (see 5.2 and 5.3).

## Check

☐ Describe the processes that occur at continent-continent convergent plate boundaries.
☐ Describe the unique characteristics that result from continent-continent convergent plate boundaries.
☐ Sketch a labeled cross section explaining the formation of the landforms at a continent- continent convergent plate boundary.

# 3.12 Transform Plate Boundaries on Land

**Key Concept:** Transform plate boundaries on land occur where two tectonic plates slide past each other. Transform plate boundaries are less complex to describe and understand than divergent and convergent plate boundaries because as the two tectonic plates slide sideways past each other few other processes occur **1**. There are two main characteristics of this type of plate boundary. First, landforms, such as river valleys, shift so they no longer line up across the plate boundary. Second, shallow to medium depth earthquakes occur as the tectonic plates move **2**.

## **1** Two tectonic plates move past each other

At a transform plate boundary on land, the tectonic plates on the two sides of the boundary move past each other in a sideways motion. This process is currently happening along the San Andreas Fault in California.

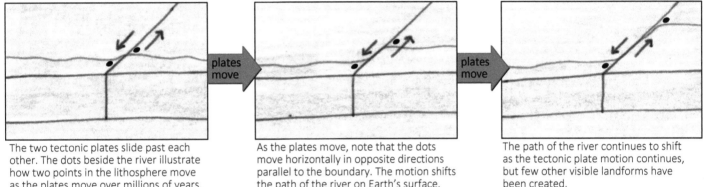

The two tectonic plates slide past each other. The dots beside the river illustrate how two points in the lithosphere move as the plates move over millions of years.

As the plates move, note that the dots move horizontally in opposite directions parallel to the boundary. The motion shifts the path of the river on Earth's surface.

The path of the river continues to shift as the tectonic plate motion continues, but few other visible landforms have been created.

## **2** Unique processes create identifiable characteristics

The processes at transform plate boundaries result in specific characteristics, which geologists use to identify this type of plate boundary on land. These processes are similar to those of transform plate boundaries in the ocean (see 3.13). Transform plate boundaries often connect divergent and convergent plate boundaries. They generally are not related to coasts or other topographical features.

San Andreas Fault

### Processes

1. Two tectonic plates slide past each other horizontally.

2. No large-scale melting of mantle rock occurs because there are no processes that cause melting to occur (such as subduction or rising mantle rock). Therefore, no volcanoes form.

3. Little to no compression means that no large mountains tend to form.

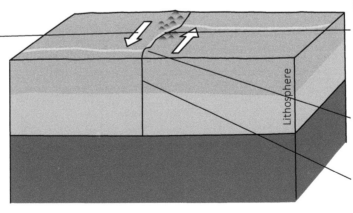

### Characteristics

Although no large mountains or valleys form where the boundary is straight, bends in a transform plate boundary may result in small mountain ranges or shallow valleys.

Landforms, such as valleys carved by rivers, are shifted so they no longer line up across the plate boundary.

Earthquakes at shallow to medium depths occur along faults along the plate boundary.

## Check

☐ Describe the processes that occur at transform plate boundaries on land.
☐ Describe any unique characteristics that result from transform plate boundaries on land.
☐ Sketch a labeled cross section explaining the formation of the landforms at a transform plate boundary on land.

# 3.13 Transform Plate Boundaries in the Ocean

**Key Concept:** Transform plate boundaries in the ocean occur where two tectonic plates slide past each other, usually **at an ocean ridge.** Remember that divergent plate boundaries in the ocean form ocean ridges. Transform boundaries form where the ocean ridge does not form a single straight line. The ocean ridge cannot curve, so the transform boundaries are the kinks in the zigzagging divergent boundary. At these shifts in the ocean ridge the tectonic plates on either side slide past each other as they move away from the divergent plate boundary **1**. As with transform plate boundaries on land, few processes other than earthquakes occur at ocean transform boundaries. Therefore, the transform plate boundary's telltale characteristic is the zigzag "cracks" in ocean ridges **2**.

## **1** Two tectonic plates move past each other

At a transform plate boundary in the ocean, the tectonic plates on the two sides of the boundary move past each other in opposite directions. This process is currently happening in segments along the Mid-Atlantic Ridge, which stretches through the middle of the Atlantic Ocean.

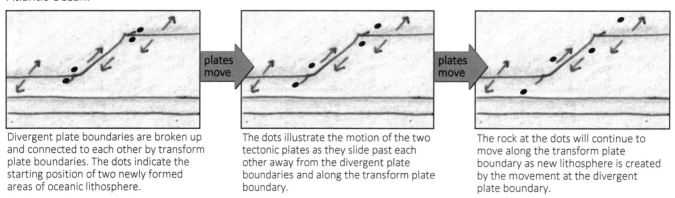

Divergent plate boundaries are broken up and connected to each other by transform plate boundaries. The dots indicate the starting position of two newly formed areas of oceanic lithosphere.

The dots illustrate the motion of the two tectonic plates as they slide past each other away from the divergent plate boundaries and along the transform plate boundary.

The rock at the dots will continue to move along the transform plate boundary as new lithosphere is created by the movement at the divergent plate boundary.

## **2** Unique processes create identifiable characteristics

The processes at transform boundaries result in specific characteristics, which geologists use to identify this type of plate boundary in the ocean. These processes are similar to those that occur at transform plate boundaries on land, described in 3.12.

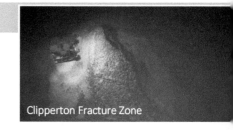

Clipperton Fracture Zone

### Processes

1. Two tectonic plates slide past each other horizontally. The transform plate boundary only exists between the divergent plate boundaries.

2. Beyond the divergent plate boundary, all areas of oceanic lithosphere are moving in the same direction away from the ridge. The areas of oceanic lithosphere are no longer moving past each other in different directions, so they are therefore on the same tectonic plate without a plate boundary between them.

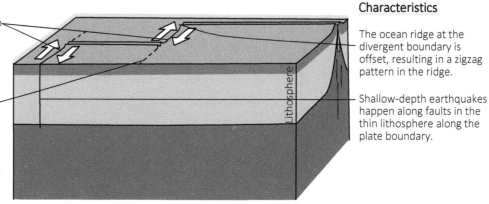

Lithosphere

### Characteristics

The ocean ridge at the divergent boundary is offset, resulting in a zigzag pattern in the ridge.

Shallow-depth earthquakes happen along faults in the thin lithosphere along the plate boundary.

## Check

☐ Describe the processes that occur at transform plate boundaries in the ocean.
☐ Describe any unique characteristics that result from transform plate boundaries in the ocean.
☐ Sketch a labeled cross section explaining the formation of the landforms at a transform plate boundary in the ocean.

# 3.14 – 3.18 Evidence for Plate Tectonics

In this section, you will learn many of the lines of evidence that overwhelmingly support the theory of plate tectonics. Like other scientific theories, the theory of plate tectonics explains a wide range of observations about how nature works.

## Frequently Used Terms

The terms listed here are used repeatedly throughout this section, so by learning them before you read this section, you can focus your mental energy on the concepts presented.

**hotspot volcanoes** Areas unrelated to plate boundaries where magma erupts and volcanoes form.

**magnetic field** This force, similar to a large magnet inside Earth, causes sensitive magnets to point north, like a compass; the magnetic field flips in opposite directions every several hundred thousand years.

**scientific theory** An exceptionally well-supported, overarching explanation of how a part of nature works; a scientific theory is so well supported that it is accepted as an accurate explanation, which is unlike the way "theory" is used in everyday language.

Scientist Marie Tharp used the data gathered on ships to create the first map of the ocean floor in the North Atlantic, published in 1957.
From marie tharpe maps at https://www.flickr.com/photos/marietharpmaps/537480113. Used under Attribution 2.0 Generic (CC BY 2.0). No changes made.

# 3.14 Evidence for Motion of the Continents

**Key Concept:** **Geologists collect a variety of data as evidence for the motion of continents.** The development of Global Positioning System (GPS) satellites has allowed geologists to measure the current movement of each tectonic plate **1**. The study of rocks has also provided geologists with evidence that continents, which are part of tectonic plates, have moved in the past. For example, a map of the continents shows that some of them fit together like puzzle pieces, hinting that they were once joined as one but separated as plates separated at divergent plate boundaries **2**. Geologists have found evidence in rocks of ancient glaciers on continents that are currently too warm for glaciers to form **3**. Geologists have also found the same fossils in rock on different continents that are now separated by an ocean **4**. These examples are just a few of many pieces of evidence that indicate the continents move.

## **1** Plate movement can be measured by GPS

The Global Positioning System (GPS) uses satellites in orbit around Earth to precisely measure the location of certain points on Earth. GPS measurements indicate that various locations on Earth have moved over the last few decades. For example, geologists set up GPS stations to collect data about the plate motions in California, along the transform plate boundary. Without plate tectonic movement, these points would remain in the same place.

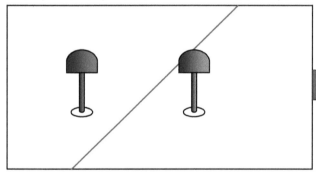
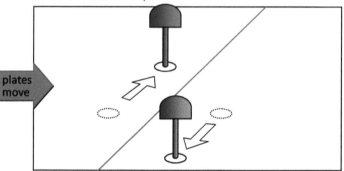

These are locations of GPS stations when they were initially set up to monitor the motions along the plate boundary.

These are locations of the same GPS stations decades later. The arrows indicate the direction of tectonic plate motion. Geologists can calculate the speed of movement by measuring the distances the stations moved over time.

## **2** The continents fit together like puzzle pieces

| Key |
| --- |
| Continent (land) |
| Ocean |
| Continental shelf (continent covered by ocean) |

The edges of continents around the Atlantic Ocean fit together like puzzle pieces because a divergent plate boundary split a single, large continent into the separate continents seen today. Without plate tectonics, the shape of the continents would be random, each with a unique shape unrelated to other continents.

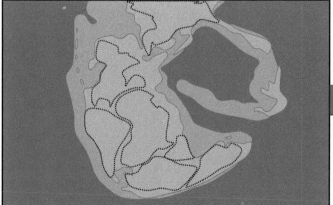

About 250 million years ago, there was just one continent on Earth, a supercontinent made up of many continents, called Pangaea.

The separate continents that exist today formed as Pangaea pulled apart at divergent plate boundaries that began forming around 180 million years ago.

## ❸ Ancient glacier locations are separated by oceans

Geologists have mapped locations and directions of movement of ancient glaciers based on evidence the glaciers leave behind in rocks as they move. Glaciers scratch, gouge, and erode the rock that they slowly flow over. Glaciers also deposit sediments in distinctive deposits. There is rock and sediment evidence of ancient glaciers in locations that today experience hot climates. This evidence supports the theory of plate tectonics, as it would be impossible for glaciers to form in those locations today. Thus we know that the continents have moved from the locations they occupied hundreds of millions of years ago.

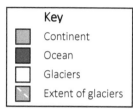

**Key**
- Continent
- Ocean
- Glaciers
- Extent of glaciers

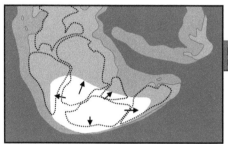
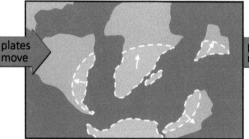
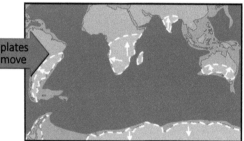

300 million years ago a supercontinent was partially covered by one large glacier flowing from its center near the South Pole.

As the plates were later pulled apart by divergent plate boundaries, the rocks with evidence for the glacier moved too.

The continents are now separated by oceans. The rocks that serve as evidence of past glaciers could not have formed in their current locations.

## ❹ Ancient fossils that formed together are now separated by oceans

Geologists have mapped the locations of unique rock types and fossils of ancient animals across the globe. The current distribution of many rocks and fossils, which initially formed together, is scattered. For example, rocks that formed together are now on opposite sides of an ocean. This distribution provides evidence for the theory of plate tectonics. The example shown in these figures features one particular fossil but the same evidence is found with other fossils and rocks that formed together in mountain ranges.

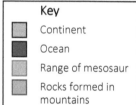

**Key**
- Continent
- Ocean
- Range of mesosaur
- Rocks formed in mountains

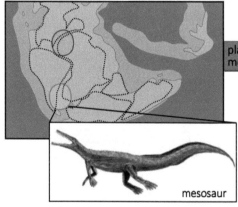
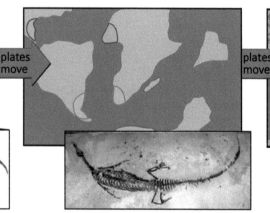
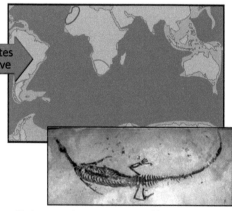

mesosaur

300 million years ago the supercontinent had many plants and animals living on it, such as mesosaurs, each adapted to a specific ecosystem. Unique series of rocks formed in ancient mountains also formed on the supercontinent.

180 million years ago, the fossils of the mesosaurs and the rocks that formed in ancient mountains were separated when the supercontinent was split by divergent plate boundaries.

Today, continents separated by oceans share the same fossils and ancient rock types. The mesosaurs could not have evolved in two widely separated locations with different climates and geography. Their fossils bear evidence to the existence of one large supercontinent.

## Check

- ☐ List four examples of evidence that support the theory of plate tectonics.
- ☐ Explain how each pieces of evidence indicates that plate tectonic movement is happening.

# 3.15 Map Evidence of Plate Boundaries

**Key Concept:** Geologists create maps of key landforms and other geologic characteristics to determine the location of plate boundaries. Examples of data used to create these maps include the locations of earthquakes **1**, volcanoes **2**, landforms **3**, and the age of the oceanic crust **4**. As described in Chapter 1, the process of science involves collecting, analyzing, interpreting, and sharing data, and maps are commonly used in geology to answer scientific questions and support scientific theories.

## 1 Earthquake locations

Geologists observe and measure earthquakes and record their locations on maps to make interpretations about the locations of plate boundaries. The theory of plate tectonics explains why most earthquakes occur in lines and patterns and do not occur in random locations.

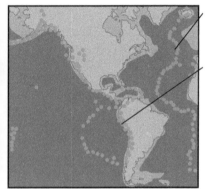

A thin line of earthquakes indicates a divergent plate boundary.

Earthquakes following a coastline indicate subduction at a convergent plate boundary.

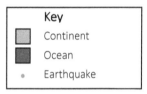

**Key**
- ▢ Continent
- ▢ Ocean
- • Earthquake

## 2 Volcano locations

Geologists observe volcanoes and record their locations on maps to make interpretations about the locations of plate boundaries. The theory of plate tectonics explains why the locations of all volcanoes are not randomly scattered and most volcanoes occur in lines.

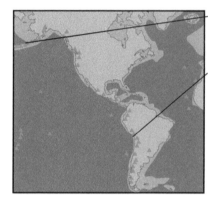

An arced line of volcanic islands indicates subduction at a convergent plate boundary.

A line of active volcanoes indicates subduction at a convergent plate boundary.

**Key**
- ▢ Continent
- ▢ Ocean
- ▲ Volcano

## 3 Landform locations

Geologists observe landforms such as mountain ranges and ocean ridges. They record their locations on maps to make interpretations about the locations of plate boundaries. The theory of plate tectonics explains why landforms are not simply randomly distributed on Earth without relation to each other.

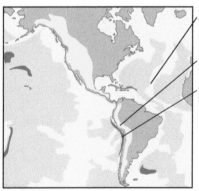

An ocean ridge that rises above the surrounding seafloor indicates a divergent plate boundary.

Mountains indicate a convergent plate boundary.

A deep ocean trench indicates subduction at a convergent plate boundary.

**Key**
- ▢ Mountains
- ▢ Other continent
- ▢ Shallow ocean
- ▢ Ocean
- ▢ Deep ocean

## 4 Seafloor ages

Geologists measure seafloor ages and record the data they collect on maps. They have found that there is new crust along ocean ridges and progressively older crust further from the ridges. If tectonic plates were not moving, the ocean floor would all be about the same age.

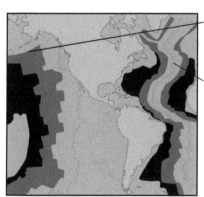

The age of ocean floor changing abruptly indicates subduction at a convergent plate boundary.

New oceanic crust indicates a divergent plate boundary

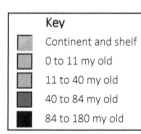

**Key**
- ▢ Continent and shelf
- ▢ 0 to 11 my old
- ▢ 11 to 40 my old
- ▢ 40 to 84 my old
- ▢ 84 to 180 my old

## Check

- ☐ Identify four types of data geologists collect to determine the location of plate boundaries.
- ☐ Describe the landforms and geologic events that indicate the location of a convergent plate boundary with subduction.
- ☐ Explain which three maps on this page would best help to identify the location of a divergent plate boundary.

# 3.16 DATA AND DIAGRAMS: Maps of Subduction Earthquakes

**Key Concept:** Maps can show characteristics of earthquakes, such as their locations and depth. This map shows the location and depth of earthquakes at a subduction zone in relation to the location of a convergent plate boundary. Recall that earthquakes occur in the rigid lithosphere **1**. To create a map like this, geologists measure earthquakes using seismometers and process the data using sophisticated computer programs to determine the exact location and depth of each earthquake. Tips on how to read this map are below **2**. Use the questions to practice interpreting maps **3**.

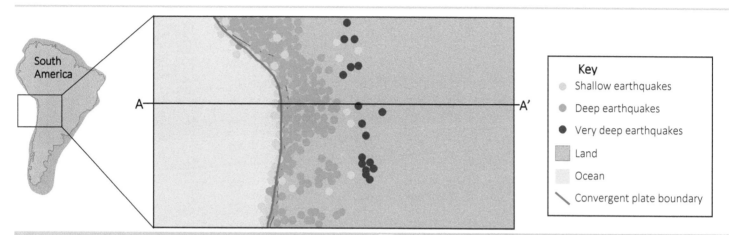

## 1 How to read the diagram

Figure out what data are being mapped. In this case the map shows an area of Earth's surface on the west coast of South America, with blue indicating ocean and brown indicating land. The dark blue line is a convergent plate boundary. The key indicates that the dots show the locations of earthquakes. The color of each dot indicates the depth below the surface at which the earthquake occurred.

## 2 An example of what you might interpret

The light colored orange dots near the plate boundary indicate that shallow earthquakes happen there.

## 3 Questions

**1. What does the map show?**
a. the size of earthquakes at different plate boundaries
b. the damage cause by earthquakes on land and ocean
c. the timing of earthquakes in different places
d. the depths of earthquakes at different locations

**2. What type of plate boundary is shown?**
a. ocean-continent convergent plate boundary with subduction
b. ocean-ocean convergent plate boundary with subduction
c. continent-continent convergent plate boundary
d. transform plate boundary with both oceanic and continental lithosphere

**3. Which statement about earthquakes does the map illustrate?**
a. Earthquakes of similar depth occur in lines along one side of the boundary.
b. Earthquakes of similar depth occur in circles surrounding a plate boundary.
c. Earthquakes of similar depth occur in a symmetric pattern on either side of a plate boundary.

**4. Which cross section most accurately shows what is happening beneath the surface of the area shown on the map?**
a. a
b. b
c. c

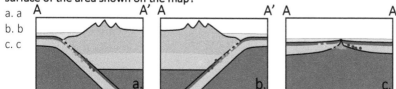

**5. What is the relationship between earthquake depth and location relative to the plate boundary?**
a. Earthquakes closer to the plate boundary tend to be deeper.
b. Earthquakes closer to the plate boundary tend to be shallower.
c. Earthquakes closer to the plate boundary occur at both shallow and deep depths.

**6. Given that earthquakes occur in the lithosphere (and not the mantle), how does the pattern of earthquake depths shown in the map serve as evidence for plate tectonics?**
a. Shallow earthquakes are related to volcanic eruptions in the lithosphere.
b. Deep earthquakes occur at all plate boundaries in the lithosphere.
c. Deep earthquakes occur where the lithosphere is subducting into the mantle beneath it.
d. Deep earthquakes occur in the lithosphere where the seafloor is the deepest.

# 3.17 Hotspot Volcanoes Are Evidence of Plate Tectonics

**Key Concept:** Hotspots volcanoes leave a track of older and older volcanism, giving evidence for the theory of plate tectonics. Hotspot volcanoes are unrelated to plate boundaries but form above unusually hot parts of the mantle **1**. As the tectonic plate above the hot part of the mantle moves, a chain of progressively older volcanoes is formed, providing evidence for the motion of tectonic plates **2**.

## **1** Hotspot volcano formation

Mauna Kea, Hawaii

Hotspot volcanoes form above unusually hot, relatively stationary parts of the mantle, called mantle plumes, that are generally unrelated to a plate boundary (see 6.12). Volcanic chains form above mantle plumes as the plate moves. Hotspot volcanic island chains, such as the Hawaiian Islands, can be distinguished from volcanoes formed by a subducting plate. Hotspot volcanic island chains are generally straight, have a single active volcano over the mantle plume, and do not have a trench next to them. Volcanoes formed at a convergent plate boundary are generally curved in an arc, have active volcanoes along the whole chain, and feature a trench located where the plate is subducting.

4. Geologists use the locations of the older hotspot volcanic islands, which were originally over the mantle plume, to determine the direction of plate motion. Geologists measure the ages and distances from the mantle plume of the older volcanic islands to determine the speed of plate motion.

5. Old hotspot volcanic islands slowly erode away.

3. Tectonic plate motion moves the newly formed volcanic island away from the mantle plume, and the volcano stops erupting. Directly over the mantle plume, a new, younger hotspot volcano begins to form.

2. Magma accumulates in magma chambers in the lithosphere and some erupts, forming lava flows. Successive lava flows may build up on the seafloor, creating an island.

1. From deep in Earth, a mantle plume slowly rises because the hot mantle rock is less dense than the surrounding rock. Some of the rock melts to become magma as it nears the surface (see 6.12).

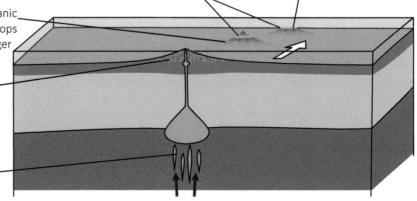

## **2** Hotspot volcano locations illustrate plate movement

The ages of the hotspot volcanoes indicate when they were over the mantle plume. Their ages give geologists information about the direction and speed of tectonic plate movement.

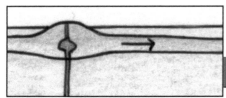

The hotspot volcano above the mantle plume grows because it has a source of magma.

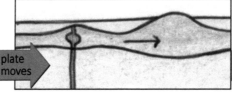

plate moves

As the plate moves, the hotspot volcano moves off the mantle plume. The volcano stops erupting, and a new hotspot volcano begins to form over the mantle plume.

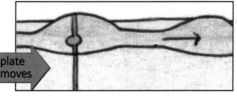

plate moves

The new hotspot volcano eventually forms a new volcanic island. The chain of progressively older volcanoes provides evidence for plate movement.

## Check

☐ Explain how hotspot volcanoes can be used as evidence for plate tectonics and plate motion.
☐ Describe how mantle plumes below hotspot volcanoes form volcanic island chains.

# 3.18 DATA AND DIAGRAMS: Ocean Floor Evidence

**Key Concept:** Time-sequence diagrams show how landforms and other characteristics form and change over time. The diagram on this page shows the change over time of the orientation of magnetic minerals at a divergent plate boundary **1**. Earth has a magnetic field, which you can picture as a large magnet within Earth lined up with Earth's north and south poles. Earth's magnetic poles flip every few hundred thousand years, reversing the direction of the magnetic field. The direction of the magnetic field affects the direction of the alignment of magnetic minerals, called magnetite, in liquid lava. When the lava cools into solid rock, the direction of alignment of the minerals is solidified and frozen in time, recording the direction of Earth's magnetic field at the time the rocks solidified. Geologists have used land-based lava flows to determine the dates that these flips have occurred in Earth's history. Other geologists used sophisticated instruments to measure the direction of magnetic minerals in the seafloor and then assigned the previously determined dates to the matching reversals on the seafloor. Tips on how to read this diagram are below **2**. Use the questions to practice interpreting time-sequence diagrams **3**.

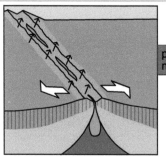 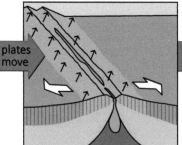 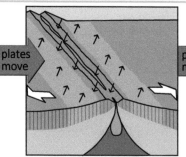 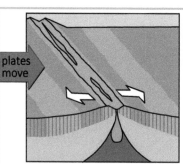

Within liquid lava at a divergent plate boundary, magnetite minerals move so they align north. The lava cools into solid rock. The color and black arrows on the diagram represent the direction the magnetite minerals are aligned.

The magnetite minerals in the newly formed solid rock lithosphere remain in this orientation, even when the magnetic poles flip causing the north magnetic pole to switch to the south pole of Earth.

After Earth's magnetic poles flip, the magnetite minerals in newly erupting lava point south. As the plates continue to separate, the magnetite minerals record the direction of the magnetic field over time in the newly formed lithosphere.

This pattern of magnetic "stripes" can be matched to rocks of known ages, and can be used to interpret the ages of the lithosphere. These ages are evidence of plate motion at divergent plate boundaries.

## **1** How to read the diagram

Read the text at the top to learn about magnetic fields and magnetic minerals. Then, scan the figure and determine what changes from diagram to diagram. The color and small black arrows indicate that the characteristic that is changing over time is the direction of the alignment of the magnetic minerals.

## **2** An example of what you might interpret

In the third panel, the magnetic minerals in the lava point "south" which is the opposite direction from the direction the minerals point in the first panel. This flip is because Earth's magnetic field has changed directions.

## **3** Questions

**1. What does this diagram show?**
a. two plates separating and the changing direction of magnetite alignment
b. two plates coming together and the changing color of the ocean floor
c. two plates sliding past each other and the changing ocean floor composition

**2. What do the different colors in the final panel of the diagram represent?**
a. One color indicates rock that formed at a convergent plate boundary, and the other color indicates rock that formed at a divergent plate boundary.
b. One color indicates rock that is magnetic, and the other color is non-magnetic.
c. One color indicates rock that formed when the magnetic field was pointing in one direction, and the other color is the opposite direction.

**3. Why are magnetic minerals useful for learning about past magnetic fields?**
a. After lava becomes rock, the minerals in the rock change orientation if the magnetic field does.
b. After lava becomes rock, the minerals in the rock do not change orientation, even if the magnetic field does.
c. After lava becomes rock, the minerals in the rock etch a path as they move to follow changes in magnetic field.

**4. How is the pattern of magnetic "stripes" on the seafloor (see the last panel) useful to geologists?**
a. Geologists can use the magnetic stripes to determine the age of the rock by matching the pattern of stripes to the dates the magnetic poles flipped.
b. Geologists can use the magnetic stripes and a compass to navigate across the ocean.
c. Geologists can use the magnetic stripes to locate volcanoes below sea level.

**5. How does the existence of magnetic stripes on the seafloor provide evidence for plate tectonics?**
a. The stripes indicate that convergent plate boundaries follow the edges of continents.
b. The stripes indicate that new seafloor forms as older seafloor moves away from the boundary.
c. The stripes indicate that the direction of the magnetic field has changed in the past.

**Chapter 3**

## End of Chapter Questions: Student Debates

For each of the following questions, determine which student you agree with and explain why.

1. **Two students are discussing the location of tectonic plates.**

   **Student 1:** Tectonic plates make up Earth's outer layer of rock, the layer that air touches and oceans sit on, because they are pieces of the lithosphere.

   **Student 2:** Tectonic plates are near the core, floating on the liquid outer core, because that is the only liquid layer in Earth.

2. **Three students are discussing how many tectonic plates are shown in the cross section. Each has numbered the plates according to their answer.**

   **Student 1:** I numbered two tectonic plates on the diagram, one is oceanic lithosphere and the other is continental lithosphere.

   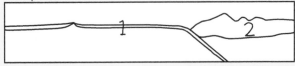

   **Student 2:** You forgot to count the divergent boundary as dividing two plates. There are three tectonic plates.

   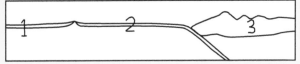

3. **Two students are discussing what a divergent plate is.**

   **Student 1:** A divergent plate has an ocean ridge in the middle where it is stretching in two different directions and growing.

   **Student 2:** I think you are mixing up terms. A plate cannot be divergent. I think you mean a divergent plate *boundary*, which is where two tectonic plates are moving apart.

4. **Two students are discussing what feature forms as two plates with oceanic lithosphere move towards each other.**

   **Student 1:** The plates form a trench because one plate bends down beneath the other plate.

   **Student 2:** The plates form a ridge because the two plates push together, and they bend upwards.

5. **Three students are discussing at which plate boundaries lava erupts.**

   **Student 1:** Rock melts where plate tectonics changes conditions in the mantle. So, lava erupts near convergent plate boundaries and at divergent plate boundaries.

   **Student 2:** Most of the mantle is molten. Lava erupts where molten rock escapes at divergent boundaries.

   **Student 3:** Rock melts where the friction between two plates raises the temperature enough to melt. So lava erupts at convergent boundaries.

## End of Chapter Questions: Short Answer

Using your own words or sketching and labeling a diagram, answer the following questions.

6. Examine a map of plate boundaries, such as the map in 3.5. List and compare in table form at least four distinct aspects of the tectonic plates and plate boundaries in the Pacific Ocean and the Atlantic Ocean. Things to consider include type of lithosphere that makes up plates, types of continental margin, types of boundaries, and locations of boundaries.

7. Explain why there are so many more geologic events, such as earthquakes and volcanic eruptions, on the West Coast of North American than there are on the East Coast.

8. Compare and contrast the three types of convergent plate boundaries in terms of geologic characteristics including landforms.

9. Imagine you discover a new planet. Identify and justify your choice of five pieces of data you could collect to determine if that planet experiences plate tectonic movement.

10. Explain why continental crust is generally older than oceanic crust.

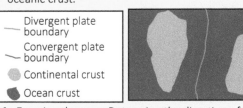

11. Examine the map. Determine the direction of motion of the plates at each boundary. Based on the motions of the plates, draw a new version of the map predicting where the areas of land and plate boundaries will be in the future.

12. Examine the map. You are designing a cruise for vacationers who want to experience a variety of landforms, both above and below sea level. Draw the path of your cruise and identify four locations where you would stop. Write a short description of each stop, identifying the landforms you would visit and why the landforms have formed where they have.

**Hints:** For each question, see the sections listed here for information relevant to answering it.

**1.** (3.1, 3.2, 3.3) **2.** (3.1, 3.2, 3.3) **3.** (3.1, 3.2, 3.3, 3.7, 3.8) **4.** (3.3, 3.7, 3.9, 3.10) **5.** (3.7,3.8,3.9,3.10,3.11,3.12,3.13) **6.** (3.1,3.2,3.3,3.4,3.5,3.14) **7.** (3.1,3.3,3.4,3.5,3.9,3.12) **8.** (3.9,3.10,3.11) **9.** (3.14,3.15,3.16,3.17,3.17,3.19) **10.** (3.4,3.7,3.8,3.9,3.10,3.18,3.19) **11.** (3.1,3.2,3.3,3.8,3.9,3.10,3.11) **12.** (3.8,3.9,3.10,3.14,3.16,3.19)

# Chapter 4: Minerals

## Chapter Objectives

When you are finished reading this chapter, you should be able to …

• define geologic minerals (4.1–4.3, 4.8).

• explain the relationship between minerals and rocks (4.3–4.4).

• summarize how the physical properties of minerals relate to the atoms that comprise them and the types of bonds between atoms (4.2, 4.5–4.6, 4.8).

• categorize minerals into groups and explain the categorizations (4.5–4.6).

• describe the physical properties of minerals and relate those properties to how minerals are identified and used (4.7–4.9).

# 4.1 – 4.4 Minerals and their Formation

In this section, you will learn what minerals are, how they form, and why they are important in geology.

## Frequently Used Terms

The terms listed here are used repeatedly throughout this section, so by learning them before you read this section, you can focus your mental energy on the concepts presented.

**atom** The smallest unit into which elements, such as oxygen or iron, can be divided; atoms are composed of protons, electrons, and neutrons; the number of protons in the nucleus defines the type of atom, and electrons can be shared or transferred to form bonds.

**bond** The attraction between atoms that holds them together; many bonds are created when an electron is shared or transferred between two atoms.

**crystallize** The process of atoms bonding together in a specific, orderly pattern to form minerals; the resulting mineral can be any shape or color.

**formula** The relative amounts of different atoms that are bonded together, such as in the form of a mineral.

**ion** An atom that has gained or lost negatively charged electrons, resulting in a negative or positive charge on the atom.

**mineral** A solid with unique physical properties made up of a particular combination of atoms that bond together in a specific, orderly pattern and form through geologic processes (such as lava cooling); they are the components of rocks; examples include quartz and pyrite.

**physical property** Something you can observe with your senses, by seeing, feeling, tasting, or smelling.

**precipitate** When ions that are mixed with water molecules bond together with other ions and become large enough that they are no longer dissolved in water and separate from the water molecules as solid minerals; "undissolve."

**rock** A geologic solid made up of minerals; the three rock types—igneous, sedimentary, and metamorphic—are categorized based on the way the rock formed and are made up of minerals that are different types, sizes, shapes, and patterns.

Many of the materials used to make this kitchen and items within it are made of minerals.

# 4.1 What Is a Mineral?

**Key Concept:** Minerals are defined as the geologically formed components of rocks that have atoms arranged in an orderly pattern. When you hear the word "mineral" you might think of the nutritious minerals in food. However, minerals are different to geologists. Two criteria define geologic minerals. First, they have a specific combination of atoms arranged in a consistent pattern, which results in a repeated, three-dimensional arrangement of atoms, and second, they must be formed by geologic processes **1**. The first criteria means that each unique mineral is a solid with a defined chemical formula and unique physical properties, such as its color and shape, which help in identification. Minerals need to fit both of these criteria, or they are not considered minerals **2**. When minerals are attached together as solid masses, they are called rock.

## **1** The definition of a mineral

The definition of a mineral is described as below and has two main criteria. More details are given in 4.2, 4.3, and 4.8, elaborating on these criteria.

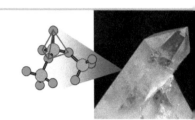

☑ A mineral has a **specific combination of atoms bonded together** in a **consistent pattern**.

| | | |
|---|---|---|
| A specific combination of atoms means that there is a **set ratio of each type of atom** described by its chemical formula. | Minerals are **solid** because atoms are bonded together, locking them in place, unlike in liquids where atoms can flow. | Atoms in a consistent pattern are **arranged in repeated, three-dimensional configurations**, such as cubes, pyramids, or sheets. |

These criteria mean that each mineral has **distinctive physical properties**, such as its hardness and shape, allowing geologists to make observations to identify it.

☑ Minerals are **formed by geologic processes.**

Geologic processes are **natural occurrences that cause geologic changes**. One example is when liquid magma cools into solid minerals. Minerals formed by biologic processes, such as animals building shells, are still considered minerals if they can also form geologically in nature.

## **2** Examples of minerals

Below are examples of minerals as well as some things that may be mistaken for minerals but are not.

**Minerals**

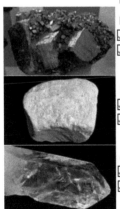

Pyrite is a mineral.
☑ Atoms arranged in a pattern
☑ Formed by geologic processes

Kaolinite is a mineral.
☑ Atoms arranged in a pattern
☑ Formed by geologic processes

Quartz is a mineral.
☑ Atoms arranged in a pattern
☑ Formed by geologic processes

**Things that are not minerals**

Glass atoms are not arranged in an orderly pattern.
☒ Atoms arranged in a pattern
☑ Formed by geologic processes

Pearl is only formed by biological processes inside oysters.
☑ Atoms arranged in a pattern
☒ Formed by geologic processes

Cubic zirconia is only formed by people in a lab.
☑ Atoms arranged in a pattern
☒ Formed by geologic processes

## Check   Before you continue, you should be able to answer each check without looking at the page.

☐ Summarize what a mineral is in your own words.
☐ Explain why each of the following terms can be used to describe minerals: not organic, naturally occurring, solid, defined chemical composition, distinct physical properties.
☐ Give examples of three things you used today that are not minerals, and explain why they are not minerals.

# 4.2 A Mineral Is Made from Atoms Bonded Together

**Key Concept:** Minerals are made of atoms that are bonded together in a three-dimensional pattern. Each mineral is made up of a specific combination of atoms bonded in a certain pattern. An atom is the smallest unit into which an element can be divided, and it is made up of a nucleus surrounded by electrons **1**. Atoms interact by forming different types of bonds that have different strengths **2**. These bonds combine atoms together to form a three-dimensional pattern **3**. If the pattern repeats itself using a specific ratio of atoms, the bonded atoms form a mineral. The characteristics of the different bonds and different atoms cause each mineral to have a unique set of physical properties that allows it to be identified, gives clues to its formation, and gives it specific uses **4**.

## **1** An atom has a nucleus surrounded by electrons

Atoms are the smallest units into which elements can be divided. They are composed of protons, electrons, and neutrons.

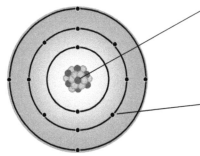

At the center of an atom is the nucleus, composed of protons and neutrons. Protons carry a positive charge and neutrons carry no charge. The number of protons determines what element the atom is.

The electrons that surround the nucleus are negatively charged and balance out the positive charge of the nucleus. If an atom gains or loses an electron, that atom is called an ion, and it has a negative or positive charge overall.

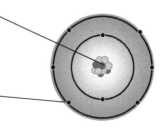

There are 14 protons in the nucleus, so this atom is called a silicon atom.

There are 8 protons in the nucleus, so this atom is called an oxygen atom.

## **2** Types of bonds between atoms

Electrons in one atom can be shared with or transferred to other atoms, creating bonds. Different types of bonds have different strengths, which affect the physical properties of minerals. The atoms in a mineral affect the types of bonds that are made. Some atoms have a tendency to gain or lose electrons, depending on how many electrons they have and how tightly the electrons are held. If electrons are gained or lost, the atom is called an ion. Ions can be attracted to other ions (and form an ionic bond, described on the left), or they can be surrounded by water molecules, thus dissolving in water.

### Ionic bonds transfer electrons between atoms.

In this example, a sodium atom has an electron it is not holding tightly, and it is transferred to a chlorine atom, which has an extra spot for an electron. The resulting sodium ion has a positive charge because it lost an electron ($Na^+$), and the chlorine ion has a negative charge because it gained an electron ($Cl^-$). The opposite charges cause the two ions to bond together with an ionic bond.

### Covalent bonds share electrons between atoms.

In this example, a silicon atom and an oxygen atom attract an electron equally, so they share an electron. Electrons are shared in a covalent bond, so the bond is typically very strong, stronger than an ionic bond, and difficult to break. Covalent bonds are not as easily broken apart by water molecules, so it is not as easy to dissolve atoms with covalent bonds.

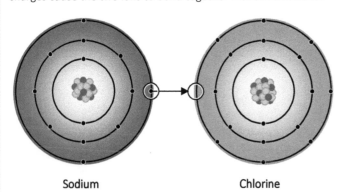

Sodium                               Chlorine

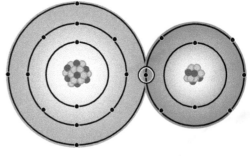

Silicon                               Oxygen

# 3 Atoms bonded together form minerals

Atoms are the building blocks of everything, including cells that make up life and minerals that make up rocks. Atoms bond together, with both ionic bonds and covalent bonds, to form minerals. Each type of mineral has a unique arrangement of specific atoms bonded in a repeating, three-dimensional pattern. The pattern of specific atoms means that there is an exact proportion of those atoms, which is described by the chemical formula.

### The mineral halite
The two types of atoms in the mineral halite are sodium and chlorine, and they are bonded together with ionic bonds. The chemical formula for the mineral halite is NaCl, which means it has one sodium atom (Na) per one chlorine atom (Cl). Chlorine and sodium atoms bond in a repeating cubic arrangement to form halite. Some other minerals also have atoms bonded in a cubic arrangement, but halite is the only one that has sodium and chlorine atoms in that pattern.

### The mineral quartz
The two types of atoms in the mineral quartz are silicon and oxygen, and they are bonded together with strong covalent bonds. The chemical formula for the mineral quartz is $SiO_2$, which means it has one silicon atom (Si) per two oxygen atoms (O). The silicon and oxygen atoms are bonded together in a repeating, four-pointed pyramid shape, called a tetrahedron, as illustrated in the diagram. Silicon-oxygen tetrahedrons are also found in other minerals, and those patterns are described in 4.6.

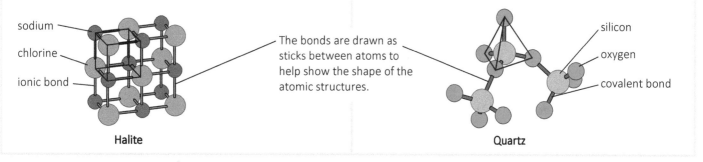

sodium

chlorine

ionic bond

The bonds are drawn as sticks between atoms to help show the shape of the atomic structures.

silicon

oxygen

covalent bond

Halite

Quartz

# 4 Types of atoms and bonds create identifiable physical properties

Each mineral is made up of particular atoms arranged in different patterns, and these differences result in each mineral having distinctive physical properties. For instance, the shape of the pattern of the atoms results in a certain shape to each mineral, which is a physical property of the mineral. These physical properties, detailed in 4.8, allow geologists to identify minerals. This identification conveys significant information such as the geologic history of an area and its potential economic importance.

### The mineral halite
Halite is the mineral name for what is commonly called table salt. Halite has the physical property of being soft because the bonds between atoms are ionic bonds, which allow the atoms in halite to break apart, or dissolve, in water easily. This property explains why you can quickly taste it. Looking carefully, it is possible to see that the cubic shape of the mineral halite reflects the cubic shape of the internal repeated pattern of atoms shown above.

### The mineral quartz
Quartz is one of the most common minerals in rocks. The strong covalent bonds between the atoms result in physical properties, such as being hard, that make quartz resistant to change and ideal for a variety of uses, including as a gemstone and in electronics. Looking carefully, it is possible to see that the mineral quartz forms six-sided points, due to the repeated pattern of silicon-oxygen tetrahedrons shown above.

**Color**
light color,
nearly white

**Shape**
cubes

**Hardness**
softer than
glass

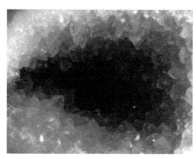

**Color**
light color,
nearly white

**Shape**
six-sided points

**Hardness**
harder than
glass

## Check

☐ Summarize two ways that atoms bond together.
☐ Describe the relationship between atoms and minerals.
☐ Explain two examples where the types of atoms and types of bonds affect the physical properties of a mineral

# 4.3 How Minerals Form

**Key Concept:** Minerals form as atoms bond together in a consistent pattern. Remember that, by definition, minerals must be formed by geologic processes. Three common ways that minerals can form are when atoms bond together as magma cools **1**; when ions dissolved in water become too concentrated and bond together as they precipitate out ("undissolve") **2**; and when pressures and temperatures are increased to a point where the original bonds are unstable, the atoms rearrange to form stable new bonds **3**. The type of rock is determined by the minerals in it, so if new minerals form, then new rock is formed. Geologists make inferences about how rocks in a given area were formed in order to learn more about the geologic history of that area, including the plate tectonic environment or past climates.

## 1 New minerals can form when magma cools

Magma is liquid rock made up of atoms, and most magma has silicon and oxygen atoms making up at least half of its composition. When magma cools, the atoms bond together to form a repeating network, creating new minerals. This process of magma cooling into minerals is called crystallizing. It describes the formation of minerals that make up the type of rock called igneous rock (see 5.1 and Chapter 6). Recall from Chapter 3 that magma forms and then cools at divergent plate boundaries, convergent plate boundaries with subduction, and hotspot volcanoes, so these are typical locations where new minerals form by cooling magma. Therefore, geologists can use the theory of plate tectonics and the types of minerals they identify to help determine the geologic history of an area. In the photo below, the black crust on the cooling lava flow is solid rock, made up of new minerals that formed when the molten rock cooled and solidified.

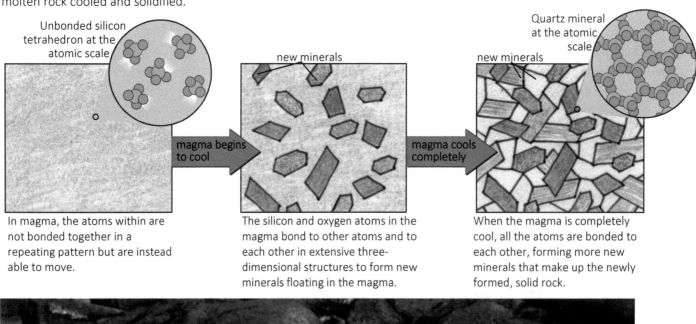

In magma, the atoms within are not bonded together in a repeating pattern but are instead able to move.

The silicon and oxygen atoms in the magma bond to other atoms and to each other in extensive three-dimensional structures to form new minerals floating in the magma.

When the magma is completely cool, all the atoms are bonded to each other, forming more new minerals that make up the newly formed, solid rock.

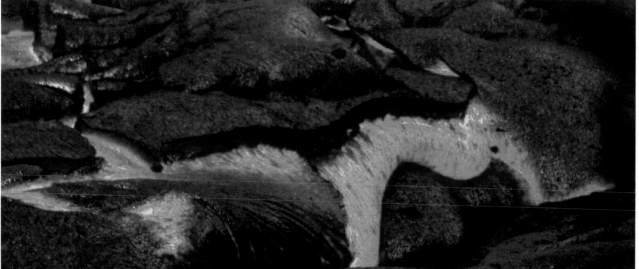

## 2 New minerals can form by precipitating from water

When minerals precipitate from water, the ions that were dissolved in the water bond together to crystallize and form new minerals. These new minerals are solid, so they settle to or grow on the water's bottom. Some animals can also precipitate minerals to create their shells. This process describes the formation of minerals that make up some of the type of rock called sedimentary rock (see 5.1 and Chapter 8). Rocks that are made up of these minerals indicate that there was abundant water at some point in the past, helping geologists determine the geologic history of an area. In the photo, the white area around the evaporating lake is solid rock made up of minerals that precipitated from the water.

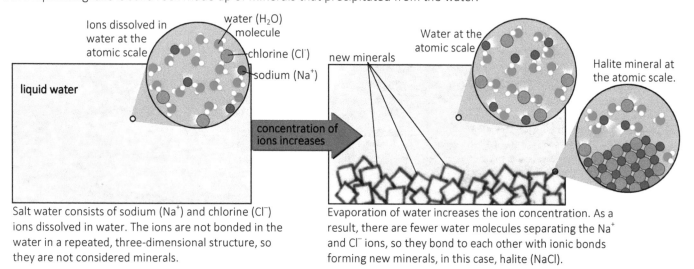

Salt water consists of sodium ($Na^+$) and chlorine ($Cl^-$) ions dissolved in water. The ions are not bonded in the water in a repeated, three-dimensional structure, so they are not considered minerals.

Evaporation of water increases the ion concentration. As a result, there are fewer water molecules separating the $Na^+$ and $Cl^-$ ions, so they bond to each other with ionic bonds forming new minerals, in this case, halite (NaCl).

## 3 New minerals can form due to high pressures and temperatures

When minerals are under very high pressures and temperatures, the bonds between their atoms break and then rearrange to recrystallize and form new minerals. Notice that these minerals form as the bonds between atoms in solid rock change, and melting does not occur. This process describes the formation of the minerals that make up the type of rock called metamorphic rock (see 5.1 and Chapter 9). High pressures and temperatures often occur at convergent plate boundaries, so when geologists observe rocks made up of minerals that have formed due to high pressures and temperatures, they can infer that the area may have been a convergent plate boundary in the past. The folded gneiss in the photo was once deep within Earth's crust, under high pressure and temperature, and is made up of minerals that formed as atoms rearranged under those conditions.

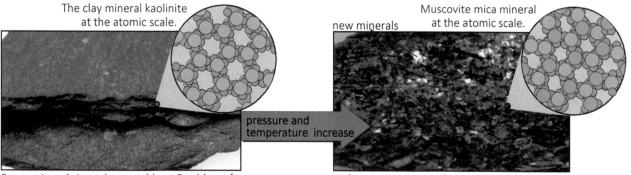

Some minerals in rock are stable at Earth's surface because the bonds between atoms are strong at the pressure and temperature conditions at the surface.

High temperatures and pressures cause bonds between atoms to rearrange, resulting in new minerals forming. These are made up of the same atoms but arranged in different three-dimensional patterns.

## Check

☐ Describe three environments in which minerals form.
☐ Summarize three changing conditions that trigger new bonds between atoms to form new minerals.

# 4.4 The Importance of Studying Minerals

**Key Concept:** Geologists study minerals to learn the geologic history of rocks and to identify valuable resources.

Rocks are made of minerals, and each mineral contains clues about how it formed, which sheds light on what an area was like at the time of formation **1**. Understanding Earth's past can help geologists better understand the processes that are working today, how people may affect them, and what may happen in the future. Minerals are also important to study because many are economically valuable, both as minerals and because of useful atoms they contain **2**.

## **1** Minerals give clues about Earth's history

Minerals are the building blocks of rocks. As discussed in 4.3, minerals form in a variety of ways, with many minerals only forming under certain conditions. Geologists can examine minerals to figure out how they formed, which in turn helps them figure out how the rock they make up formed. Learning about how rocks formed allows geologists to interpret the geologic history of an area.

### Minerals in the rock granite

In this example, a geologist is making observations of the rock granite. Based on the types of minerals and their arrangement in the rock, geologists have determined that the minerals in granite formed as atoms bonded together in cooling magma with abundant silicon and oxygen. When geologists see granite, they can interpret that the area in the past was once deep under the volcanoes at a convergent plate boundary with subduction.

what a geologists observes

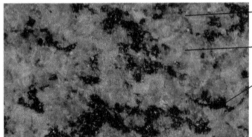 quartz

potassium feldspar

amphibole

what a geologists interprets

 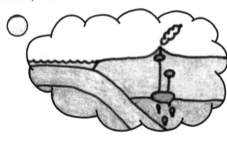

## **2** Minerals are valuable

In addition to giving clues about Earth's history, many minerals are used by people and are important economically. There are hundreds of known minerals, but only a few of them form the majority of rocks. Some minerals are used as they are. For these minerals, the physical properties caused by the structure and bonding of atoms are important. Other minerals have value because they contain uncommon atoms. These minerals are called ores and are typically less common. Examples of things produced from minerals are shown below and detailed in 5.5 and 5.6.

**In their life, every American will use...**

| gold | zinc | lead | copper | clays | iron ore | salt | other minerals |
|------|------|------|--------|-------|----------|------|----------------|
| 50 g | 250 kg | 400 kg | 450 kg | 5,200 kg | 11,800 kg | 15,100 kg | 25,500 kg |
| 2 oz | 550 lbs | 900 lbs | 1,000 lbs | 11,500 lbs | 26,000 lbs | 33,200 lbs | 56,000 lbs |

## Check

☐ Describe two reasons geologists study minerals.
☐ Summarize how minerals can be used to learn about Earth's past.

# 4.5 – 4.9 Mineral Groups and Physical Properties

In this section, you will learn that geologists divide minerals into groups based on the atoms that compose them. Additionally, all minerals also have particular physical properties that allow them to be identified.

## Frequently Used Terms

The terms listed here are used repeatedly throughout this section, so by learning them before you read this section, you can focus your mental energy on the concepts presented.

**hardness** Referring to minerals, hardness is a physical property that describes how easily a mineral is scratched or how easily a mineral scratches something else; for example, a hard mineral scratches most other things while a soft mineral is scratched by most other things.

**luster** A physical property of minerals describing how a mineral reflects light; many minerals have a glassy luster, meaning they reflect light and are shiny like glass; other minerals may have an earthy luster, meaning the mineral is dull, like dirt, or a metallic luster, meaning the mineral reflects light like a metal.

**silicate mineral** A mineral with both silicon and oxygen in the chemical formula.

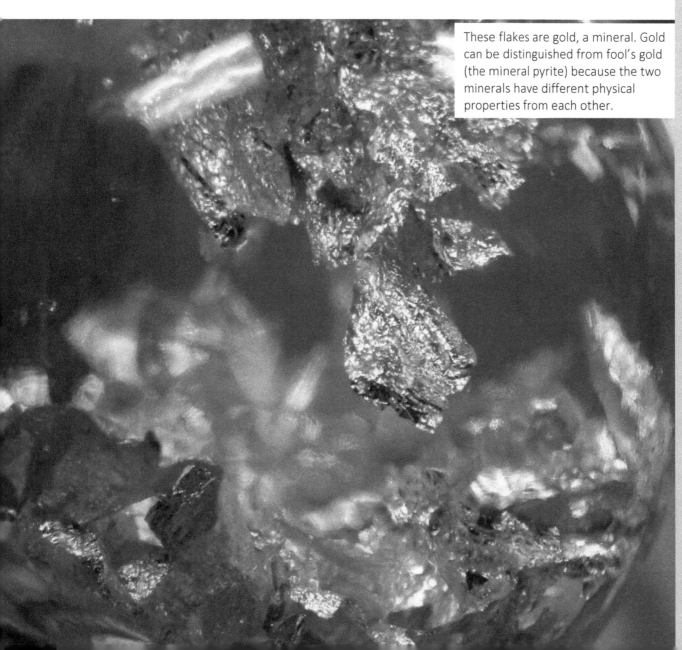

These flakes are gold, a mineral. Gold can be distinguished from fool's gold (the mineral pyrite) because the two minerals have different physical properties from each other.

# 4.5 Mineral Groups

**Key Concept:** **Minerals are divided into groups based on the types of atoms in their structure.** Just as you can categorize pies based on their key ingredients, such as cream or fruit, geologists categorize minerals based on their atoms. Geologists divide minerals this way to organize information and help identify relationships between minerals. The most abundant group is the silicate group, in which all the minerals contain the atoms silicon and oxygen bonded together **1**. One example is quartz. Silicate minerals can be further divided into iron-free silicate minerals, which do not contain iron and magnesium atoms, and iron-rich silicate minerals, which do. Another common group is the carbonate group, in which the minerals contain the atoms carbon and oxygen **2**. Although silicates and carbonates are the major groups of minerals, there are several other minor groups that are not abundant in typical rocks but can be important economically **3**.

## **1** Silicate minerals

Silicate minerals contain silicon (Si) and oxygen (O) atoms strongly bonded together. This is the largest group of minerals and is subdivided into two groups, silicate minerals with or without iron and magnesium. Both subgroups of silicate minerals form in all the ways that minerals can form (see 4.3). For example, many silicate minerals form when magma cools or when other minerals recrystallize due to high pressures and temperatures. However, the two silicate mineral subgroups often behave differently during the geologic processes that form them or destroy them, which is why they are subdivided here. Silicate minerals are important because most rocks are made up of predominantly silicate minerals. An example is granite, which is often used as kitchen countertops.

### Iron-rich silicate minerals and examples

Iron-rich silicate minerals must contain silicon (Si) and oxygen (O) because they are a subset of the silicate group. In addition, they contain iron (Fe) and magnesium (Mg), which means these minerals are generally dark in color, as shown in the examples below. Iron-rich silicate minerals tend to form before iron-free silicate minerals when atoms bond as magma cools, but they also tend to break apart and weather faster at Earth's surface.

**hornblende**
$(Ca_2(Mg,Fe^{2+},Fe^3,Al)_5(Si,Al)_8O_{22}(OH)_2)$

**olivine**
$((Mg,Fe)_2SiO_4)$

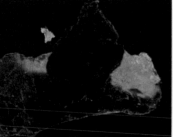 

**biotite mica**
$(K(Mg,Fe)_3AlSi_3O_{10}(OH)_2)$

**garnet**
$((Mg,Fe,Mn,Ca)_3(Al, Fe, Cr)_2Si_3O_{12})$

### Iron-free silicate minerals and examples

Iron-free silicate minerals must contain silicon (Si) and oxygen (O) because they are a subset of the silicate group. These minerals do not contain any iron (Fe) or magnesium (Mg). As a result, a key physical property of this group is that the minerals are light in color, as shown in the examples below.

**potassium feldspar**
$(KAlSi_3O_8)$

**quartz**
$(SiO_2)$

**muscovite mica**
$(KAl_2(AlSi_3O_{10})(F,OH)_2)$

**sodium plagioclase**
$(NaAlSi_3O_8)$

## ❷ Carbonate minerals

Carbonate minerals contain both carbon (C) and oxygen (O). Although not as common as the two groups of silicate minerals, carbonate minerals play an important role in forming some rocks, such as marble that is often made into tiles. Many carbonate minerals form by precipitating out of water or when atoms bond together as they recrystallize due to high pressures and temperatures (see 4.3).

calcite
($CaCO_3$)

### Carbonate minerals and examples
The bonds between other atoms and the carbon and oxygen atoms are ionic bonds, and acid will break them apart. Therefore, a key physical property of this group is that when acid is added to the carbonate mineral, it breaks the bonds and forms ions, water molecules, and carbon dioxide gas. Therefore, most carbonates react to acid by dissolving and fizzing. The most common example of a carbonate mineral is calcite, shown here.

## ❸ Other groups of minerals

Minerals that are not silicate minerals and not carbonate minerals can also be divided into different categories, including oxides, sulfides, sulfates, and native minerals. Although these groups are not commonly found in most rocks, they are often important economically because the minerals have desired physical properties or they contain useful atoms that can be extracted from the minerals.

### Other minerals and examples
The native mineral diamond is a gemstone that has the desired physical property of vividly sparkling in light and being hard. Other minerals contain metal atoms. Examples of these include the oxide mineral magnetite that contains the metal iron and the sulfide minerals pyrite and galena that contain the metals iron and lead. Note the variety of physical properties as you examine the examples below.

halite (salt)
(NaCl)

pyrite (fool's gold)
($FeS_2$)

gypsum
($CaSO_4 \cdot 2H_2O$)

magnetite
($Fe_3O_4$)

galena
(PbS)

copper
(Cu)

## Check

- ☐ List the major groups of minerals.
- ☐ Describe the two subgroups of silicate minerals and explain what differentiates them from each other.
- ☐ Compare and contrast the compositions and physical properties of the major groups of minerals.

# 4.6 Silicate Mineral Groups

**Key Concept:** Silicate minerals can be divided into additional subgroups based on how the silicon-oxygen tetrahedrons are bonded together. 4.5 describes one way to divide silicate minerals, based on the presence of iron and magnesium. The diagrams below show the four basic groups of silicate minerals when dividing them based on how the tetrahedrons are bonded together. The tetrahedrons may be bonded only to other atoms and not to each other **1**, they may be bonded to each other as long chains **2**, they may be bonded to each other in two-dimensional sheets **3**, or they may be bonded to each other forming a three-dimensional framework **4**. Silicate minerals within each group have some similar physical properties and similar numbers of oxygen atoms compared to silicon atoms.

## 1 Isolated tetrahedron silicate minerals

In this group, silicon-oxygen tetrahedrons are bonded only to other atoms, so the silicon atoms do not "share" oxygen atoms with each other. The bonds between silicon and oxygen atoms are strong covalent bonds, but bonds to other atoms tend to be weaker. Isolated tetrahedron silicate minerals tend to have the physical property of being equally strong in all directions. They tend to be iron-rich silicate minerals. Olivine and garnet are examples.

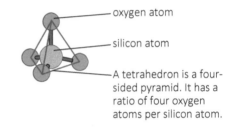

oxygen atom

silicon atom

A tetrahedron is a four-sided pyramid. It has a ratio of four oxygen atoms per silicon atom.

## 2 Chain silicate minerals

Silicon-oxygen tetrahedrons form long chains with silicon atoms sharing oxygen atoms with neighboring tetrahedrons. The bonds within chains are strong covalent bonds, but the chains are bonded to other atoms with weaker bonds. Chain silicate minerals tend to break in two directions along the strong chains without cutting across them. They also tend to be iron-rich silicate minerals. Pyroxene and amphibole are examples.

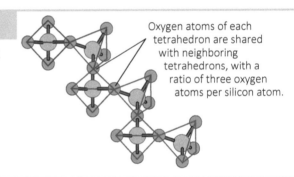

Oxygen atoms of each tetrahedron are shared with neighboring tetrahedrons, with a ratio of three oxygen atoms per silicon atom.

## 3 Sheet silicate minerals

Silicon-oxygen tetrahedrons form two-dimensional sheets with silicon atoms sharing three of their four oxygen atoms with surrounding tetrahedrons. The bonds within sheets are strong covalent bonds, but the sheets are bonded to other atoms with weak bonds. Sheet silicate minerals tend to break in flat layers along the weak bonds between the sheets, resulting in soft minerals. They may be iron-rich or iron-free silicate minerals. The clay mineral kaolinite, muscovite mica, and biotite mica are examples.

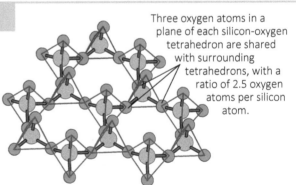

Three oxygen atoms in a plane of each silicon-oxygen tetrahedron are shared with surrounding tetrahedrons, with a ratio of 2.5 oxygen atoms per silicon atom.

## 4 Framework silicate minerals

Silicon-oxygen tetrahedrons form a three-dimensional framework with silicon atoms sharing all of their oxygen atoms. The silicon-oxygen bonds creating the framework are all strong bonds, so framework silicate minerals tend to be hard. They tend to be iron-free silicate minerals. Quartz, potassium feldspar, and plagioclase feldspar are examples.

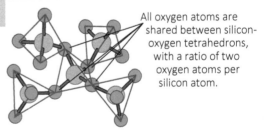

All oxygen atoms are shared between silicon-oxygen tetrahedrons, with a ratio of two oxygen atoms per silicon atom.

## Check

☐ Name and describe four groups of silicate minerals and the arrangement of silicon-oxygen tetrahedrons in each.
☐ Explain how the bonding of silicon-oxygen tetrahedrons affects some physical properties of minerals.
☐ Compare the relative abundance of different atoms (the ratio of Si to O, presence of Fe and Mg) for four groups of silicate minerals.

# 4.7 Identifying Minerals

**Key Concept:** Minerals can be identified by performing a chemical analysis or by examining their physical properties.
Geologists do not identify minerals for the sake of learning their names, but rather they identify minerals in rocks to learn about how the rocks formed, which tells a story about the geologic history of the area. For any mineral, geologists can perform a chemical analysis to determine the atoms present and their arrangement, which, as you may recall, together are different for every mineral **1**. Some minerals are large enough have physical properties that you can observe, such as color and shape, that allow a geologist to identify them **2**. Additional information about the physical properties of minerals is given in the next section.

## **1** Identifying minerals using chemical analysis

Geologists can determine what minerals are present in a rock by identifying the types of atoms in the rock and their three-dimensional arrangement. One method requires grinding the mineral into a powder and measuring the strength of x-rays after they interact with the atoms as they travel through that powder, giving information about the arrangement of atoms. This kind of geochemical analysis is especially useful if the minerals making up the rock are incredibly small and not observable, even with a microscope. However it is not practical to identify most minerals this way because of the time involved, the cost, and the lab equipment needed.

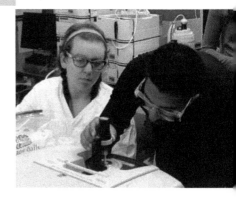

Geologists, as shown in this photo, determine the types of minerals in a rock to learn more about how the rock formed. This information may give clues about the geologic history and plate tectonic environment of the area in which it was found.

## **2** Identifying minerals using physical properties

Minerals have specific physical properties, so those properties can be used to identify the mineral. Examples of properties include luster (how it reflects or shines in light), hardness, shape, and color. In 4.8 we explore how geologists measure and describe these properties in mineral samples. These properties are dependent on the atoms present and the way they are arranged and bonded together. Some physical properties are more useful than others for different minerals. Usually a combination of several different physical properties is required in order to identify a mineral.

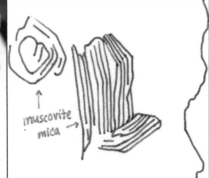

Minerals shown on this and the following pages were selected because they are unusually large, large enough to easily observe their physical properties. Most minerals in a rock tend to be smaller and crowded together, making it more difficult to identify them.

For example, the physical properties of the mineral muscovite mica in the first photo include its tan color, flakey shape, and glassy luster. The physical properties of the smaller muscovite mica minerals in the rock in the second photo are less easy to distinguish.

## Check
□ Describe two ways geologists identify minerals.
□ Compare and contrast the advantages and disadvantages of the two methods of identifying minerals.

# 4.8 Physical Properties of Minerals

**Key Concept:** Geologists observe the many different physical properties of minerals in order to identify them. As previously discussed, minerals can be identified because each mineral has distinct physical properties. These physical properties apply to individual minerals and not to the entire rock in which they are found. Examples of physical properties include the mineral's luster **1**, hardness **2**, shape due to how it breaks **3**, shape due to how it grows **4**, color **5**, color when it is ground to a powder **6**, as well as a few physical properties that are unique to certain minerals **7**. It is helpful to observe multiple physical properties of a mineral, since one alone rarely gives enough information to identify it.

## **1** Mineral luster

Luster is how a mineral reflects light. A mineral with a metallic luster is opaque and reflects light the way a metal does; a glassy luster reflects light in a shiny way, as glass does, although it does not need to be clear; and an earthy luster is dull, with no shine. For some mineral uses it is important to have a particular luster. For example, diamond has an exceptionally shiny luster, making it valuable as a gemstone.

### How do we test it?

Look at a mineral and see how it reflects light. Unfortunately, photographs do not do a good job of showing luster.

Pyrite has a metallic luster.

Plagioclase feldspar has a glassy luster.

Hematite has an earthy luster.

## **2** Mineral hardness

Mineral hardness is how easily a mineral is scratched. The way the atoms in a mineral are arranged and the type of bonds between the atoms determine the hardness of the mineral. For example, framework silicate minerals, such as quartz, are hard because there are strong covalent bonds connecting the silicon and oxygen tetrahedrons to one another. Hardness is measured on a scale called the Mohs hardness scale, where 1 is the softest mineral, and 10 is the hardest. For some mineral uses, such as minerals in toothpaste or in sandpaper, it is important to have a particular hardness: minerals in toothpaste must be soft to avoid damaging teeth (hardness of around 3) and minerals in sandpaper must be hard in order to scratch other materials (hardness greater than 7).

### How do we test it?

A mineral can scratch anything that is softer than it. The Mohs hardness scale below shows some minerals and other objects and their hardness. Mineral with higher numbers will scratch minerals with lower numbers.

### Mohs Hardness Scale

| Minerals and other objects | Scale number |
|---|---|
| Talc | 1 |
| Gypsum | 2 |
| Fingernail | 2.5 |
| Calcite | 3 |
| Fluorite | 4 |
| Apatite | 5 |
| Glass | 5.5 |
| Potassium feldspar | 6 |
| Quartz | 7 |
| Topaz | 8 |
| Corundum | 9 |
| Diamond | 10 |

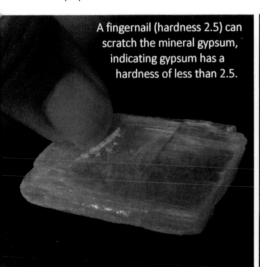
A fingernail (hardness 2.5) can scratch the mineral gypsum, indicating gypsum has a hardness of less than 2.5.

The mineral quartz can scratch a glass plate (hardness 5.5), indicating quartz is harder than 5.5.

# 3 Mineral shape: cleavage

The word "cleave" means "to break," so mineral cleavage describes the shape of a broken mineral. The arrangement of atoms in a mineral and the strength of bonds between the atoms determine how a mineral cleaves. Some minerals have weak bonds along specific planes that create cleavage along that plane, meaning they break easily along that plane. For some mineral uses, it is important to have excellent cleavage, such as mica minerals that break perfectly along one plane into shiny flakes. They are used to give makeup and paint their sparkle.

**How do we test it?**
Examine the shape of a broken mineral, and look for shiny planes, which appear as flashes of reflected light. Count the number of planes, keeping in mind that parallel sides are considered to be one plane, and measure the angle between planes.

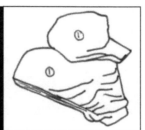

The mineral muscovite mica has one excellent cleavage plane, so it tends to split into flat flakes.

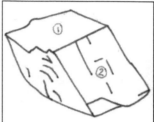

The mineral potassium feldspar has two cleavage planes at right angles, so it tends to break into rectangle-shaped blocks.

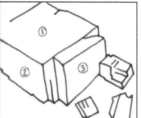

The mineral halite has three cleavage planes at right angles to each other, so it tends to break into cubes.

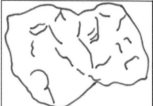

The mineral quartz does not have cleavage planes because its internal structure is uniformly strong in all directions. Geologists call where it breaks fracture instead of cleavage.

# 4 Mineral shape: habit

Mineral habit is the shape a mineral takes as it grows if it is not crowded by other minerals, unlike minerals in most rocks. As with cleavage, the arrangement of atoms in a mineral determines its habit. The habit shape may be the same as the cleavage shape of a broken mineral, or it may be different. If a mineral grows in a confined space, such as in a rock with many other minerals, its shape will be affected by nearby minerals. In such cases the mineral's habit will be difficult or impossible to determine. For some mineral uses, such as decorative pieces like geodes, it is important to have a particularly attractive habit.

**How do we test it?**
Look at the shape of a mineral that has not been broken or grown into other minerals. This is not always possible.

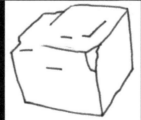

Halite grows as a cube, which is the same as its cleavage.

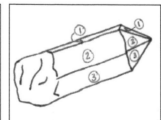

Quartz grows as a six-sided mineral. Notice that quartz does have a specific habit shape, but it does not have cleavage.

→

## 5 Mineral color

The mineral color is the color a mineral appears to be. It depends on key atoms present and whether or not the mineral is contaminated by tiny amounts of other atoms. Some minerals are consistently the same color, making color a useful property for helping to identify them. Other minerals can be a range of colors, so color is not useful to identify them. The color of many minerals, such as gemstones in jewelry and minerals in countertops, make them particularly desirable.

### How do we test it?
Mineral color can be determined by looking at a mineral. The top row shows minerals for which color is a useful physical property. The bottom row shows the mineral quartz, illustrating color is not always useful for identification.

Biotite is black.

Olivine is olive green.

Galena is silvery gray.

Crystalline quartz is colorless.

Citrine quartz is yellow or orange.

Amethyst quartz is purple.

## 6 Mineral streak color

The streak color is the color of the mineral in powdered form. A few minerals have a streak color that is different from the mineral color, which makes it particularly useful when identifying those minerals. The streak color of some minerals is important commercially because the minerals are powdered and used as pigments to color paints.

### How do we test it?
The streak color can be determined by rubbing a mineral on a very hard surface and looking at the color of the resulting powder.

The mineral pyrite has a gold mineral color, but it has a gray streak color.

The mineral hematite has a silver or red mineral color, but the streak color is always reddish or brown.

## 7 Other properties

Some minerals have other unique properties to help identify them.

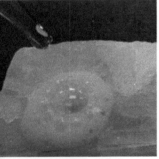

The mineral calcite fizzes when it reacts with acid to form carbon dioxide gas.

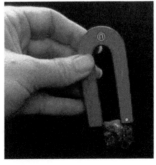

The mineral magnetite is attracted to a magnet because it is magnetic.

The mineral galena feels heavy because it has a high density.

## Check
- □ Describe six properties that can be used to identify minerals, and provide an example of each property.
- □ Identify three tests you could perform to determine different properties of a mineral.

# 4.9 DATA AND DIAGRAMS: Mineral Uses

**Key Concept:** Tables can show the relationships among several characteristics. This table gives information about the physical properties, characteristics, and uses of certain minerals **1**. To create a table like this, geologists observe and measure the physical properties of minerals and compile information about how minerals are used in everyday life. Tips on how to read this table are below **2**. Use the questions to practice interpreting tables **3**.

| Mineral | Mohs hardness | Cleavage planes | Other | Mineral Group | Select uses |
|---|---|---|---|---|---|
| Muscovite mica | 2 – 2.5 | 1 | • splits into thin, flexible sheets | silicate (sheet, iron-free) | • glitter in paint and cosmetics |
| Quartz | 7 | none | • vibrates with electricity<br>• chemically stable | silicate (frame-work, iron-free) | • glass<br>• abrasive (grinding, polishing)<br>• household scrubbing agent<br>• electronics<br>• jewelry (amethyst, citrine) |
| Calcite | 3 | 3, not at right angles | • chemically reacts with acid | carbonate | • cement<br>• neutralize acid in soil<br>• antacid for people<br>• household scrubbing agent |
| Gypsum | 2 | 1 (plus 2 not as good planes) | • after it is powdered and heated, adding water recrystallizes new minerals as it dries | other | • drywall<br>• cement<br>• plaster of Paris |
| Halite | 2.5 | 3, at right angles | • chemically dissolves in water<br>• tastes like salt | other | • table salt<br>• road salt |
| Diamond | 10 | 4 | • chemically stable | other | • abrasive (cutting, grinding, polishing)<br>• jewelry |

## 1 How to read the diagram

Identify what information is placed in each column and row. The first column indicates what mineral is described in each row. For each mineral, physical properties and other characteristics are listed in the middle columns, and uses are listed in the last column.

## 2 An example of what you might interpret

Reading across the last row tells us that, among other things, diamonds are very hard and are used as an abrasive and in jewelry.

## 3 Questions

1. **What does the table show?**
a. A ranking of some minerals based on their cost, organized by uses
b. Some geologic minerals, organized by their physical properties and other characteristics
c. Select physical properties and uses of some minerals, organized by mineral group
d. The most important criteria used to identify some minerals, organized by hardness

2. **How would you figure out the hardness of minerals used as household scrubbing agents?**
a. Examine the column headings.
b. Examine the second column.
c. Examine the first column and then the second column.
d. Examine the last column and then the second column.

3. **What is a distinctive physical property of minerals used as gemstones in jewelry?**
a. They are hard.
b. They have cleavage planes.
c. They are brightly colored.

4. **What relationship is the purpose of this table?**
a. How the physical properties of minerals affect how they are used
b. How the uses of minerals affect their value
c. How the hardness of a mineral makes it more useful
d. How one physical property affects other physical properties of minerals

## End of Chapter Questions: Student Debates

For each of the following questions, determine which student you agree with and explain why.

**1. Two students are discussing whether ice is a mineral.**

**Student 1:** Ice is not a mineral because it is made of water molecules that can be a liquid, and ice melts when it is at room temperature.

**Student 2:** Ice is a mineral because it is a solid formed naturally by freezing and made up of atoms in a three-dimensional pattern.

**2. Two students are discussing whether there are minerals in vegetables.**

**Student 1:** Vegetables contain minerals, which is why vegetables are so healthy and help our bodies grow.

**Student 2:** That's not the geologic use of the word mineral. Minerals in geology are not formed by plants.

**3. Two students are discussing the fundamental reason why a geologist studying the geological history of an area identifies minerals.**

**Student 1:** When a geologist identifies a mineral, it can reveal information about how it formed.

**Student 2:** When a geologist identifies a mineral, it can be classified and put into a category.

**4. Two students are discussing the location of minerals in the microscopic image.**

**Student 1:** The minerals fill up the entire image. Some are gray and some are clear in the microscopic image.

**Student 2:** The minerals are the areas that are black, and the grey areas are gaps between those minerals and filled with something else.

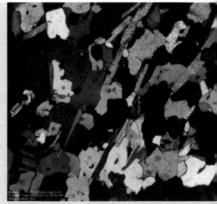

**5. Two students are discussing the relative sizes of atoms and minerals.**

**Student 1:** Minerals and atoms both make up larger things like rocks, so they are both very, very small.

**Student 2:** Atoms are much smaller than minerals because millions of billions of atoms make up minerals.

**6. Two students are discussing the best way to identify minerals.**

**Student 1:** You can look at the color of the mineral, such as whether it is dark or light, and that gives most of the information you need.

**Student 2:** You need to look at a variety of things in addition to color, since color works to identify some minerals but not others.

## End of Chapter Questions: Short Answer

Using your own words or sketching and labeling a diagram, answer the following questions.

**7.** Both of these rocks formed from magma. Determine which one is made up of minerals with a higher percentage of silicon and oxygen atoms. Justify your answer.

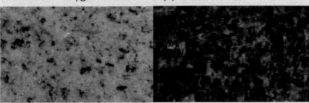

**8.** Choose five minerals and give an example for each one of how the atoms, the types of bonds between them, or their arrangement affects the physical properties of that mineral.

**9.** The mineral pyrite (FeS) has a mineral habit of cubes, just like the mineral halite (NaCl). Draw a labeled diagram showing how the atoms are arranged in pyrite.

**10.** Explain the role, if any, of liquid (liquid water or liquid magma) in the three ways that minerals form.

**11.** A friend says "Minerals that form from cooling lava are black." Do you agree or disagree? Justify your response with at least three lines of supporting evidence.

**12.** Identify at least five ways in which you used minerals yesterday, and explain the physical properties that made them useful.

**13.** A friend calls you to help her identify a mineral. Identify four questions you would ask her about the mineral over the phone. Explain what information you would learn from each question.

**14.** Imagine you took this photo. Write a hypothesis explaining what mineral is shown and why you think so. To test your hypothesis, describe four observations or experiments you could make and what each observation would tell you about your hypothesis.

**Hints:** For each question, see the sections listed here for information relevant to answering it.

**1.** (4.1, 4.2) **2.** (4.1, 4.2, 4.3) **3.** (4.4, 4.5, 4.6) **4.** (4.3, 4.4) **5.** (4.2) **6.** (4.7, 4.8, 4.9) **7.** (4.2, 4.3, 4.5, 4.6) **8.** (4.2, 4.5, 4.6, 4.8, 4.9) **9.** (4.2, 4.8) **10.** (4.3, 4.4, 4.5) **11.** (4.3, 4.4, 4.5) **12.** (4.4, 4.9) **13.** (4.7, 4.8) **14.** (4.7, 4.8)

# Chapter 5:
# Rocks and Resources

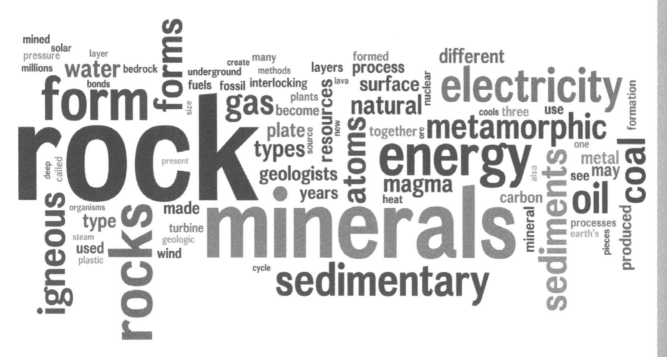

## Chapter Objectives

When you are finished reading this chapter, you should be able to ...

• distinguish how each of the three rock types form and explain how that influences their distinctive characteristics (5.1–5.4).

• explain how rocks change over time and how plate tectonics plays a role (5.1, 5.3).

• identify examples of rock, mineral, and energy resources; explain how they form; and compare how they are removed from the ground and used (5.5–5.8, 5.10).

• compare ways electricity is produced and advantages and disadvantages of each method (5.7–5.11).

# 5.1 – 5.4 Rocks and the Rock Cycle

In this section, you will learn that in geology, the way that rocks form is so important that it provides the basis for how geologists categorize rock. Rock can change and reform into a new rock that may be a different rock type.

## Frequently Used Terms

The terms listed here are used repeatedly throughout this section, so by learning them before you read this section, you can focus your mental energy on the concepts presented.

**bedrock** The rock that makes up the solid component of Earth's crust; every place on Earth has bedrock underneath it, sometimes exposed at the surface where you can see it and sometimes deep beneath soil, sediments, and buildings; bedrock forms in large, continuous areas.

**crystallize** The process of atoms bonding together in a specific, orderly pattern to form minerals that make up rock.

**igneous rock** The rock type that forms from magma (molten rock underground) or lava (molten rock that has erupted on the surface) that cools and solidifies (crystallizes) into solid rock.

**metamorphic rock** The rock type that forms from a preexisting rock when its minerals change shape or composition, generally under high pressure and temperature.

**mineral** A solid with unique physical properties made up of a particular combination of atoms that bond together in a specific, orderly pattern and form through geologic processes; they are the components of rock, and different combinations of minerals form distinctive rocks.

**plate boundary** The edge of tectonic plates where two plates touch each other; there are three types—convergent, divergent, and transform—each resulting in key geologic processes that affect rocks and their formation, such as magma forming and cooling, rock compressing, and mountains growing and eroding.

**rock** A geologic solid made up of minerals; the three rock types—igneous, sedimentary, and metamorphic—are categorized based on the way the rock formed.

**sedimentary rock** The rock type that forms from sediments that form together into a new rock; sediments are pieces resulting from weathering of preexisting rock, either pieces of broken rock or pieces that form when dissolved ions bonds together.

The colors and grays in this microscopic view of the igneous rock gabbro are minerals that formed slowly over millions of years in a cooling magma chamber.

# 5.1 Rocks

**Key Concept:** The categories geologists use to group rocks are based on their method of formation. Rocks are geologic solids made up of minerals, and they compose the solid bedrock making up Earth's crust **1**. They are divided into three categories based on how they form **2**. It is the process of formation that makes each rock type unique and allows scientists to study them and form conclusions about the Earth.

## **1** Rocks and minerals

Rock is made of minerals, which form as described in 4.3. Geologists distinguish different types of rock from each other by the types and shapes of minerals that comprise them. One example rock with its component minerals is given below. The rock in the rectangle photo is close to actual size, and the circular photo on the right is showing the rock as it looks through a microscope.

Geologists identify rock in nature, and may bring pieces of it to a lab to study the minerals.

This rock is made up of minerals discussed in Chapter 4, such as quartz, biotite mica, and plagioclase feldspar.

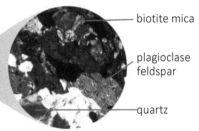

biotite mica

plagioclase feldspar

quartz

This microscopic view allows geologists to study the properties of the minerals in detail.

## **2** Rock classification

Geologists classify rocks into three categories by how the rocks formed. This classification system is useful because the method of formation gives geologists clues about what Earth was like when the rocks formed in the past. Observations of rock characteristics and interpretations of how the rock formed allow geologists to test hypotheses about Earth's past, present, and future as well as determine where resources might be (see 5.5).

| Igneous rock | Sedimentary rock | Metamorphic rock |
|---|---|---|
| Igneous rock forms when magma or lava cools and solidifies into minerals that form solid rock. This process can occur deep in the crust or at the surface where the magma erupts as lava. Studying igneous rocks can give geologists clues about Earth, such as the locations of plate boundaries in the past and the processes that cause volcanoes to erupt. More information about igneous rocks is in Chapter 6. You may have seen igneous rock as granite counter tops, as walls of some buildings, or as some curbstones. | Sedimentary rock forms either from pieces of rock, called sediment, deposited on Earth's surface or from dissolved ions that precipitate out on Earth's surface. Because these processes occur at or near Earth's surface, studying sedimentary rocks can give geologists clues about environments that existed when the sediments were deposited, including details about what lived (preserved as fossils) and the climate. More information about sedimentary rocks is in Chapter 8. You may have seen sedimentary rocks as layers in the Grand Canyon or as brownstone building materials. | Metamorphic rock forms when minerals in a preexisting rock deep in the crust change shape, size, or composition, generally because of a significant increase in pressure and temperature, and form a new rock. Studying metamorphic rocks can give geologists clues about the Earth, such as the history of mountain ranges and what early Earth was like. More information about metamorphic rocks is in Chapter 9. You may have seen metamorphic rocks as marble carved into a statue or as part of the United States Capitol building. |

**Check**    Before you continue, you should be able to answer each check without looking at the page.

☐ Describe the relationship between rocks and minerals.
☐ Explain the purpose of classifying rocks by their method of formation, including an example of what geologists can learn by studying each rock type.

# 5.2 The Rock Cycle

**Key Concept:  Rocks form and can change, resulting in new rocks.**  Rocks are divided into three categories based on how they form: igneous **1**, sedimentary **2**, and metamorphic **3**. However, once rock forms, it does not permanently stay that way, because it will change if the conditions change. The rock cycle is a model that describes how rock forms and changes between the three rock types, shown in the diagram **4**. The rock cycle is a major theme in this book.

## **1** Igneous rock

Igneous rocks, such as the granite and basalt shown, form when magma cools. As magma cools, bonds form between the atoms to form a solid. This process, when atoms in liquid magma bond together to form solid minerals, is called crystallizing. The size and types of minerals give clues about the crystallizing process (see 6.4).

### Magma
Magma is molten rock. Magma is made up of the same atoms that compose minerals in rock, but it is a liquid because most atoms are not bonded together as minerals. They instead flow freely. Magma forms from hot rock when bonds between atoms in the minerals break. This process when a solid becomes liquid is called melting. Magma is called lava if it erupts at the surface.

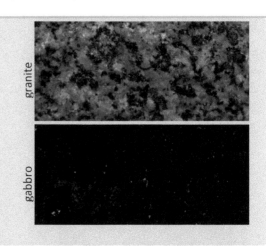

## **2** Sedimentary rock

Sedimentary rocks, such as the conglomerate and limestone shown, form from sediments and dissolved ions that were moved from where they were weathered in a process called transporting. When sediments stop moving and settle, that is called depositing. They can become a solid rock when layers of additional sediments push the sediments tightly together, compacting them, and when atoms form bonds and attach sediments together, cementing them. Transported dissolved ions also bond together to form minerals making up a sedimentary rock, a process called precipitating. The minerals present and the size and shape of sediments give clues about these processes (see 8.7).

### Sediments
Sediments are pieces that result from the breakdown of rock. There are two types of sediments: pieces of broken rock and minerals that form when dissolved ions bond together. The first type of sediment forms when a process called weathering breaks bonds between atoms, breaking rock into pieces that can be seen or felt, like mud or sand. The second type of sediment forms after the weathering process causes some of the atoms to dissolve in water. Those dissolved ions bond together to form minerals during a process called precipitating.

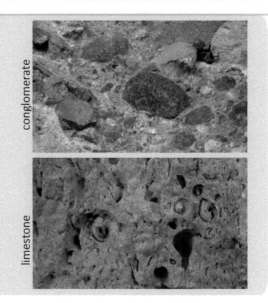

## **3** Metamorphic rock

Metamorphic rocks, such as the marble and gneiss shown, form when changing pressure and temperature conditions result in minerals that are no longer stable. The minerals then recrystallize, which means their atoms rearrange and form new bonds, creating new minerals. When minerals recrystallize, the rock is undergoing a process called metamorphosing. The minerals present and their orientation and size give clues about the metamorphosing process (see 9.4).

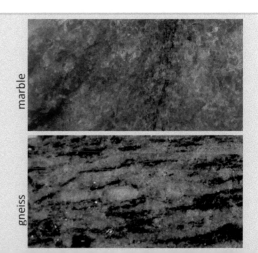

## 4 The rock cycle model

The three rock types are interconnected through the processes shown in the diagram below. This cycling of atoms through the various rock types is called the rock cycle. A model depicting how rocks change is useful because the processes usually happen on timescales that are too long for people to watch. Atoms commonly take tens of thousands of years to go through a single step in the rock cycle, but some atoms are "stuck" for billions of years as a particular rock without changing.

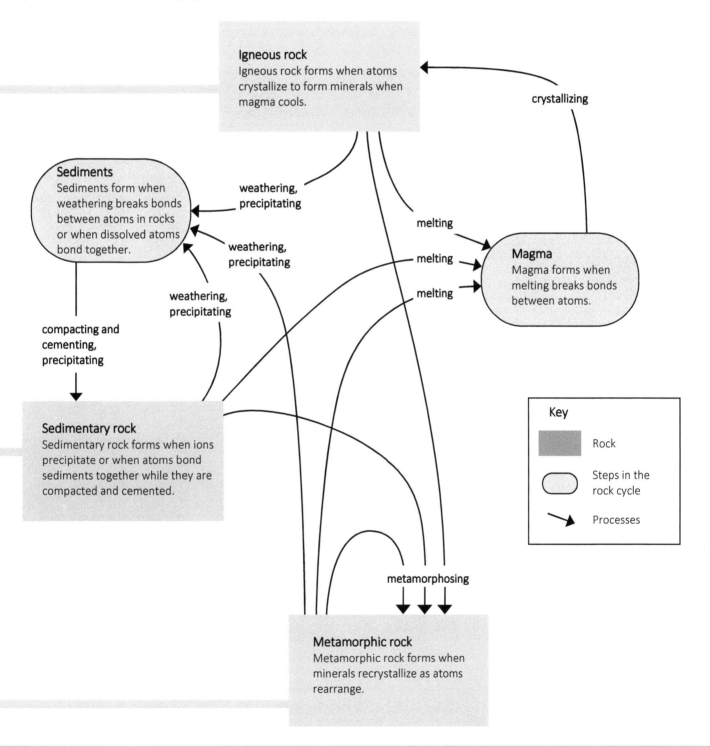

## Check

☐ Summarize the processes necessary to form each of the three rock types.
☐ Describe at least four steps involved along two possible paths through the rock cycle.

# 5.3 Rocks and Plate Tectonics

**Key Concept:** Certain rock types tend to form in specific plate tectonic settings. As discussed in 5.1, each of the three rock types forms in different environments, and many of these environments are defined by plate tectonics. For example, magma formed at divergent plate boundaries cools to become igneous rock **1**. In contrast, convergent plate boundaries with subduction create a variety of environments, and all three rock types can form **2**. Convergent plate boundaries without subduction also form sedimentary and metamorphic rocks but not igneous rock because they do not create magma **3**. Transform plate boundaries are not associated with the formation of a particular rock type. In addition, there are some environments not related to plate boundaries in which some rock types typically form **4**. As a result of these relationships, geologists can interpret the geologic history of an area by identifying the rock types present.

## **1** Divergent plate boundary

Magma forms as plates move apart, so igneous rocks form here. Sediments may be deposited, but they do not become sedimentary rock.

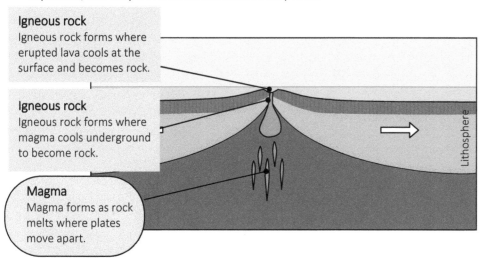

**Igneous rock**
Igneous rock forms where erupted lava cools at the surface and becomes rock.

**Igneous rock**
Igneous rock forms where magma cools underground to become rock.

**Magma**
Magma forms as rock melts where plates move apart.

Erupting volcanoes form new igneous rock.

## **2** Convergent plate boundary with subduction

Mountains and volcanoes form as two plates move together, and one plate subducts under the other, forming magma. Igneous, sedimentary, and metamorphic rocks form here.

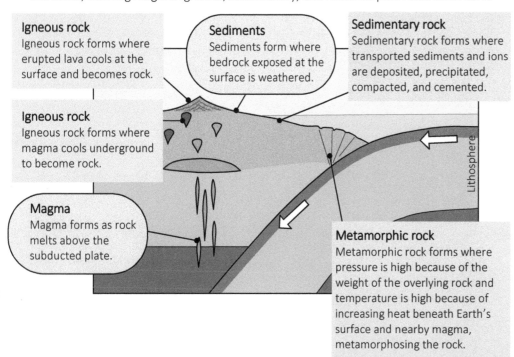

**Igneous rock**
Igneous rock forms where erupted lava cools at the surface and becomes rock.

**Sediments**
Sediments form where bedrock exposed at the surface is weathered.

**Sedimentary rock**
Sedimentary rock forms where transported sediments and ions are deposited, precipitated, compacted, and cemented.

**Igneous rock**
Igneous rock forms where magma cools underground to become rock.

**Magma**
Magma forms as rock melts above the subducted plate.

**Metamorphic rock**
Metamorphic rock forms where pressure is high because of the weight of the overlying rock and temperature is high because of increasing heat beneath Earth's surface and nearby magma, metamorphosing the rock.

The volcano in the distance formed when lava flows cooled to become igneous rock. Some of the igneous rock has been weathered and transported away as sediments in the stream.

# 3 Convergent plate boundary without subduction

Two plates of continental lithosphere come together, forming mountains. Sedimentary and metamorphic rocks form here.

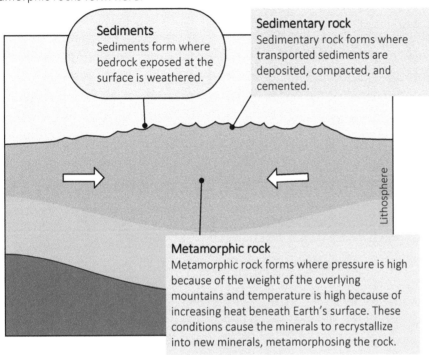

**Sediments**
Sediments form where bedrock exposed at the surface is weathered.

**Sedimentary rock**
Sedimentary rock forms where transported sediments are deposited, compacted, and cemented.

**Metamorphic rock**
Metamorphic rock forms where pressure is high because of the weight of the overlying mountains and temperature is high because of increasing heat beneath Earth's surface. These conditions cause the minerals to recrystallize into new minerals, metamorphosing the rock.

Lithosphere

This metamorphic rock formed deep within a mountain range, but the overlying mountains of rock above it have eroded away, exposing the metamorphic rock.

# 4 Continental margins with no plate boundary

Some locations where certain rock types typically form are areas that are not related to plate boundaries. One example is igneous rocks tend to form where lava erupts at hotspot volcanoes. Another example, shown below, is where sediments are deposited in the shallow ocean, especially along the edges of continents where there is no plate boundary, called passive margins (see 15.3). Sedimentary rock forms here.

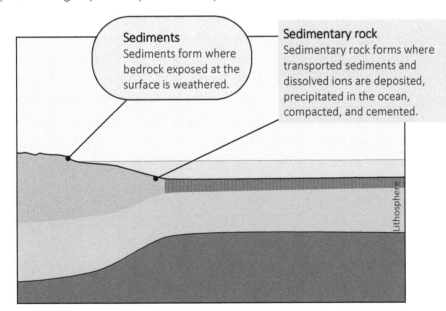

**Sediments**
Sediments form where bedrock exposed at the surface is weathered.

**Sedimentary rock**
Sedimentary rock forms where transported sediments and dissolved ions are deposited, precipitated in the ocean, compacted, and cemented.

Lithosphere

This sand is sediment that was weathered from land and deposited in the water. If it gets buried, compacted, and cemented, it may become sedimentary rock over millions of years.

# Check

☐ Summarize the rock types that form in three different plate tectonic settings and continental margins.
☐ Compare the similarities between the different plate tectonic settings and continental margins that cause the same rock types to form.

# 5.4 Key Characteristics to Identify Rocks

**Key Concept:** The arrangement of minerals in rock gives clues to identify the rock type. Unique processes form each of the three rock types, so the way the minerals are arranged is different for each rock type. These differences allows rocks to be identified by observing the minerals **1**. The descriptions on this page are useful as an introduction to the identification of rock types, although there are exceptions to these generalizations. Igneous rocks have minerals that are interlocking and are usually randomly oriented **2**. Metamorphic rocks also have minerals that are interlocking, but unlike igneous rocks the minerals may be aligned parallel to each other or the rock may be made up of only one type of mineral **3**. Sedimentary rocks may have gaps between the sediments **4**. However, to complicate matters, a few sedimentary rocks have minerals that are interlocking, and in these cases other characteristics need to be observed to determine if the rock is igneous, metamorphic, or sedimentary.

**There is more than one type of mineral.**
There is more than one type of mineral in the rock.

**Minerals are randomly oriented.**
The minerals are not aligned in any particular direction.

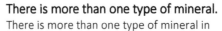

**Minerals are not randomly oriented.**
The minerals are lined up parallel to each other or are in bands.

## **2** Igneous rocks

Minerals in igneous rocks are interlocking because, during their formation, the atoms in the liquid magma bond together to form minerals as it cools and crystallizes, leaving no space between minerals. The minerals crystallize in liquid with no pressure squeezing them in a particular direction, so they generally do not have a common orientation. Igneous rock is further classified by the minerals present and their size.
The photo on the left shows randomly-oriented interlocking minerals in diorite at approximately actual size. The photo on the right shows randomly-oriented interlocking minerals in basalt. These minerals are much smaller, so viewing them through a microscope allows geologists to study the minerals' arrangement.

## **3** Metamorphic rocks

Minerals in metamorphic rocks are interlocking because the pressure during their formation generally prevents spaces between minerals. These minerals are often aligned if the pressure squeezes the rock more in one direction than another. Metamorphic rock is further classified by the minerals present, their orientation, and their size.
The photo on the left shows the variety of minerals in gneiss that are aligned in bands of light and dark at approximately actual size. The photo on the right shows a variety of microscopic minerals that are aligned parallel to each other in slate.

# ❶ Start here with unknown rock

Geologists ask the scientific question of how a particular rock formed. They form a hypothesis of whether the rock is igneous, metamorphic, or sedimentary and then test that hypothesis by making careful observations of its component minerals. To identify a rock like a geologist, follow the suggested guidelines below. The first observation you want to make is to determine whether or not the minerals are interlocking.

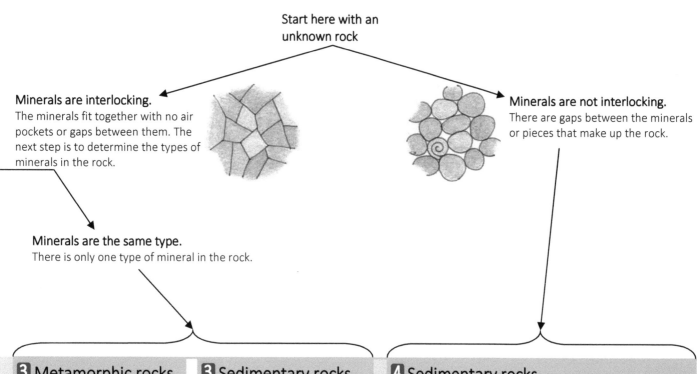

Start here with an unknown rock

**Minerals are interlocking.**
The minerals fit together with no air pockets or gaps between them. The next step is to determine the types of minerals in the rock.

**Minerals are not interlocking.**
There are gaps between the minerals or pieces that make up the rock.

**Minerals are the same type.**
There is only one type of mineral in the rock.

## ❸ Metamorphic rocks

Metamorphic rocks with interlocking minerals may be made of a single type of mineral, such as calcite or quartz.
The photo shows the interlocking calcite minerals in marble.

## ❸ Sedimentary rocks

Minerals in sedimentary rocks may be interlocking if they precipitated out of water. They are generally a single type of mineral.
The photo shows the interlocking halite minerals in rock salt.

## ❹ Sedimentary rocks

Sedimentary rocks may form from deposited sediments, such as shells or sand. Spaces between sediments during deposition may remain even after the sediments become rock. Sedimentary rock is further classified by the minerals present and the size and shape of sediments.
The photo on the left shows gaps exist between the shells in limestone at approximately actual size. The photo on the right shows gaps between the microscopic sediments in sandstone.

## Check

☐ Explain how the arrangement and type of minerals can assist in identifying the rock type.
☐ Sketch or describe a possible arrangement of minerals for each of the three rock types.

# 5.5 – 5.11 Resources

In this section, you will learn that you use many resources that relate to geology. These resources were formed by geologic processes and they are found by geologists.

## Frequently Used Terms

The terms listed here are used repeatedly throughout this section, so by learning them before you read this section, you can focus your mental energy on the concepts presented.

**carbon dioxide** A gas, comprised of two oxygen atoms bonded to one carbon atom ($CO_2$), that makes up a very small proportion (0.04%) of Earth's atmosphere; although it is present in such small quantities, it plays a large role in controlling climate because it traps heat in the atmosphere.

**fossil fuel** Fuel—such as coal, natural gas, and oil—that formed from the remains of ancient organisms, such as plants and single-celled organisms.

**resource** Something that benefits people, such as materials and energy; many resources people currently use may eventually run out because they take millions of years to form.

**turbine** A device, often a wheel or cylinder with blades around its edges, that converts energy from moving water, steam, or air into mechanical energy by spinning; the spinning motion is then converted into electricity.

These plastic bags require many geologic resources to produce, including oil to make the plastic; rock, minerals and metals to make the factories that make the plastic; and fossil fuels to burn to generate electricity.

# 5.5 Mineral and Rock Resources

**Key Concept:** Igneous, sedimentary, and metamorphic rocks may be mined and used as whole rocks or as sources for minerals. The formation process and minerals that comprise igneous, sedimentary, and metamorphic rocks affect the usefulness of the rocks **1**. After geologists locate rock and mineral resources, the rock can be mined, or removed, from the bedrock through surface mining or underground mining **2**. After it is removed, whole rock can be used for many purposes, such as building materials and art. If the rock contained useful minerals, those minerals can be removed from the rock for their own uses **3**.

## **1** Rock formation and resource characteristics

The formation processes and types of minerals affect the resulting characteristics of rocks, giving them unique properties that make some rocks more useful as resources than other rocks. Depending on how the rock formed, the type of minerals that comprise each rock type varies.

| Igneous rock | Sedimentary rock | Metamorphic rock |
| --- | --- | --- |
| When magma cools, the resulting igneous rock is made up of interlocking silicate minerals, which tend to be hard. Therefore, many igneous rocks tend to be hard and resistant to weathering. Some igneous rocks contain large, exotic minerals that form as less common atoms in magma crystallizes. | Properties of sedimentary rocks generally depend on the types of minerals that form the sediments. Sediments are commonly made up of silicate minerals and carbonate minerals, but some sedimentary rocks form from less common minerals. Some sediments, such as gravel and sand, are also mined. | Metamorphic rock comprised of recrystallized silicate minerals tends to be hard, whereas rock comprised of carbonate minerals is softer and can be carved. Flat clay minerals result in metamorphic rock that breaks along flat planes. Other metamorphic rocks contain large, exotic minerals. |

## **2** Finding and excavating rocks and minerals

Geologists examine bedrock and the minerals within it, as shown to the right, to identify where rock and mineral resources are located and can be mined. They use the data they collect to create geologic maps. A geologic map is an interpretation of an area's geology and can be used to predict where to find resources. Once a location is identified, the resources are removed from the ground in a mine or quarry, like the large mine in the photo on the right. It takes many millions of years and particular circumstances for most rocks and minerals used as resources to form, so most exist in limited amounts. In addition to finding rock and mineral resources, geologists also help try to minimize the negative environmental impact of mines.

## **3** How we use rocks and minerals

Whole rock can be used for building materials, art sculptures, and more, but it can also be crushed and the minerals removed. Sediments are commonly used in construction. Minerals in igneous, sedimentary, and metamorphic rocks have many uses, including in construction, jewelry, electronics, makeup, paints, and food. For example, sheetrock, used in construction as shown, is made from the mineral gypsum, which forms as a sedimentary rock. Jewelry often contains gemstones, such as the minerals sapphire and diamond in the photo, which forms in igneous and metamorphic rocks.

## Check

☐ Explain how the formation of a rock and the minerals within it impact its usefulness.
☐ Explain how geologists find and mine rocks and minerals.
☐ Explain four ways that you have used mineral and rock resources.

# 5.6 Ore Resources

**Key Concept:** **An ore is a rock that is mined for the metals it contains.** The minerals in an ore have enough metal atoms bonded in the mineral structure that they can be a resource for that metal. They can be any rock type: igneous, sedimentary, or metamorphic **1**. Once mined, the minerals are processed, often using chemical reactions, to break the bonds and remove the metal atoms from the structure of the minerals in the rock **2**. After the metal is extracted, it can be used for many purposes, including wire, jewelry, electronics, cars, and building materials **3**.

## **1** How ore forms

Ore is rock in which metals have concentrated through geologic processes. Special circumstances are usually required for the metal atoms to become this highly concentrated.

**Igneous rock**
When magma cools, the first minerals that form use the common atoms in the magma, so the last minerals to form have a higher concentration of the more unusual metal atoms, such as copper and uranium. Some minerals with metal atoms in their structures have a high density and sink to the bottom of the magma chamber, concentrating metals, such as chromium, there.

**Sedimentary rock**
In ancient oceans, dissolved iron precipitated iron-rich minerals on the seafloor. In other sedimentary ores, the process of transporting sediments concentrates heavy minerals with a high metal content, so the resulting sedimentary rocks have a high metal content, such as gold or platinum.

**Metamorphic rock**
During the process of metamorphism, hot fluids that are often associated with nearby magma chambers carry metal atoms. The metals, such as gold, can become concentrated in rocks, especially along cracks in the rocks.

## **2** Refining ore into metal

The atoms of metal in an ore are bonded to other atoms to form minerals. Therefore, the minerals need to be processed to extract the metal from the rock. This process usually begins with crushing the rock into smaller pieces and then using chemical reactions to break the bonds holding the metal atoms in the mineral. For example, copper can be extracted through chemical reactions from the mineral chalcocite, shown on the top, right. In contrast, some metals, like the gold shown on the bottom, right, may occur as a pure metal within rocks. Metals are present in ores in high enough quantities to be cost-effective to mine. However, most ores contain less than a couple percent of the metals, meaning that over 90% of the ore is mined but not used.

## **3** How we use metal extracted from ore

Metal processed from ores can be used in a wide range of ways. For example, the copper extracted from the ore shown above is often made into large plates as shown here. These plates are then shipped to factories where it is made into a variety of things, such as wire used to conduct electricity. Different metals are valuable components in buildings, structures, machinery, cellphones, computers, cars, tools, and more. Some metals, such as the gold, are made into jewelry, like the ring shown to the right.

## Check

☐ Identify one way that metal atoms can be concentrated in igneous, sedimentary, and metamorphic rocks.
☐ Describe four ways that you have used metal resources extracted from ore.

# 5.7 Oil and Natural Gas Resources

**Key Concept:** Oil and natural gas form from dead organisms and are pumped out of the ground. Although you may have thought that oil and natural gas formed from dinosaurs, they actually have a less glamorous origin. After single-celled organisms in the ocean died, were buried, and reached the right pressure and temperature range, the carbon atoms bonded in their bodies slowly decayed into oil and natural gas **1**. Oil companies drill into rock that trap oil and gas to remove them from the ground to use them **2**. Both oil and natural gas are burned for energy, and oil has other uses as well, such as making plastic **3**.

## 1 How oil and natural gas form

It takes millions of years for oil and natural gas (often called just oil and gas) to form in sedimentary rock.

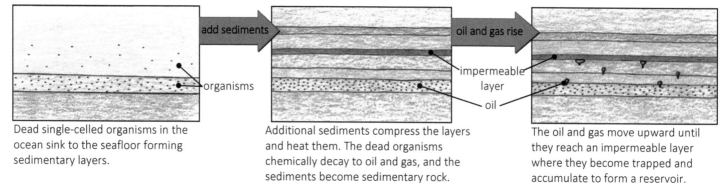

Dead single-celled organisms in the ocean sink to the seafloor forming sedimentary layers.

Additional sediments compress the layers and heat them. The dead organisms chemically decay to oil and gas, and the sediments become sedimentary rock.

The oil and gas move upward until they reach an impermeable layer where they become trapped and accumulate to form a reservoir.

## 2 Getting oil and natural gas out of the ground

Geologists look for impermeable layers in sedimentary rock that can form a trap by stopping the upward movement of oil and gas, resulting in reservoirs. Oil companies drill through the impermeable layer into the reservoir and pump the oil and gas out of the ground. If the oil or gas is locked within an impermeable rock, it may be removed by splitting the rock with high-pressure water, allowing the oil and gas to move through the cracks. This process is called hydraulic fracturing, or fracking.

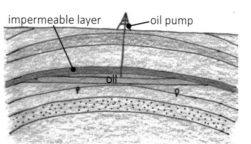

Sedimentary rock layers fold upward, forming an oil and gas trap. Geologists use geologic maps and other technologies to determine locations like this to drill for oil.

This oil rig is drilling for trapped oil or gas that form a reservoir in the sedimentary bedrock underground.

## 3 How we use oil and natural gas

People use oil and natural gas to burn for heat or as fuel for transportation. Oil and natural gas are also burned, and the heat is used to create electricity (see 5.10). Oil is used to produce things, such as plastic. See 5.11 for environmental impacts of burning oil and natural gas.

## Check

☐ Describe how oil and natural gas initially form.
☐ Explain one method of how geologists discover oil and natural gas reservoirs and remove oil and natural gas from them.
☐ Give three examples of how oil and natural gas are used by people.

# 5.8 Coal Resources

**Key Concept:** **Coal forms from dead swamp plants and is removed from the bedrock to be used for energy.** Unlike oil and natural gas, coal typically forms from million-year-old swamp plants. If swamp plants die and the environmental conditions are right, the carbon will be concentrated to form coal **1**. Coal can be removed from the rock layers through surface mining or underground mining **2**. After it is removed, coal is burned to produce heat and electricity **3**. Coal is not only useful as a resource, but it also helps geologists learn about past environments, including ancient climates and plants.

## **1** How coal forms

Coal is made up of mostly carbon with some oxygen and hydrogen. It takes millions of years and the right pressure and temperature conditions for plants in ancient swamps and other wetlands to become layers of coal within sedimentary rock layers.

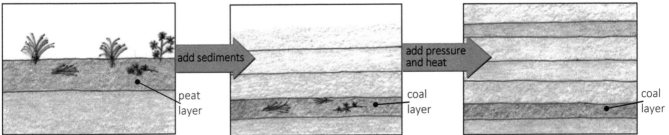

Plants die and sink in a swamp where low amounts of oxygen slow decomposition. The partially decayed plants form brown, soil-like peat which is made up of mostly carbon, oxygen, and hydrogen.

The deeply buried peat layers are compressed and heated, breaking the bonds between atoms and concentrating the carbon content by driving off other atoms. The peat changes into coal.

Higher pressures and temperatures result in higher quality coal. However, if it gets too hot, the carbon atoms bond together forming the mineral graphite, which is not a burnable energy resource.

## **2** Getting coal out of the ground

Coal can be excavated by removing the land on top of it if it is near the surface, or it can be mined from deeper underground.

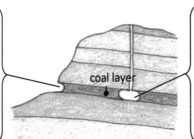

**Surface mine**
At surface mines, coal layers near the surface are mined by removing the sedimentary rock layers on top of them.

coal layer

**Underground mine**
Deep coal layers are removed from underground mines by digging through the sedimentary rock layers, deep underground.

## **3** How we use coal

Most coal is burned to create electricity (see 5.10). Burning higher quality coal releases fewer other components that act as pollutants to the atmosphere than burning lower quality coal. Environmental impacts of burning coal are described in 5.11. This power plant burns coal to produce electricity.

## Check

☐ Describe the three major steps in how coal forms.
☐ Explain how people remove coal from rock.

# 5.9 DATA AND DIAGRAMS: How Deadly is Your Electricity?

**Key Concept:** Bar graphs show the relationship between varying factors, and pie charts compare pieces of a whole.

These diagrams show the mortality rate and percentage of global energy for different methods of producing electricity **1**. Although the data are not from a scientific publication reviewed by other scientists (see 1.7), this perspective provides an interesting approach to looking at costs and benefits of different types of electricity. To create a diagram like this, scientists examine both records of reported deaths in different countries and records of electricity produced. Tips on how to read these graphs are below **2**. Use the questions to practice interpreting bar graphs and pie charts **3**.

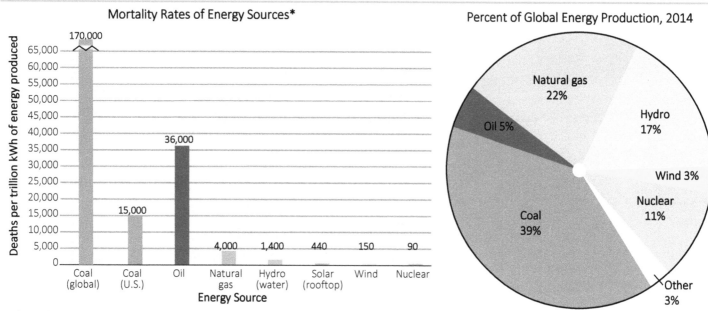

*Mortality rate includes deaths from resource and electricity production as well as related health effects, from 2012; data from:
http://www.forbes.com/sites/jamesconca/2012/06/10/energysdeathprint-a-price-always-paid/#5f222ee749d2

## **1** How to read the diagram

Determine what the variables are. In this case, the horizontal axis of the bar graph on the left shows different sources of energy, and the vertical axis shows the related mortality rate. The pie chart on the right shows the same sources of energy, but this time the whole graph represents all of the energy produced globally, and each slice is the percentage that source contributes.

## **2** An example of what you might interpret

If you examine the energy source of nuclear energy on both graphs, you will see that it is the source of energy with the lowest related mortality rate, at 90 deaths per trillion kilowatt hour (kWh) produced, but it only produces 11% of global energy.

## **3** Questions

**1. What does the bar graph show?**
a. The relationship between the number of related deaths and the global amount of electricity produced
b. The number of related deaths for a certain amount of electricity produced by different methods
c. The amount of energy produced by different methods
d. A comparison of the proportion of energy produced by different methods

**2. What does the pie chart show?**
a. The total amount of global electricity generated by each energy source.
b. The proportion of global electricity generated by each energy source.
c. The average household usage of each energy source.

**3. Approximately what proportion of the world's electricity is produced by fossil fuels (coal, natural gas, and oil)?**
a. About one-third.
b. About one-half.
c. About two-thirds.

**4. Why are the two diagrams shown together?**
a. They allow the same data to be presented in two different ways.
b. They allow different but related data to be compared.
c. They allow a global perspective for U.S. data.

**5. What is one main point that requires both diagrams to be examined together?**
a. The largest source of electricity, coal, is also the most harmful.
b. Nuclear energy is a harmful source of electricity.
c. Coal in the United States is safer than most forms of energy.
d. Oil is not a significant source of electricity.

# 5.10 Producing Electricity

**Key Concept:** Electricity is produced in a variety of ways. Although you use electricity every day, have you wondered how it is produced? Most electricity is generated using a turbine, which is a wheel that can convert the energy of moving steam, air, or water into electricity by spinning magnets past wire **1**. The actual method used to spin the turbine varies. For example, many power plants spin a turbine with steam, produced by heating water using nuclear energy **2** or burning fossil fuels **3**. Turbines can also be turned directly by wind **4** and flowing water **5**. Energy from the sun, or solar energy, may involve either concentrating sunlight enough to boil water to create steam to turn a turbine or using the sun's light energy to directly produce electricity with a solar panel **6**. All of these methods, as well as other methods not mentioned here, use resources from Earth's rocks, either as fuel or as building materials.

## **1** Electricity is produced by spinning

Most electricity is produced by causing magnets to spin within a coil of wire in a generator. Electrons behave like tiny magnets, so the electrons in wire move when a magnet is moving, and these moving electrons produce an electric current in the wire. The diagram on these pages illustrates the steps to generate electricity, mostly using different strategies to spin the generator containing magnets in a coil of wire.

## **2** Nuclear energy

Uranium ore is mined and put into a nuclear reactor where fast-moving particles break apart the nucleus of uranium atoms. Released heat energy boils water into a jet of steam, which spins turbine blades. The power plant shown in 5.11 converts nuclear energy into electricity.

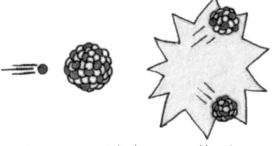

A uranium atom is broken apart and heat is released from the breaking atom.

## **3** Fossil fuel energy

Fossil fuels, such as coal and natural gas, are mined (see 5.7 and 5.8) and burned. The process of burning releases heat energy which is used to boil water. The water expands to become a jet of steam, which spins turbine blades.

Fossil fuels, such as coal and natural gas, are burned to produce heat.

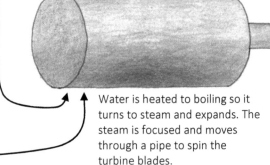

Water is heated to boiling so it turns to steam and expands. The steam is focused and moves through a pipe to spin the turbine blades.

## 4 Wind energy

Wind spins the turbine blades of each wind mill directly. Hundreds of turbines may be on wind farms such as the one shown in 5.11, with each windmill converting wind energy into electricity.

Wind blows through an area and spins the turbine blades of the windmill. The generator is inside the windmill.

## 5 Water energy (hydro)

Flowing water spins turbine blades in a hydroelectric dam directly. The turbines inside the large dam shown in 5.11 convert the energy from flowing water into electricity.

Water builds up in a reservoir behind a dam. The water at the bottom is under high pressure and rushes through a pipe, spinning the turbine blades.

## 6 Direct solar energy

The Sun's energy directly produces electricity with solar panels, such as the one shown on 5.11, which include rare metals that are mined from ores. In addition, the Sun's energy can also be used to heat water to steam to indirectly create electricity.

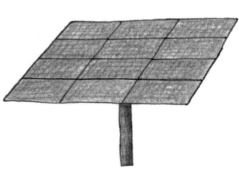

Light energy from the Sun hits the surface of the solar panel. Light energy causes electrons in the panel to move, pushing other electrons along a wire, producing electricity.

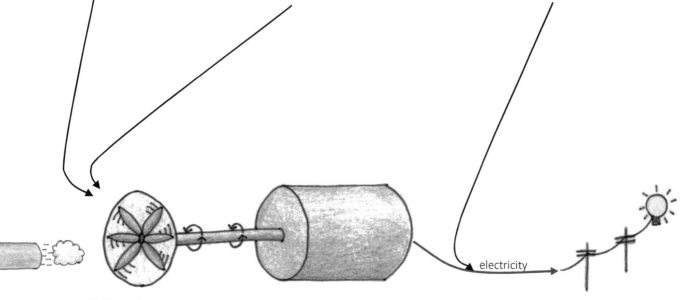

electricity

Turbine blades spin a rod connected to the generator.

Magnets rotate around a coil of wire in the generator, generating electricity.

## Check

□ Explain how steam, wind, and flowing water are similar in how they generate electricity.
□ Compare and contrast how electricity is generated with each of the following types of energy: nuclear energy, fossils fuels, wind energy, water energy, and direct solar energy.

# 5.11 Comparing Electricity Sources

**Key Concept:** There are advantages and disadvantages to each of the different ways of producing electricity. The various methods of producing electricity described on the previous pages are compared in this section. The relative amount of electricity produced is graphed in 5.9. Coal and natural gas are called fossil fuels because they formed from organisms that died millions of years ago **1**. Fossil fuels have advantages as sources of electricity because they are abundant and relatively cheap. However, they pollute the environment and add carbon dioxide to the atmosphere. Alternative methods of producing electricity other than fossil fuels include nuclear, wind, hydroelectric, and solar **2**. These tend to pollute less, but they have a variety of disadvantages as well. All methods require rock and mineral resources to build the power plant, turbine, dam, or panel. While reading, keep in mind that this page only describes some of the advantages and disadvantages. No energy source is perfect, which emphasizes our need to reduce the amount of electricity that we use.

## **1** Fossil fuels

Fossil fuels are fuels such as coal, natural gas, and oil that are formed from the remains of ancient organisms and are burned for energy.

**Coal:** Coal is burned to generate electricity.

### Select Advantages

- currently abundant
- relatively cheap for each unit energy
- people have invested in developing current technology that uses coal

### Select Disadvantages

- burning releases carbon dioxide into the atmosphere, affecting the atmosphere and Earth's climate (see Chapter 12)
- burning releases contaminants, such as mercury and soot, which can cause health issues in people living downwind from power plants
- causes more deaths per unit energy than other forms of energy, predominantly through mining and health problems caused by pollution (see 5.9)
- surface mining changes Earth's surface, destroys ecosystems, and may cause contamination of water in the ground
- it takes millions of years to form, so coal is a nonrenewable resource; we will run out, likely in the next couple hundred years

**Natural gas:** Natural gas is burned to generate electricity.

### Select Advantages

- currently abundant
- relatively cheap for each unit energy
- burns relatively cleanly compared to other fossil fuels
- people have invested in developing current technology that uses natural gas

### Select Disadvantages

- burning releases carbon dioxide into the atmosphere, affecting the atmosphere and Earth's climate (see Chapter 12)
- drilling and hydraulic fracturing may cause contamination of water in the ground
- it takes millions of years to form, so natural gas is a nonrenewable resource; we will run out, likely in less than 100 years

## 2 Alternative energy

Alternative energy sources include methods of producing electricity that use resources other than fossil fuels.

**Nuclear energy:** Atoms are split to generate electricity.

| Select Advantages | Select Disadvantages |
| --- | --- |
| • uranium is currently abundant<br><br>• does not release carbon dioxide<br><br>• causes the least number of deaths per unit energy compared to other forms of energy | • using uranium produces nuclear waste which is radioactive for many thousands of years<br><br>• nuclear power plants can have meltdowns, releasing radioactive materials into the air and water, although this is less likely with new designs<br><br>• it takes millions of years to form, so uranium is a nonrenewable resource; we will run out, likely in the next few hundred years |

**Wind energy:** Wind spins turbines to generate electricity.

| Select Advantages | Select Disadvantages |
| --- | --- |
| • unlimited<br><br>• does not release carbon dioxide | • wind turbines can only be built in areas with consistently strong wind<br><br>• takes up a lot of space compared to the amount of energy produced and may be considered an eyesore |

**Hydroelectric energy:** Water spins turbines to generate electricity.

| Select Advantages | Select Disadvantages |
| --- | --- |
| • unlimited once dams are built<br><br>• does not release carbon dioxide<br><br>• the reservoir can be used for other purposes, such as drinking water and recreation | • dams can only be built in certain places on rivers<br><br>• the dam and the reservoir behind it destroy the natural river system, impacting related ecosystems<br><br>• dams trap sediments, filling the reservoir and preventing the sediments from reaching the ocean and replenishing beaches<br><br>• dams may break |

**Solar energy:** Panels convert the sun's energy into electricity.

| Select Advantages | Select Disadvantages |
| --- | --- |
| • unlimited sunshine<br><br>• does not release carbon dioxide | • solar panels must be built in sunny areas<br><br>• currently expensive per unit energy compared to other forms of energy<br><br>• takes up a lot of space compared to the amount of energy produced<br><br>• manufacture of solar panels uses rare earth elements that need to be mined |

## Check

☐ Compare and contrast advantages and disadvantages for six different ways of producing electricity.
☐ Summarize the importance of generating electricity with methods other than coal and natural gas.
☐ Explain why it is important to reduce the amount of electricity we use in regard to damaging the environment.

## Chapter 5

### End of Chapter Questions: Student Debates

For each of the following questions, determine which student you agree with and explain why.

1. **Two students are discussing the direction rocks travel through the rock cycle.**

   **Student 1:** Rocks travel through one circular path, making a circle allowing geologists to predict what rock type it will be next.

   **Student 2:** Rocks may travel along any path, so they can become any rock type depending on the environment they are in.

2. **Two students are discussing why geologists study rocks.**

   **Student 1:** Geologists make observations of rocks in order to describe them and identify them.

   **Student 2:** Geologists use information in rocks to learn about the processes changing Earth.

3. **Two students are discussing how rocks change.**

   **Student 1:** Rocks can change, like when they are weathered or melted, but it happens very slowly.

   **Student 2:** That explains how rocks formed, but once they form, they are very stable and not do change.

4. **Three students are discussing how oil forms.**

   **Student 1:** Tiny, microscopic organisms become oil after they die and are buried.

   **Student 2:** Dinosaurs and other large animals become oil after they die and are buried.

   **Student 3:** Coal dissolves in underground water and becomes oil.

5. **Two students are discussing the relationship between where swamps and coal mines are located today.**

   **Student 1:** Coal mines are found where swamps are currently located, although the swamp may be destroyed when the mine is created.

   **Student 2:** Coal mines are found where swamps were located millions of years ago, so the current environment is likely not swampy anymore.

### End of Chapter Questions: Short Answer

Using your own words or sketching and labeling a diagram, answer the following questions.

6. A friend says, "Why would anyone want to learn about minerals in rocks? They don't tell you anything interesting." Do you agree or disagree with your friend? Justify your response with at least five lines of supporting evidence.

7. Using what you understand about the rock cycle, create a story about how a silicon atom in an igneous rock can become part of a metamorphic rock in a mountain range and then a sedimentary rock. Explain each step in the processes in detail (on the atomic level).

8. Two towns are located in two different areas. Town A has more ore resources than Town B. Hypothesize at least two distinct explanations why there is a difference

9. Imagine you took this photo of a countertop made of igneous rock. Explain to your friends how this rock formed.

10. Identify and explain at least five ways in which you used geologic resources (such as rock, mineral, ore, energy) yesterday.

11. Draw a table to compare and contrast at least five separate pieces of information about natural gas and coal. Things to consider include formation processes, removal from the ground, uses, how they are used to produce electricity, and advantages/disadvantages of each.

12. Draw a diagram or flow chart explaining how swamp plants can eventually be used to generate electricity.

13. Imagine that your school is building a new library. Make a recommendation as to whether fossil fuels or alternative energy (be specific with the type you recommend) should be used to provide electricity to the library. Support your recommendation with at least three separate arguments, including your local geologic conditions as appropriate.

**Hints:** For each question, see the sections listed here for information relevant to answering it.

**1.** (5.1) **2.** (5.1, 5.2, 5.3, 5.4) **3.** (5.1, 5.3) **4.** (5.7) **5.** (5.8) **6.** (5.1, 5.2, 5.3, 5.4) **7.** (5.1, 5.3) **8.** (5.3, 5.6) **9.** (5.1, 5.2, 5.3, 5.4) **10.** (5.5, 5.6, 5.7, 5.8, 5.10) **11.** (5.7, 5.8, 5.9, 5.10, 5.11) **12.** (5.8, 5.10) **13.** (5.7, 5.8, 5.9, 5.10, 5.11)

# Chapter 6:
# Igneous Rocks

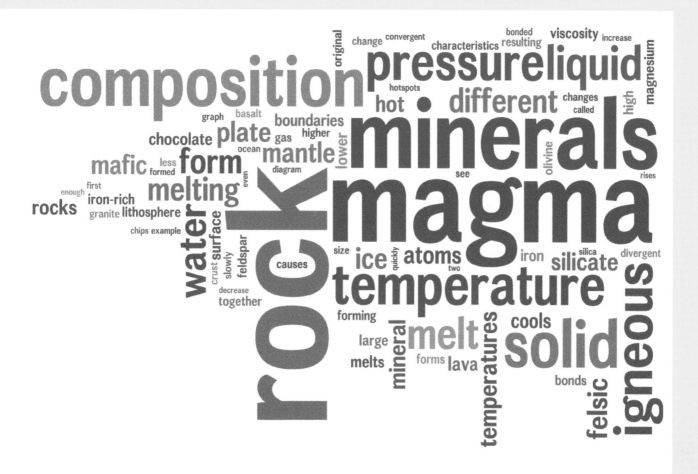

## Chapter Objectives

When you are finished reading this chapter, you should be able to …

• distinguish the characteristics of igneous rock color and mineral size, and use them to identify and categorize igneous rocks (6.1–6.4).

• explain how minerals melt to become magma and contrast that process with how magma cools to become igneous rock (6.5–6.7).

• compare and contrast the processes that cause rock to melt at divergent plate boundaries, convergent plate boundaries, and hotspots (6.8–6.12).

• classify magma based on its characteristics and explain how those characteristics affect volcanic eruptions (6.13–6.14).

# 6.1 – 6.4 Igneous Rock Characteristics

In this section, you will learn that the names of igneous rocks are defined by their color and mineral size. These characteristics give geologists information about the composition of the igneous rocks and how long it took for the lava or magma to cool.

## Frequently Used Terms

The terms listed here are used repeatedly throughout this section, so by learning them before you read this section, you can focus your mental energy on the concepts presented.

**extrusive igneous rock**  Erupted lava of any composition that cools quickly to form igneous rock with a texture of small minerals.

**felsic composition**  The composition of magma, lava, or igneous rock that contains a high amount of silica, approximately 70% silica.

**igneous rock**  The rock type that forms from magma or lava that cools and solidifies (crystallizes) into solid rock.

**intermediate composition**  The composition of magma, lava, or igneous rock that contains an intermediate amount of silica, between felsic and mafic compositions.

**intrusive igneous rock**  Magma of any composition that cools slowly beneath the surface to form igneous rock with a texture of large minerals.

**mafic composition**  The composition of magma, lava, or igneous rock that contains a low amount of silica, approximately 50% silica.

**silica**  Silicon bonded with oxygen ($SiO_2$); silica is the primary ingredient of magma or lava and bonds together upon cooling to form minerals in igneous rock; the amount of silica varies with composition.

This counter top is made from the igneous rock that geologists call gabbro, although it is frequently called granite when sold.

# 6.1 Igneous Rock Composition

**Key Concept:** The composition of an igneous rock is defined by the percentage of silica, which affects the types and colors of minerals that form. Each row in the diagram below shows a different composition of igneous rock, cooled from the same composition of magma or lava. The percentage of silica ($SiO_2$) in magma, lava, and igneous rocks decreases for the four igneous compositions of felsic, intermediate, mafic, and ultramafic. At the same time, the percentage of iron and magnesium increases **1**. As you look through the table, you will see that the change in these key components affects the types of minerals that can form **2**, which in turn influences the overall color of the rock **3**, with the felsic rocks having a lighter color and the mafic rocks having a darker color.

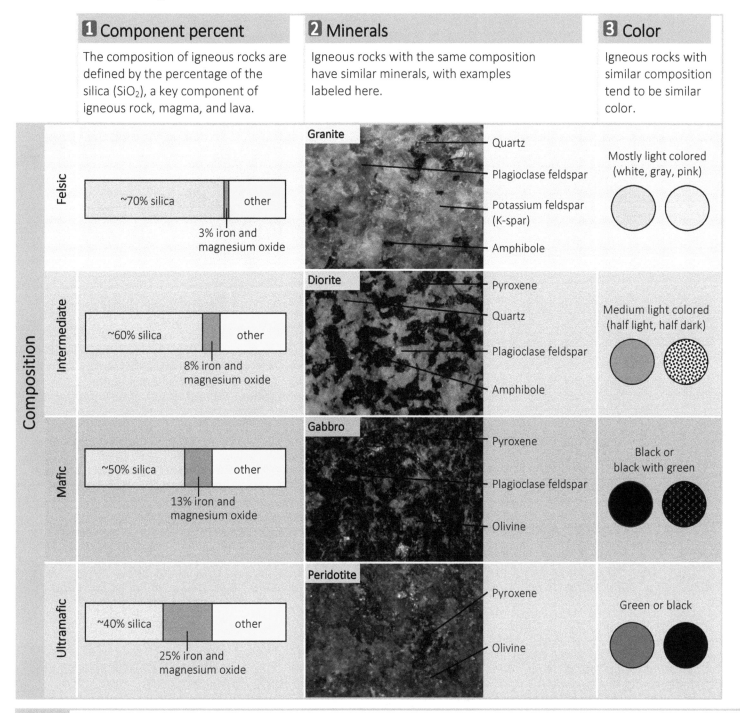

**1 Component percent**

The composition of igneous rocks are defined by the percentage of the silica ($SiO_2$), a key component of igneous rock, magma, and lava.

**2 Minerals**

Igneous rocks with the same composition have similar minerals, with examples labeled here.

**3 Color**

Igneous rocks with similar composition tend to be similar color.

**Composition**

**Felsic**

Granite — Quartz, Plagioclase feldspar, Potassium feldspar (K-spar), Amphibole

~70% silica | other
3% iron and magnesium oxide

Mostly light colored (white, gray, pink)

**Intermediate**

Diorite — Pyroxene, Quartz, Plagioclase feldspar, Amphibole

~60% silica | other
8% iron and magnesium oxide

Medium light colored (half light, half dark)

**Mafic**

Gabbro — Pyroxene, Plagioclase feldspar, Olivine

~50% silica | other
13% iron and magnesium oxide

Black or black with green

**Ultramafic**

Peridotite — Pyroxene, Olivine

~40% silica | other
25% iron and magnesium oxide

Green or black

**Check** Before you continue, you should be able to answer each check without looking at the page.

☐ Explain how the color of an igneous rock relates to its relative silica content and iron and magnesium content.
☐ Identify two example minerals in each of the four different compositions of igneous rocks.

# 6.2 DATA AND DIAGRAMS: Mineral Percentage; Rock Composition

**Key Concept:** Diagrams can show the relationship between the overall composition of an igneous rock and the percentages of the related minerals. Each composition, from felsic to mafic, corresponds to a particular set of minerals ❶. To create a diagram like this, geologists in labs have measured the percentage of minerals present in igneous rocks with a great variety of overall composition. Tips on how to read this diagram are below ❷. Use the questions to practice interpreting this type of diagram ❸.

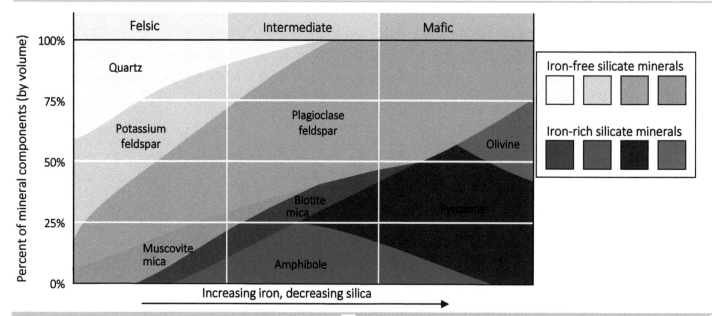

## ❶ How to read the diagram

Determine what the variables are. In this case, the horizontal axis is igneous rock composition from felsic on the left to mafic on the right, and the vertical axis is the percentage of different minerals that make up the rock.

## ❷ An example of what you might interpret

If you find an igneous rock with roughly equal parts quartz, potassium feldspar, and plagioclase feldspar with some muscovite mica and biotite mica, you can find on the diagram where a vertical line is made through those components. That vertical line is in the middle of the felsic rock composition, so you can determine that the rock is felsic.

## ❸ Questions

**1. What does the graph show?**
a. The amount of different minerals in rocks of different compositions
b. The order in which you would encounter different minerals if you drilled into rocks of different compositions
c. The size of minerals in rocks of different compositions
d. A cross section of what you would see if you cut open part of Earth's crust

**2. Why was the color scheme chosen for the different mineral regions?**
a. The colors are arranged mostly from light to dark from the top to the bottom of the figure.
b. The earth-tone colors are chose by an artist and randomly assigned to mineral regions.
c. The light and dark colors for each mineral region represent how the minerals actually appear.

**3. What does the horizontal length of each mineral's region in the diagram tell you?**
a. The range of rock compositions in which that mineral is found.
b. The amount of that mineral in a particular rock composition.
c. The size of that mineral in a particular rock composition.

**4. If you want to know the amount of a mineral in a particular rock composition, what is the most important feature of each mineral region in the graph?**
a. The shape of the whole region
b. The vertical height at the composition in question
c. The maximum horizontal distance of the region

**5. If you identify the mineral quartz in a rock, which mineral is LEAST likely to also be part of that rock?**
a. Plagioclase feldspar      b. Olivine      c. Mica

**6. What is the relationship between rock composition and minerals present?**
a. Felsic composition rocks are mostly made up of iron-free silicate minerals; mafic composition rocks are mostly made up of iron-rich silicate minerals.
b. Felsic composition rocks are mostly made up of iron-rich silicate minerals; mafic composition rocks are mostly made up of iron-free silicate minerals.
c. There is no clear relationship between rock composition and minerals present.

# 6.3 Igneous Rock Mineral Size

**Key Concept:** The size of minerals that make up an igneous rock depends on how quickly the magma cools, with larger minerals forming when magma cools slowly. Magma erupted from a volcano as a lava flow on Earth's surface cools much more quickly than magma deep beneath Earth's surface. These different cooling rates create igneous rocks with different mineral sizes. Geologists call the pattern of mineral sizes in igneous rocks the rock texture. In magma that cools quickly, minerals have very little time to grow, and are therefore small **1** compared to magma that cools slowly underground **2**. If magma cools nearly instantaneously, no minerals have time to form **3**. Some igneous rocks have two mineral sizes **4**.

## 1 Small minerals

If magma cools quickly (days to years), minerals have little time to grow, so they remain small and can only be seen with a microscope. Magma cools quickly when it erupts at the surface. Igneous rock that forms in this way is called extrusive igneous rock, and the texture is called aphanitic. For example, the rock andesite primarily has minerals that are only visible through a microscope.

## 3 No minerals

If magma cools nearly instantaneously, no minerals form because there is no time for them to grow, resulting in volcanic glass called obsidian. Obsidian with gas bubbles is called pumice. The obsidian shown does not have minerals, even when viewed through a microscope.

lava flow
(extrusive)

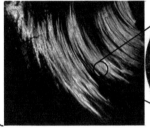 

## 2 Large minerals

If magma cools slowly (thousands to millions of years), minerals have a long time to grow, so they grow large and are clearly seen with the naked eye. Magma cools slowly when it remains underground in a magma chamber. Igneous rock that forms in this way is called intrusive igneous rock, and the texture is called phaneritic. The rock diorite below has minerals that are visible by the naked eye and through a microscope.

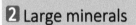

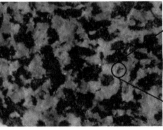 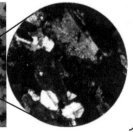

## 4 Two mineral sizes

Igneous rock with minerals of two distinct sizes went through two stages of cooling—first slowly underground, forming the large minerals, and then cooling more quickly, often by erupting out of a volcano, forming the smaller minerals. Igneous rock that forms in this way is called porphyry, and the texture is called porphyritic. The porphyry below has large olivine minerals next to smaller minerals that are only visible with a microscope.

magma chamber
(intrusive)

## Check

☐ Describe what the mineral size of an igneous rock tells you.
☐ Relate the cooling rate of magma to the geologic location in which the igneous rock formed.
☐ Describe a situation in which an igneous rock could form with two different sizes of minerals.

# 6.4 Identifying Igneous Rocks

**Key Concept:**  Igneous rocks are given names based on both the composition of the rock and the size of minerals.
In order to figure out the name of an igneous rock, observations of both the composition **1**, which is indicated by the
color of the rock, as well as the mineral size **2**, which is related to the cooling rate of the magma, are needed. Each
specific combination of mineral size and composition defines a specific igneous rock and is shown in the table below.
For example, an igneous rock that is felsic in composition and has large minerals is called granite. The rocks' defining
characteristics can also shed some light on the geologic history of an area. Identifying bedrock as granite indicates
that the area was constituted of iron-free, silica-rich magma that cooled slowly underground in a magma chamber.

## **1** Rock characteristic: Composition

The rows in the chart are based on the composition of
igneous rock. Composition can be determined by the types
of minerals in or colors of the igneous rock. Felsic rock
tends to have a lighter color then mafic rock.

## **2** Rock characteristic: Mineral size

The columns in the chart are based on the size of
minerals in the igneous rock. Mineral size depends on
how fast magma cools. Rocks in the first column
cooled more slowly than rocks in the second column.

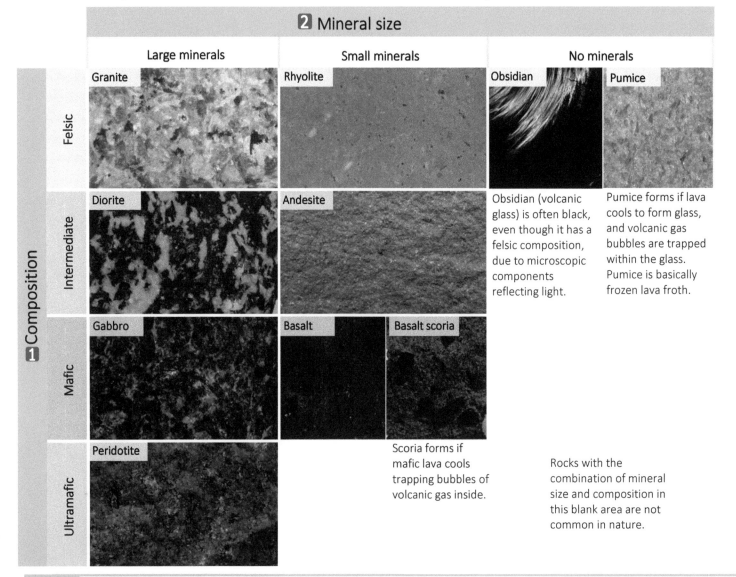

**2** Mineral size

|  | Large minerals | Small minerals | No minerals |
|---|---|---|---|

Felsic: Granite, Rhyolite, Obsidian, Pumice

Obsidian (volcanic glass) is often black, even though it has a felsic composition, due to microscopic components reflecting light.

Pumice forms if lava cools to form glass, and volcanic gas bubbles are trapped within the glass. Pumice is basically frozen lava froth.

Intermediate: Diorite, Andesite

Mafic: Gabbro, Basalt, Basalt scoria

Scoria forms if mafic lava cools trapping bubbles of volcanic gas inside.

Ultramafic: Peridotite

Rocks with the combination of mineral size and composition in this blank area are not common in nature.

**1** Composition

## Check

☐ Give the two pieces of information you need to know about an igneous rock in order to determine its name.
☐ For each of the igneous rocks listed, identify the combination of color and mineral size.
☐ For each of the igneous rocks listed, explain how their specific characteristics can be interpreted to determine how the rock formed.

# 6.5 – 6.7 From Rock to Magma and Back

In this section, you will learn that the processes of melting rock to become magma and cooling magma to become igneous rock happen in predictable steps.

## Frequently Used Terms

The terms listed here are used repeatedly throughout this section, so by learning them before you read this section, you can focus your mental energy on the concepts presented.

**freeze**  The process in which atoms that are not bonded together in a liquid bond together to form a solid which often occurs as temperatures cool, although rock freezes, or crystallizes, when the temperature is still very hot.

**iron-free silicate mineral**  Minerals with primarily silicon and oxygen atoms that do not contain iron and magnesium atoms; they are generally light colored, and examples include quartz and potassium feldspar.

**iron-rich silicate mineral**  Minerals with primarily silicon and oxygen atoms that also contain iron and magnesium atoms; they are generally dark colored, and examples include pyroxene and olivine.

**melt**  The process of breaking bonds between atoms in a solid to form a liquid in which the atoms are not bonded together; melting is the opposite of freezing.

**mineral**  The solid components of rock (see Chapter 4).

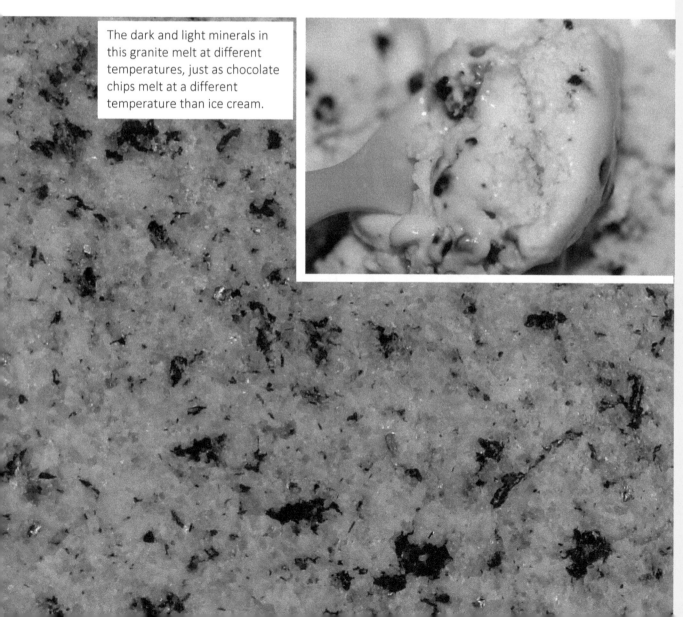

The dark and light minerals in this granite melt at different temperatures, just as chocolate chips melt at a different temperature than ice cream.

Chapter 6: Igneous Rocks    Section 2

# 6.5 Melting Minerals in Rock

**Key Concept:** Different minerals that make up rock will melt at different temperatures resulting in partially melted rock and magma with a different composition. Contrary to melting ice, when rock melts to become magma, the whole rock does not melt at the same time. Instead certain minerals melt first because they have lower melting temperatures than other minerals **1**, just as ice melts at lower temperatures than chocolate **2**. As a result, it is common for only some minerals in a solid rock to melt and become magma, leaving behind many still-solid minerals. The solid minerals are denser than the liquid magma, so they settle out of the magma. Therefore, the resulting magma has a different composition than the original whole rock.

## **1** Magma composition

The composition of magma is different than the original rock if only some of the minerals melt. The idea that the entire rock does not melt at once because minerals melt at different temperatures is called partial melting.

**Rock at 600°C**

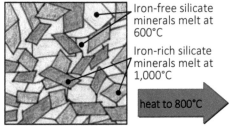

Iron-free silicate minerals melt at 600°C

Iron-rich silicate minerals melt at 1,000°C

heat to 800°C

Iron-rich silicate minerals and iron-free silicate minerals in a rock have different melting temperatures. Often, melting rock only reaches the melting temperature of some of its component minerals.

**Magma with minerals at 800°C**

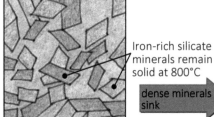

Iron-rich silicate minerals remain solid at 800°C

dense minerals sink

In general, iron-free silicate minerals will melt to become magma before iron-rich silicate minerals. When atoms bonded together in a solid mineral break bonds during the melting process, the resulting liquid magma is less dense than solid minerals.

**Magma with minerals at 800°C**

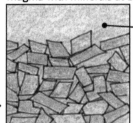

Magma with a more felsic composition than the original rock

The lower density magma rises. The composition of the new magma is more felsic than the original rock because it does not include the iron and magnesium from the unmelted iron-rich silicate minerals.

## **2** Ice and chocolate chip analogy

In the analogy below the composition of the water "magma" is different than the original ice-chocolate "rock" if only the ice melts and the chocolate settles to the bottom. Similar to the rock, partial melting is occurring because only part of it is melting at this temperature.

**Ice and chocolate at -2°C**

Ice melts at 0°C

Chocolate melts at 35°C

heat to 15°C

An ice block with chocolate chips represents "rock" with different "minerals" (ice + chocolate chips). The ice "minerals" and the chocolate chip "minerals" have different melting temperatures.

**Water and chocolate at 15°C**

Chocolate remains solid at 15°C

chocolate sinks

The ice and chocolate "rock" is heated to a temperature at which the ice melts to water "magma", but it remains below the melting temperature of the chocolate chips.

**Water and chocolate at 15°C**

Water with no chocolate

Water "magma" is less dense than solid chocolate chips and will rise. The composition of the melt (water) is different than the composition of the original "rock" (water + chocolate).

## Check

☐ Describe why rock might only partially melt at a given high temperature.
☐ Explain how the composition of newly-formed magma might differ from the rock from which it formed, and why the composition change occurs.

# 6.6 Forming Minerals from Magma

**Key Concept:** As magma cools, different minerals form at different temperatures, resulting in a rock that has a variety of minerals with different compositions. The previous section describes how minerals melt at particular temperatures to form magma. Individual minerals form as they freeze from cooling magma at those same particular temperatures **1**. Once a mineral has formed and settles out, the left-over magma has a changed composition because it no longer contains that mineral type. The new, changed magma composition then results in different minerals forming, and the process, called fractional crystallization, repeats itself. A useful illustration is a rock that has large and small minerals **2**.

## **1** Different minerals form as the magma cools

As magma cools, atoms bond together to form newly crystallized minerals. The composition of the magma determines which minerals crystallize, removing certain atoms from the magma. This process is called fractional crystallization because only a fraction of the magma crystallizes. The order in which the minerals form from magma tends to be the same, allowing geologists to better understand the cooling of magma and the resulting rock as conditions change (see Bowen's Reaction Series in 6.7).

| Magma at 1,200°C | Magma at 900°C | Magma at 900°C | Magma at 800°C |
|---|---|---|---|
| 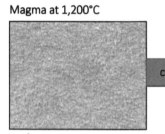 | 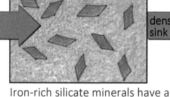 |  | 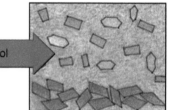 |
| Mafic composition magma has a relatively high percentage of iron and magnesium atoms and is completely liquid at 1,200°C. As the magma cools, minerals form by crystallizing when atoms bond together. | Iron-rich silicate minerals have a higher freezing temperature than iron-free silicate minerals, so they form first at higher temperatures as the magma cools. There are both solid minerals and liquid magma at this temperature. | The denser minerals may sink. Note that the remaining magma is more felsic than the original magma because the formation of the iron-rich silicate minerals removed iron and magnesium atoms from the magma. | Different minerals form because the magma now has a more felsic composition than the original magma. |

## **2** Porphyry as an example

A porphyritic rock has large and small minerals due to a time of slow cooling followed by quick cooling, often because it erupts (see 6.3). The example of an olivine basalt porphyry is shown below. In this example, the large, green olivine minerals formed slowly and then the remaining magma that was more felsic in composition cooled quickly.

| | | | |
|---|---|---|---|
| 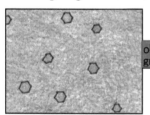 | 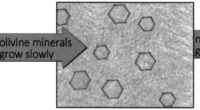 | 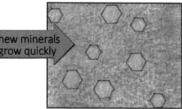 |  |
| Olivine minerals form, removing iron and magnesium atoms from the magma. | The resulting magma composition shifts to be more felsic than it was. | The magma cools forming smaller pyroxene and plagioclase feldspar minerals. | |

## Check

☐ Compare the order of formation of iron-rich silicate minerals with iron-free silicate minerals as magma cools.
☐ Explain why the composition of magma changes as minerals form.
☐ Explain why igneous rocks are composed of different types of minerals instead of one mineral that has the same composition as the original magma.

# 6.7 DATA AND DIAGRAMS: Melting and Freezing Temperatures

**Key Concept:** Diagrams can show how individual characteristics relating to a single variable can change as that variable is altered. This diagram shows the relationship between the temperature and the melting and freezing points of a variety of minerals in mafic magma **1**. To create a diagram like this, geologists slowly cooled basalt magma and observed what minerals formed at each temperature. Geologists particularly noted the order in which the minerals formed, and this order is called Bowen's Reaction Series. Tips on how to read this diagram are below **2**. Use the questions to practice interpreting this type of diagram that shows how a characteristics can change as a variable is altered **3**.

| Minerals that form and melt at cooler temperatures (e.g., iron-free silicate minerals) | | Minerals that form and melt at hotter temperatures (e.g., iron-rich silicate minerals) | |
|---|---|---|---|
| Quartz | Biotite mica | Amphibole | Pyroxene | Olivine |
| Muscovite mica | Sodium-rich plagioclase feldspar | Sodium-calcium plagioclase feldspar | Calcium-rich plagioclase feldspar |
| Potassium feldspar | | | |

Cooler = solid rock    600°C            800°C            1,000°C            1,200°C    Hotter = liquid magma

If the temperature increases, minerals melt from solid rock in this order.

If the temperature decreases, minerals form from liquid magma in this order.

## 1 How to read the diagram

Determine what the variable is. In this case the horizontal axis indicates changing temperature (in Celsius). This graph is two dimensional, so the vertical component (how high or low something is on the graph) does not have a meaning. The characteristics affected by the variable (the changing temperature) are the melting and freezing points of different minerals.

## 2 An example of what you might interpret

You can read that olivine melts and freezes at approximately 1,200°C, a much higher temperature than quartz.

## 3 Questions

1. **What does the graph show?**
a. The order in which minerals melt or freeze in mafic solid rock or liquid magma.
b. The minerals that occur in different compositions of igneous rock.
c. How the minerals in an igneous rock change as the solid rock is heated or cooled.

2. **If mafic solid rock mostly melts into liquid magma, what are the last minerals to remain solid?**
a. Quartz, muscovite mica, potassium feldspar
b. Biotite mica, amphibole, pyroxene
c. Olivine, calcium-rich plagioclase feldspar
d. Potassium feldspar, all plagioclase feldspars

3. **If a mafic solid rock partially melts, what is the composition of the liquid magma based on the minerals that melt first?**
a. More felsic (less iron) than the original rock
b. More mafic (more iron) than the original rock
c. More plagioclase than the original rock

4. **What is the relationship between mineral composition and the melting and cooling temperature?**
a. Iron-free silicate minerals melt and form at hotter temperatures than iron-rich silicate minerals.
b. Iron-free silicate minerals melt and form at cooler temperatures than iron-rich silicate minerals.
c. There is no clear relationship.

5. **As minerals progressively form from liquid magma cooling into solid rock, how does the composition of the remaining magma change?**
a. The minerals that form first contain abundant iron and magnesium, so the remaining liquid is more felsic.
b. The minerals that form first contain abundant iron and magnesium, so the remaining liquid magma is more mafic.
c. The minerals that form first contain little iron and magnesium, so the remaining liquid magma is more felsic.
d. The minerals that form first contain little iron and magnesium, so the remaining liquid magma is more mafic.

# 6.8 – 6.13 Magma

In this section, you will learn that rock usually melts in Earth for reasons other than increasing the temperature. You will also learn at what plate tectonic locations melting occurs and why.

## Frequently Used Terms

The terms listed here are used repeatedly throughout this section, so by learning them before you read this section, you can focus your mental energy on the concepts presented.

**basalt** Igneous rock that has the combination of a mafic composition and extrusive texture; it is dark-colored with small minerals.

**granite** Igneous rock that has the combination of a felsic composition and intrusive texture; it is light-colored with large minerals.

**lava** Molten rock that has erupted on Earth's surface.

**magma** Molten rock that is below Earth's surface.

**viscosity** The resistance of a liquid to flowing, or the opposite of how runny something is; lava with a high viscosity does not flow well, while lava with a low viscosity flows quickly and far.

This geologist is collecting recently erupted basalt lava from the hotspot volcano on Hawaii to learn information about the characteristics of the lava.

# 6.8 Why Magma Forms

**Key Concept:** Rock in Earth melts primarily because of decreased pressure and added water and rarely because of **increased temperature.** Although the mantle is nearly completely solid, there are specific locations related to plate tectonics where it melts **1**. As shown in the diagrams, rock melts primarily near the top of the mantle, forming magma, which may erupt at the surface. There are three processes within Earth that can cause rock to melt: decreasing pressure on very hot rock **2**, adding water to very hot rock **3**, and increasing temperature of cool rock **4**.

## **1** Melting locations in the mantle

The mantle and crust are solid except where plate tectonics or mantle plumes cause rock to melt in the upper mantle. Mantle plumes are unusually hot parts of the mantle where the mantle rock rises beneath hotspot volcanoes. A hot air balloon rises because hot air is less dense than the surrounding air, and in a similar way, melted rock rises because it is hotter and therefore less dense than the surrounding solid rock.

| Divergent plate boundary | Convergent plate boundary | Hotspot volcano |
| --- | --- | --- |

Lithosphere
Mantle

The decreased pressure on hot rock as plates separate and the rock rises causes melting at divergent plate boundaries.

The adding of water from the subducted lithosphere to hot mantle rock causes melting at convergent plate boundaries.

The decreased pressure on hot rock in mantle plumes as it rises in the mantle causes melting at hotspot volcanoes.

## **2** Decreased pressure

If a solid is hot enough to melt, it will continue to be a solid if it is under enough pressure. For example, if a rock is 1,300°C (2,400°F) it may remain solid because high pressure holds the atoms close to each other. Decreasing pressure is a common way for rock to melt to form magma at divergent plate boundaries and hotspot volcanoes (see 6.10 and 6.12).

### Melting rock

As shown below, the pressure is higher deeper in Earth's interior than it is at the surface. Therefore, rock can melt by moving shallower, as it does at divergent plate boundaries and within mantle plumes under hotspot volcanoes. Pressure may also decrease as rock pulls apart at divergent plate boundaries.

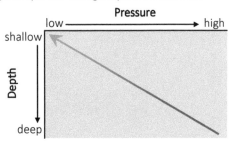

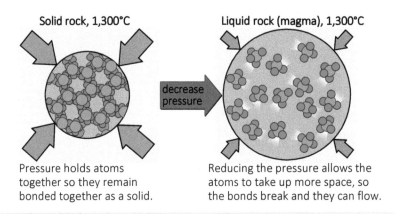

Solid rock, 1,300°C                    Liquid rock (magma), 1,300°C

decrease pressure

Pressure holds atoms together so they remain bonded together as a solid.

Reducing the pressure allows the atoms to take up more space, so the bonds break and they can flow.

### Analogy

The reason that hot rock changes from a solid to a liquid due to a decrease in pressure is similar to the reason that water changes from liquid to gas when pressure is decreased in a pressure cooker. In both cases, the reduction of pressure allows the atoms that were held tightly together to separate, resulting in a change of phase, even though the temperature does not change.

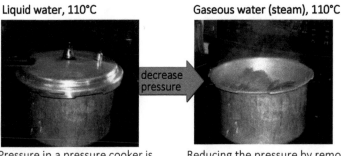

Liquid water, 110°C                    Gaseous water (steam), 110°C

decrease pressure

Pressure in a pressure cooker is kept high by the lid, so water that is hot enough to become steam remains a liquid.

Reducing the pressure by removing the lid makes space for the water molecules to move apart and become gas rising over the pot.

# 3 Added water

If water molecules are added to very hot rock, it changes its chemistry and causes the rock to melt at a lower temperature than it would without water. Added water is a common way for rock to melt to form magma at convergent plate boundaries with subduction (see 6.11).

 water molecule

### Melting rock

If rock or sediment with water bonded in minerals is heated, as may occur when oceanic lithosphere is subducted, the water molecules are released. These water molecules may migrate to nearby hot mantle rock. This addition of water changes the chemistry of the hot mantle rock, causing it to melt at a lower temperature than it would without water.

Solid rock, 1,300°C     Solid rock, 1,300°C     Liquid rock (magma), 1,300°C

add water → bonds break

Atoms in solid rock are bonded together even if the solid is very hot.

Added water disrupts bonds between atoms in a very hot, solid rock.

Once the bonds break, the atoms can flow, even if the temperature remains the same.

### Analogy

The reason that rock changes from a solid to a liquid due to the addition of water is similar to the reason ice and snow change from a solid to a liquid due to the addition of salt. In both cases, the addition of something else to the solid disrupts the bonds holding the atoms together as a solid, resulting in melting, even though the temperature does not change.

Solid water (ice), -2°C     Solid water (ice), -2°C     Liquid water, -2°C

add salt → bonds break

Snow is made up of solid ice crystals.

Added salt disrupts the bonds between the atoms in the ice crystals.

The ice crystals melt, even if the temperature remains the same.

# 4 Increased temperature

If the temperature is increased enough, rock will melt. However, increasing the temperature is not the way most magma forms on Earth.

### Melting rock

The temperature is higher deeper in Earth's interior than at the surface. However, this increase does not cause melting because the also-increasing pressure prevents melting. Nevertheless, raising the temperature of rock plays a role when already-created magma rises through cooler crust. The hot magma heats up and melts some of the rock that makes up the crust.

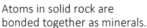

Solid rock, 600°C     Liquid rock (magma), 1,300°C

increase temperature →

Atoms in solid rock are bonded together as minerals.

Increasing the temperature breaks the bonds between atoms, which then flow as a liquid.

### Analogy

The reason that rock changes from a solid to a liquid due to an increase in temperature is similar to reason that ice changes from a solid to a liquid due to an increase in temperature. In both cases, the increase in temperature causes the atoms to move and strain against their bonds, finally breaking them, resulting in melting.

Solid water (ice), 0°C     Liquid water, 10°C

increase temperature →

Water molecules in ice are bonded together to form a solid.

Increasing the temperature breaks the bonds, and it becomes liquid.

## Check

☐ Summarize what changes in pressure, water, and temperature cause rock to melt.
☐ Describe at an atomic level why rock melts for each of the three causes of melting.
☐ Explain why rock melts at: divergent plate boundaries, convergent plate boundaries with subduction, and hotspots.

# 6.9 DATA AND DIAGRAMS: P-T Solid-Liquid Line

**Key Concept:** Graphs can show how a characteristic dependent on two variables changes as both of those variables change. This graph shows whether rock is solid or liquid at different combinations of pressure and temperature **1**. For comparison, just 1 gigapascal (GPa) of pressure is the equivalent of the pressure under a stack of 5,000 cars or 30 kilometers (20 mi) of rock. To create a graph like this, geologists use specialized technology in labs to measure the particular combinations of pressure and temperature that result in solid rock or liquid magma. Tips on how to read this graph are below **2**. Use the questions to practice interpreting this type of graph showing changes dependent on two variables **3**.

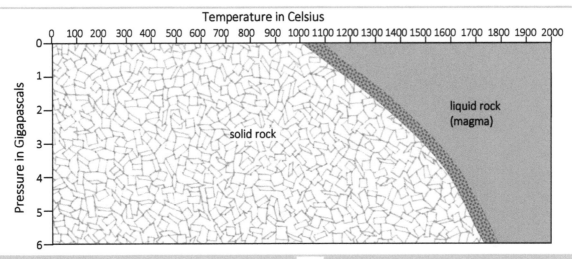

## **1** How to read the diagram

Determine what the variables are. In this case the vertical axis is pressure (in gigapascals) and the horizontal axis is temperature (in Celsius). The characteristic on the graph that is dependent on the two variables is whether a rock is solid or liquid.

## **2** An example of what you might interpret

If you look at the conditions of 1,300°C and 2 gigapascal, you will see that there will be solid rock and not magma, but if you increase the temperature by about 200°C or decrease the pressure by about 1 gigapascal, then the rock will melt and become magma.

## **3** Questions

**1. What does the graph show?**
a. How to change the pressure and temperature of a rock in order to melt it into magma
b. The combination of pressure and temperature at which a rock is either solid or liquid
c. How to change the pressure and temperature of a rock in order to solidify it into an igneous rock
d. All of the above

**2. Why do the numbers on the vertical axis showing pressure on the graph increase as you go down, not up?**
a. Earth's surface is along the top line, and the deeper you go, the higher the pressure gets.
b. The graph is drawn upside down, to make the line between the solid and liquid rock curve down.
c. The numbers are negative pressure, so the highest pressures are at the top of the graph.

**3. What does the gray patterned, curved line in the graph indicate?**
a. The shape of a magma chamber at different depths and pressures
b. The temperature at which solid rock melts to liquid, regardless of pressure
c. The temperature and pressure at which there is both solid and liquid rock at the same location

**4. Based on the graph, what could happen to a rock that moves from deep to shallow in the mantle?**
a. The pressure on it would decrease, so it could cross the line and melt into magma.
b. The pressure on it would decrease, so it could cross the line and solidify into igneous rock.
c. The pressure on it would increase, so it could cross the line and melt into magma.
d. The pressure on it would increase, so it could cross the line and solidify into igneous rock.

**5. Near the top of the mantle, the pressure is 2 GPa and the temperature is 1200°C. Is this part of the mantle solid or liquid?**
a. It is liquid.
b. It is solid.
c. It is not possible to determine with the information given.

**6. How do the pressure and temperature affect whether a rock is solid or liquid?**
a. Rock is solid under higher pressures and higher temperatures; it is liquid under lower pressure and lower temperatures.
b. Rock is solid under higher pressures and lower temperatures; it is liquid under lower pressure and higher temperatures.
c. Rock is solid under lower pressures and higher temperatures; it is liquid under higher pressure and lower temperatures.
d. Rock is solid under lower pressures and lower temperatures; it is liquid under higher pressure and higher temperatures.

# 6.10 Magma at Divergent Plate Boundaries

**Key Concept:** At divergent plate boundaries, magma forms because hot mantle rock is under lower pressure where plates pull apart. As we saw in Chapter 3, hot mantle rock moves upward where tectonic plates move apart at divergent plate boundaries **1**. The solid mantle rock is hot enough to melt, except the high pressure deep in the mantle keeps it solid. As it rises and as the plates separate, the pressure on this very hot mantle rock decreases, which causes it to melt into liquid magma **2**. This magma rises and cools into igneous rock, forming new gabbro ocean crust where magma cools slowly underground and new basalt ocean crust at the surface where it erupts at an ocean ridge **3**. Although a divergent boundary in the ocean is shown and described here, this melting process is the same at divergent plate boundaries in continents.

## **1** Decreasing pressure

Hot, lower density mantle rock moves upward as the two tectonic plates above move apart at a divergent plate boundary, decreasing the pressure on the mantle rock.

## **2** Melting rock

The rising mantle rock is at a constant very high temperature, and the decreasing pressure causes the rock to melt. The melted rock (magma) has a mafic composition and moves toward the surface because it is less dense than solid rock.

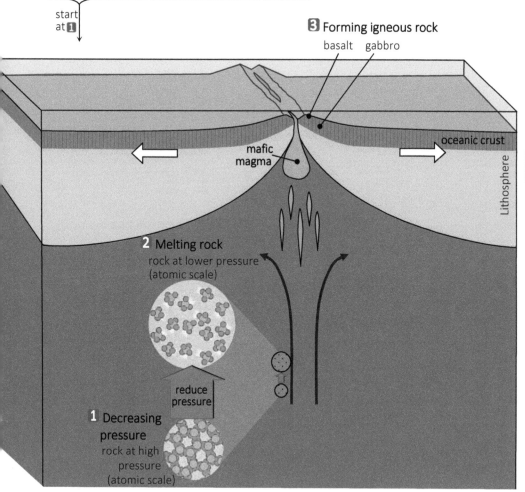

**3** Forming igneous rock

basalt   gabbro

start at **1**

mafic magma

oceanic crust

Lithosphere

**2** Melting rock
rock at lower pressure (atomic scale)

reduce pressure

**1** Decreasing pressure
rock at high pressure (atomic scale)

## **3** Forming igneous rock

As the plates move apart, the pressure is reduced enough so the newly generated magma can force its way up through a crack. If the mafic magma cools slowly below the surface, it becomes new gabbro ocean crust. The mafic magma that erupts at the surface forms an ocean ridge and cools quickly to form new basalt ocean crust.

**Note:**
This page and the next two are presenting related concepts in a similar way. This organization was designed to help identify the similarities and differences between these locations where magma forms.

## Check

☐ Explain why magma forms at divergent plate boundaries.
☐ Discuss why the ocean crust is made up of basalt and gabbro.

# 6.11 Magma at Convergent Plate Boundaries

**Key Concept:** At convergent plate boundaries, magma forms because added water lowers the melting temperature of hot mantle rock. As we saw in Chapter 3, oceanic lithosphere subducts when plates come together at convergent plate boundaries. Water is bonded in minerals in the subducting ocean lithosphere, and at high temperatures, this water is released into the very hot, solid mantle rock **1**. As discussed previously, this addition of water causes the rock to melt. The magma rises and increases the temperature of surrounding felsic rock in the crust, causing some of it to melt as well **2**. Intermediate and felsic magmas result, forming the igneous rocks rhyolite, andesite, granite, and diorite **3**.

## **1** Adding water by subduction

Subducting oceanic lithosphere rock and sediments take water bonded within minerals with them down past the trench and into the mantle. As the plate subducts deeper into Earth's interior, as shown by the white arrows, the temperature of the subducting minerals increases. The mineral structure changes, and the water bonded within the minerals is released into the mantle.

## **2** Melting rock

The released water molecules are added to the mantle rock, breaking the bonds between atoms. It lowers the melting point and causes the mantle rock to melt into magma. The mantle, not the subducting plate, melts because the plate is not hot enough, even with added water. The newly melted magma moves upward because it is less dense than solid rock. It melts part of the overlying felsic lithosphere by increasing the temperature, since the magma is hotter than the surrounding lithosphere.

## **3** Forming igneous rock

The intermediate and felsic composition magma resulting from the combination of melting mantle and overlying lithosphere accumulates in magma chambers. If it cools slowly beneath the surface, it forms granite and diorite. Some magma erupts and builds up to form volcanoes of andesite and rhyolite.

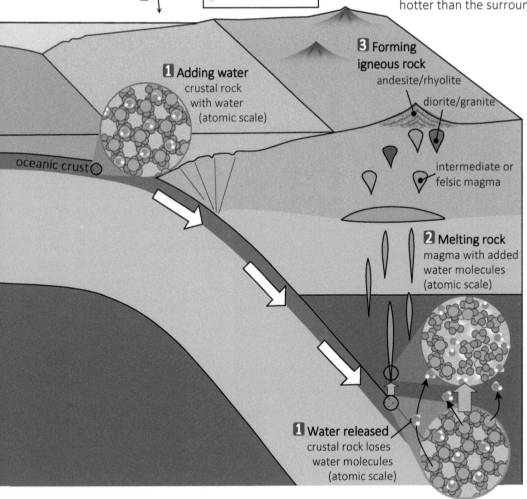

start at **1**

water molecule

**1** Adding water
crustal rock with water (atomic scale)

oceanic crust

**3** Forming igneous rock
andesite/rhyolite
diorite/granite
intermediate or felsic magma

**2** Melting rock
magma with added water molecules (atomic scale)

**1** Water released
crustal rock loses water molecules (atomic scale)

## Check

☐ Explain why magma forms at convergent plate boundaries with subduction.
☐ Discuss why volcanoes here are made up of intermediate and felsic composition igneous rock.

# 6.12 Magma at Hotspot Volcanoes above Mantle Plumes

**Key Concept:** Magma forms at locations other than plate boundaries where hot mantle rock rises in a mantle plume, decreasing in pressure and forming hotspot volcanoes above it. As discussed in 3.17, a mantle plume beneath a hotspot volcano consists of unusually hot, solid mantle rock. This mantle rock slowly rises because it is less dense than the surrounding mantle rock **1**. The rock does not melt because it is unusual hot. Instead, the very hot rock is under lower pressure as it rises, which causes it to melt forming magma **2**. The magma rises until it cools, forming a variety of igneous rock types, depending on whether the mantle plume is under oceanic or continental lithosphere **3**. As you examine this page, flip back a page and notice how magma formation at hotspot volcanoes above mantle plumes is similar to magma formation at divergent plate boundaries.

## **1** High temperature and decreasing pressure

A mantle plume is an unusually hot part of the mantle. Although geologists are unsure why and how they form, mantle plumes likely start at the core–mantle boundary. The solid mantle rock slowly moves up because it is hotter and therefore less dense than the surrounding mantle rock.

## **2** Melting rock

The rising solid mantle rock in a mantle plume beneath a hotspot volcano is a constant hot temperature, but the decreasing pressure causes the rock to melt, forming a magma chamber.

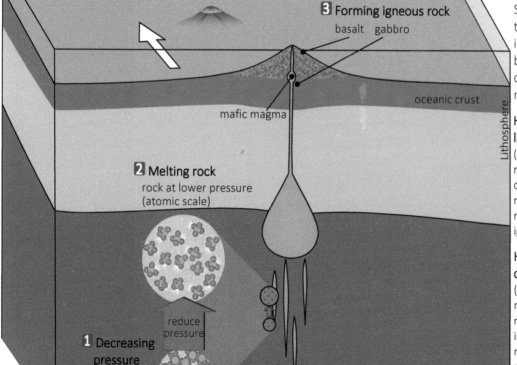

## **3** Forming igneous rock

Some magma erupts and builds up to form volcanoes. Mantle plumes in the ocean form volcanoes of basalt, and mantle plumes in the continent result in a variety of magma compositions.

### Hotspot volcanoes within oceanic lithosphere

(shown) If the mafic composition magma chamber melts the mafic ocean crust, the composition of the magma does not change much, resulting in mafic composition igneous rock.

### Hotspot volcanoes within under continental lithosphere

(not shown) Mafic composition magma chambers frequently heat and melt felsic continental crust, resulting in intermediate or felsic composition magma in addition to the mafic composition magma.

## Check

☐ Explain why magma forms at mantle plumes beneath hotspot volcanoes unrelated to plate boundaries.
☐ Compare the types of magma that erupt at hotspot volcanoes due to mantle plumes under oceanic lithosphere or under continental lithosphere.

# 6.13 Characteristics of Magma

**Key Concept:** Felsic and mafic composition magmas have different characteristics, such as temperature, composition, gas content, and viscosity (how well the magma flows). As you recall, there is a wide range in compositions of magma, from felsic to mafic. While reading through the diagram below, focus on how the characteristics of felsic and mafic compositions of magma differ. Compared to mafic composition magma, felsic composition magma has more silicon and oxygen and less iron and magnesium **1**, a lower temperature **2**, more gas dissolved in the magma **3**, and a higher viscosity, meaning it does not flow as well **4**. Intermediate magmas have characteristics between mafic and felsic magmas. These characteristics are important because they play a large role in governing how different composition magmas erupt **5** in a variety of plate tectonic settings **6**.

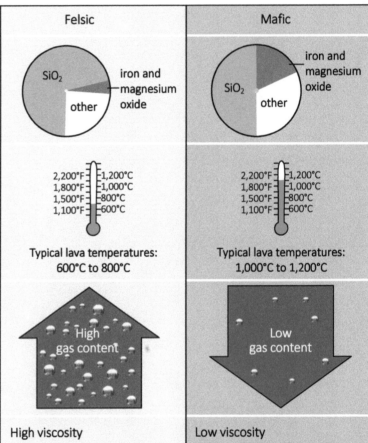

## **1** Composition

The composition is the amount of different elements in the magma. The composition of magma affects the viscosity (see below).

## **2** Temperature

The temperature has a strong effect on the minerals that melted or formed, since more mafic minerals melt at higher temperatures. The temperature of magma also affects the viscosity (see below).

## **3** Gas content

Gas is dissolved in magma in the same way that gas is dissolved in coke in a bottle before it is opened. Gas content is important when discussing volcanic eruptions because high gas contents in magma will often result in explosive volcanic eruptions.

## **4** Viscosity

Viscosity is the resistance of a liquid to flowing. It is the opposite of how fluid or runny a liquid is. The viscosity of magma is related to how easily atoms can move with respect to each other, so it is primarily dependent on the temperature and composition of the magma, as described. Viscosity is important when discussing volcanic eruptions, as discussed on the next page.

**High viscosity**
Does not flow well, flows slowly, and is not runny

**composition**—more silicon and oxygen in a magma results in a higher viscosity because the silicon and oxygen atoms bond together, forming a tangle of molecules that cannot flow past each other.

**temperature**—lower temperature magmas have a higher viscosity, just like cold honey and peanut butter do not flow well. The bonds between atoms are strong, so there is a high resistance to flow, and therefore a high viscosity.

**Low viscosity**
Flows easily, flows relatively quickly, and is fairly runny

**composition**—magma with relatively little silicon and oxygen has no tangle of molecules. The freely moving molecules allow the magma to flow well, with a lower viscosity.

**temperature**—higher temperature magmas have a lower viscosity. The bonds between atoms are more easily broken at higher temperatures, so there is lower resistance to flow, and therefore a lower viscosity.

|  | Felsic | Mafic |
| --- | --- | --- |

## 5 Eruption style

The viscosity and gas content of magma play a large role in determining if magma will erupt peacefully or explosively. An eruption with a felsic composition is explosive because the high-viscosity magma does not easily allow the high amount of dissolved gas to escape, resulting in the gas exploding out and forming large clouds of ash. In contrast, an eruption with a mafic composition results in peacefully erupting lava flows because the low-viscosity magma flows well and allows the small amount of dissolved gas to escape easily. Intermediate composition eruptions have a combination of these characteristics. A more detailed explanation is given in 7.2.

This eruption of felsic composition lava from Mt. St. Helens is explosive as seen by the large clouds of ash.

This eruption of mafic composition lava in Hawaii has peacefully-erupting, long-flowing lava flows.

## 6 Plate tectonic setting

As described in 6.10 to 6.12, the composition of magma is largely determined by the plate tectonic setting in which magma forms. Therefore, magma characteristics and the resulting eruption style of the lava are related to the plate tectonic setting. Generally, explosive felsic and intermediate eruptions occur at convergent plate boundary volcanoes and some hotspot volcanoes in continental crust. Peaceful mafic eruptions occur at hotspot volcanoes in the ocean and divergent plate boundaries.

Explosive eruptions, such as this one in Alaska, form where felsic and intermediate lava erupts at convergent plate boundaries.

Peaceful, mafic lava flows, such as this lava erupting underwater in the South Pacific, erupt at divergent plate boundaries.

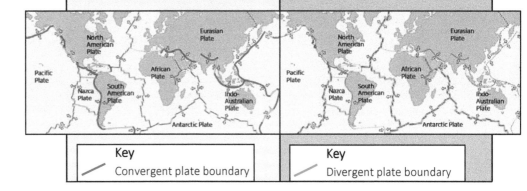

| Key | Key |
| --- | --- |
| — Convergent plate boundary | ⁄ Divergent plate boundary |

## Check

☐ Compare felsic and mafic composition magmas in terms of composition, temperature, gas content, viscosity, eruption style, and location.
☐ Describe the two things that affect the viscosity of magma and how.

## End of Chapter Questions: Student Debates

For each of the following questions, determine which student you agree with and explain why.

1. **Three students are discussing how large igneous rocks are when they first form.**

   **Student 1:** I think igneous rocks form as huge magma chambers or lava flows. Pieces break off, which is what we see.

   **Student 2:** I think igneous rocks form as medium-sized pieces, approximately the size of a table or car. They break into smaller pieces over time.

   **Student 3:** I think igneous rocks form small enough to hold in your hand, since that is what you tend to see when you look at rocks.

2. **Two students are discussing which rock formed from magma erupting from a volcano.**

   **Student 1:** If I look at a rock and see large black minerals, I know it must have erupted from a volcano.

   **Student 2:** If I look at a rock and see it has small minerals, then I know it must have erupted from a volcano.

3. **Two students are discussing where magma forms in Earth.**

   **Student 1:** As you go deeper in Earth, it gets hotter, so there is a layer of melted rock below the crust. There are a few places on Earth where the magma in the layers erupts onto the surface.

   **Student 2:** As you go deeper, the pressure increases too, keeping the crust and mantle solid. There are a few unusual places in Earth where solid rock melts to form magma that may erupt at the surface.

4. **Three students are discussing where rock melts at convergent plate boundaries with subduction.**

   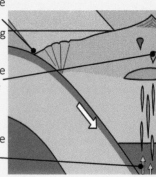

   **Student 1:** I think it forms in the trench, because that is where the plates rub together, making it hot enough to melt rock.

   **Student 2:** I think it forms in the magma chambers beneath the volcanoes, because that is where you find the magma.

   **Student 3:** I think it forms in the mantle above the subducting plate, because that is where subducted water is added to already hot rock.

5. **Three students are discussing how granite forms.**

   **Student 1:** Granite forms when atoms making up magma in a magma chamber bond with each other to form a variety of minerals.

   **Student 2:** Granite forms when a variety of minerals making up the walls of the magma chamber group together within the magma chamber.

   **Student 3:** Granite forms when sediments get trapped in magma, and these sediments come together to form a solid rock.

## End of Chapter Questions: Short Answer

Using your own words or sketching and labeling a diagram, answer the following questions.

6. List two key characteristics of this rock that you can observe. Explain what you can interpret based on those two observations.

7. Imagine you are on a hike and pick up a piece of granite. Explain what you can determine about the geologic history of the area. Include information about the past geologic setting and plate tectonic environment.

8. Based on the minerals present, explain why granite will partially melt at a lower temperature than basalt.

9. Explain two reasons why butter melting all at once by being heated on the stove is not a good analogy for rock melting in Earth.

10. Compare and contrast the reasons that mantle rock melts at hotspots, divergent plate boundaries, and convergent plate boundaries with subduction. Use diagrams to explain your answers. It may help to organize your answer in a chart.

11. Combine information from the diagram in 6.2 with other information in the chapter to explain why different types of minerals form from mafic composition magma compared to felsic composition magma.

12. Compare and contrast the formation of basalt and the formation of granite from magma, including the plate tectonic location in which they form. It may help to organize your answer in a chart.

13. Predict a large mineral you might see in a porphyry igneous rock formed at a convergent plate boundary with subduction. Justify your prediction.

**Hints:** For each question, see the sections listed here for information relevant to answering it.

**1.** (6.3, 6.10, 6.11, 6.12) **2.** (6.3, 6.4) **3.** (6.8, 6.9. 6.10, 6.11, 6.12) **4.** (6.11) **5.** (6.3, 6.6) **6.** (6.1, 6.3, 6.4) **7.** (6.1, 6.3, 6.4, 6.11) **8.** (6.2, 6.5, 6.7, 6.9) **9.** (6.5, 6.7) **10.** (6.8, 6.10, 6.11, 6.12) **11.** (6.2, 6.6, 6.7) **12.** ( 6.2, 6.3, 6.4, 6.10, 6.11, 6.12) **13.** (6.4, 6.7, 6.11)

# Chapter 7: Volcanoes

## Chapter Objectives

When you are finished reading this chapter, you should be able to ...

• relate the types of volcanoes and igneous rock formations to magma composition and plate tectonic boundaries (7.1–7.6).

• compare the influence of the composition of lava to how it relates to volcanic hazards (7.2, 7.7–7.11).

• summarize how people try to reduce volcanic hazards (7.9–7.10).

# 7.1 – 7.6 Volcanoes and Igneous Rock Formations

In this section, you will learn how different compositions of magma erupt and how geologists classify the resulting volcanoes that are built from the eruptions.

## Frequently Used Terms

The terms listed here are used repeatedly throughout this section, so by learning them before you read this section, you can focus your mental energy on the concepts presented.

**mafic, intermediate, and felsic composition** The composition of magma from lower silica to higher silica, which results in a low to high viscosity; the erupted lava of these compositions form the rocks basalt, andesite, and rhyolite.

**magma** Molten rock that is below Earth's surface; after it erupts at the surface and volcanic gases escape, it is called lava.

**pyroclast** A fragment of lava and rock that erupts out of volcanoes.

**shield volcano** A large, flat volcano made from layers of lava flows that have a mafic composition and low viscosity.

**stratovolcano** A medium-sized, steep-sided volcano made of layers of lava flows and pyroclasts of felsic or intermediate composition.

**viscosity** The resistance of a liquid to flowing, or the opposite of how runny something is; lava with a high viscosity, such as felsic composition lava, does not flow well, while lava with a low viscosity, such as mafic composition lava, flows quickly and far.

**volcanic gas** The gases erupted from a volcano, such as water vapor, carbon dioxide, and sulfur gases.

**volcano** The location from which lava, pyroclasts, and gases erupt and accumulate; the resulting mountain-like formation from the buildup of lava and pyroclasts is also called a volcano.

Pyroclastic flows, like this one raging down the side of Soufriere Hills on the Caribbean Island of Montserrat, are an unpredictable and dangerous aspect of volcanic eruptions.

Chapter 7: Volcanoes    Section 1

# 7.1 Volcanoes and Underground Igneous Rock Formations

**Key Concept:** Before it cools to form igneous rock, magma may take a variety of shapes, such as volcanoes, dikes, sills, and plutons. These igneous rock formations can be distinguished by their size, shape, and relationship to the surrounding, preexisting bedrock. Lava flows form where lava erupts from a vent at the surface, and volcanoes form where erupted lava flows pile up **1**. Dikes and sills are long, narrow igneous rock formations that form where magma cuts through rock underground **2**. Plutons form where magma cools in large magma chambers within the crust instead of erupting at the surface **3**.

## 1 Lava flow and volcano

Lava flows are molten rock flowing along the surface and are still called lava flows after they have solidified. Lava flows frequently stack, layer upon layer, to form a volcano. A volcano is both the location from which lava, ash, and volcanic gases erupt and the resulting igneous rock formation shaped like a mountain. Lava erupts at the surface, so it cools to form rock with predominantly small minerals, like andesite or basalt (see 6.4).

## 2 Dike and sill

Dikes and sills are sheet-like igneous rock formations with a long and narrow shape. Dikes form as the pressure of intruding magma creates cracks that cut across the surrounding bedrock. Magma immediately fills the cracks, often bringing magma to the surface. Sills extend between sedimentary bedrock layers.

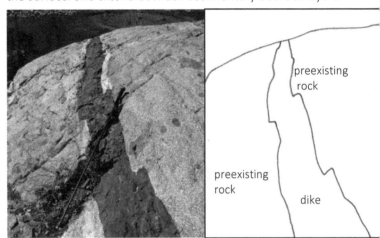

## 3 Pluton

Plutons are large, blob-shaped igneous rock formations in the surrounding bedrock. They form where magma cools and solidifies underground in magma chambers. They form deep within the crust, so it cools to form rock with large minerals, like granite or diorite (see 6.4).

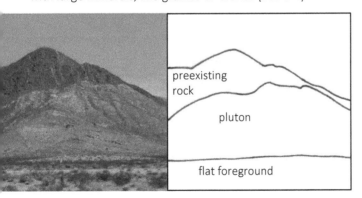

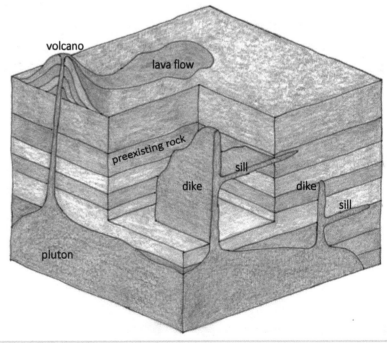

**Check**  Before you continue, you should be able to answer each check without looking at the page.
- ☐ Describe characteristics of four examples of igneous rock formations.
- ☐ Summarize how four different igneous rock formations form.

# 7.2 Formation of a Volcano

**Key Concept:** Volcanoes form where erupted lava and pyroclasts come out of the ground and pile up over time.

After mantle rock melts to become magma, it rises into the crust where it forms a magma chamber **1**. In some cases, magma from the magma chamber rises toward the surface. The resulting decreased pressure allows the volcanic gases dissolved in the magma to form bubbles **2**. Magma is called lava once it erupts from a volcano. It may erupt peacefully as lava flows or explosively forming small pyroclasts **3**. The lava and pyroclasts build up to form a volcanic landform, and the characteristics of each volcano are dependent on the style of volcanic eruptions that formed it **4**.

## **1** Magma rises

Melting occurs when the bonds between atoms in solid rock break. Unbonded atoms take up more space, so liquid magma is less dense, which is why it rises through solid rock (see 6.8). As it rises, it may melt some of the crust that then mixes with the original magma, changing the composition through contamination.

unbonded atoms in melted magma take up more space

densely arranged atoms in solid rock

## **2** Volcanic gases

As magma rises towards the surface, the pressure on it decreases, so dissolved gases in it start to bubble out and move up. This process is similar to how dissolved gas in a bottle of coke forms bubbles when the pressure is lowered by removing the cap.

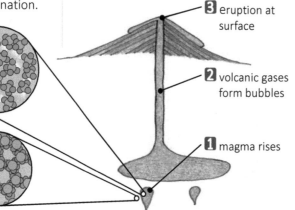

**3** eruption at surface

**2** volcanic gases form bubbles

**1** magma rises

## **3** Eruption

Magma erupts out of the vent at the surface as lava, pyroclasts, and volcanic gases. Pyroclasts are small fragments of lava and rock, such as ash. The magma composition plays a role in determining whether the volcano erupts peacefully as lava or explosively as pyroclasts (see 7.3).

### Mafic eruptions
In the example to the left, mafic lava erupts peacefully as volcanic gases bubble out, forming long lava flows and few pyroclasts (see 7.3).

### Felsic eruptions
When gas bubbles escape explosively from felsic magma, the lava spatters and forms pyroclasts that cool as they are erupted (see 7.7). Intermediate composition lavas tend to erupt with a combination of styles.

## **4** A volcano is built

In this example of an intermediate composition volcano, the erupted lava and pyroclasts pile up on the surface to form the volcano and make it larger. The lava and pyroclasts frequently erupt out of the central vent at the top of the volcano, but in some cases there may also be vents on the sides of the volcano.

Lava and pyroclasts erupt from a vent and form a volcano. Few eruptions have occurred, and the volcano is small.

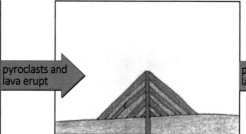

pyroclasts and lava erupt

Layers of pyroclasts and lava are added, though the volcano has periods of inactivity between times when it is erupting.

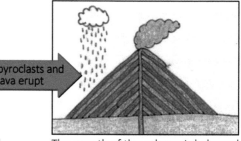

pyroclasts and lava erupt

The growth of the volcano is balanced by erosion of the rock by rain and glacier ice.

## Check

☐ Explain the sequence of events that cause a volcanic eruption.
☐ Summarize how a volcano grows.

# 7.3 Magma Viscosity Affects Eruptions

**Key Concept:** The viscosity of magma (how resistant it is to flow) has a strong effect on how it erupts. As discussed in 6.13, the composition of magma affects its viscosity, which in turn affects the eruption style of a volcano. Some common foods can help you picture these characteristics. All magma has a higher viscosity than chocolate milk **1**. Mafic magma has about the same viscosity as a milkshake, so it flows relatively easily and gas can escape **2**. In comparison, felsic composition magma is more like peanut butter, with a very high viscosity, so it flows very slowly and it prevents air bubbles from escaping easily **3**.

| | **1 Very low viscosity** | **2 Low viscosity** | **3 High viscosity** |
|---|---|---|---|
| | No type of magma has viscosity this low. | Mafic magma has a relatively low viscosity. | Felsic magma has a high viscosity. |
| **Magma viscosity** | No lava has viscosity this low. | The low viscosity of mafic magma allows it to spread out and form lava flows, such as this one in Hawaii, or flow underground through cracks in the bedrock, forming dikes and sills. | Felsic magma barely flows, so it frequently remains in magma chambers and forms plutons. If it erupts, the lava piles up near where it erupted, as in this flow in Oregon. |
| **Food viscosity analogy** | Chocolate milk flows easily, so it spreads out as it is poured onto a surface and does not pile up. | Similar to mafic magma, milkshakes flow some, so it spreads out some as it is poured onto a surface and piles up a little. | Similar to felsic magma, peanut butter barely flows, so it piles up high without spreading as it is poured onto a surface. |
| **Gas trapped in magma** | No lava has viscosity this low. | Mafic magma allows dissolved gases to bubble out with little difficulty, so pressure does not build up. Therefore, the eruptions are generally peaceful, as seen in these lava fountains on Hawaii. | Felsic magma traps dissolved gases and does not allow them to escape, so pressure builds until the gas bubbles burst out suddenly, resulting in explosive eruptions like this one of Mt. St. Helens. |
| **Gas trapped in food analogy** | If you blow bubbles with a straw into very low viscosity chocolate milk, the bubbles very easily rise to the surface. | Similar to gases in mafic magma, bubbles blown into medium viscosity milkshakes rise to the surface with a little difficulty. | Similar to gases in felsic magma, bubbles trapped in very high viscosity peanut butter cannot rise to the surface and escape. |

## Check

☐ Explain how the viscosity of magma affects lava flow characteristics and volcano shape.
☐ Discuss why the viscosity of the magma and gas content affect the eruption style of volcanoes.

# 7.4 Types of Volcanoes

**Key Concept:** The type of volcano is defined by what is erupted and its shape, which depends on the composition and amount of erupting lava. Lava erupts differently depending on its composition and viscosity, so different composition lavas generally produce different types of volcanoes. Mafic composition lava with the lowest viscosity tends to flow easily and produce long lava flows. These form very large, broad shield volcanoes, though some may erupt in small, steep piles called cinder cones **1**. Felsic to intermediate composition lava, with a higher viscosity, tends to erupt as pyroclasts or pile up as thick lava flows. These produce large stratovolcanoes and small volcanic domes **2**. Some volcanoes have a complex structure that indicates more than one eruption style over the course of their eruptive history, but this basic categorization is a good starting point for understanding volcanoes.

## **1** Mafic composition volcanoes

Mafic composition lava has a low viscosity, so it forms shield volcanoes and cinder cones. Shield volcanoes are the largest type of volcano, although they are so broad and flat they may not look like a volcano. Cinder cones are much smaller mafic composition volcanoes that are often found in groups and on the sides of shield volcanoes. Sometimes fluid lava flows do not erupt from a central vent and build up a volcano but instead flood a large area; these flows are called flood basalts.

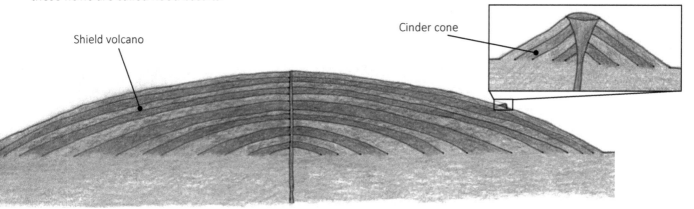

Shield volcano

Cinder cone

### Shield volcano

Mafic composition lava forms long, thin lava flows that cool into basalt. Shield volcanoes are built of layer upon layer of these low-viscosity lava flows, forming broad, gently sloping volcanoes that may be up to a hundred kilometers (many tens of miles) across. Shield volcanoes typically erupt peacefully and rarely result in abundant pyroclasts. Mauna Kea in Hawaii is an example of a broad, flat, peacefully erupting shield volcano. The small bumps on the broad shield volcano are cinder cones.

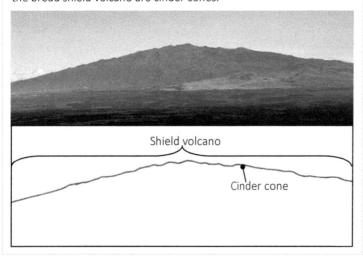

Shield volcano

Cinder cone

### Cinder cone

Cinder cones are piles of mafic composition pyroclasts, especially gravel-sized pieces of basalt called volcanic cinders. Cinder cones are relatively small, short-lived volcanoes. Small amounts of volcanic gases bursting out of the mafic lava cause small "spitting" eruptions, which result in pyroclasts building up around the central erupting vent. These cinder cones formed in less than 10 years on the side of the shield volcano Mauna Kea in Hawaii.

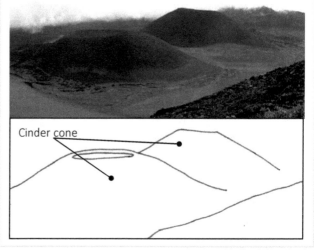

Cinder cone

# 2 Intermediate and felsic composition volcanoes

Intermediate and felsic lava have a high viscosity, so they form stratovolcanoes and volcanic domes. Stratovolcanoes are large volcanoes, generally with a conical shape and are what you probably think of when you picture a volcano. Volcanic domes are also made from intermediate or felsic lava, but they are much smaller and may form on stratovolcanoes. Sometimes felsic and intermediate lava may erupt so explosively that the volcano collapses into the emptied magma chamber, leaving behind a broad, bowl-shaped depression called a caldera.

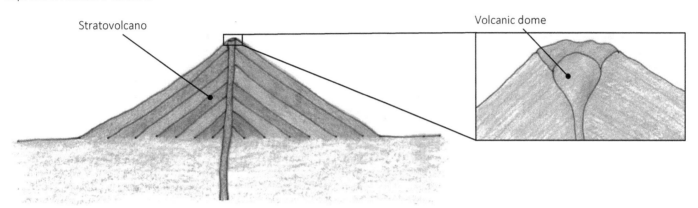

## Stratovolcano

Felsic and intermediate composition lavas have a high enough viscosity that they tend to produce large amounts of pyroclasts, such as ash. In some cases, especially with intermediate compositions, they form thick, slow lava flows that cool into andesite. Stratovolcanoes are built up of layers of pyroclasts and lava flows, forming steep-sided volcanoes, typically a couple tens of kilometers (couple tens of miles) across. Stratovolcanoes produce large, explosive eruptions. This photo shows Mt. Saint Helens before the 1980 eruption.

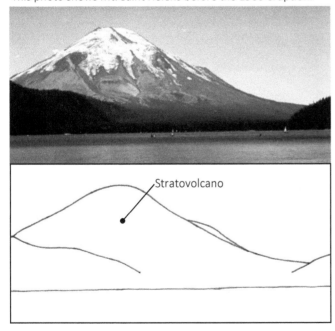

## Volcanic dome

Volcanic domes form from very high viscosity felsic lava that has lost its dissolved gas content, so it does not erupt explosively. Instead, the lava oozes out and piles up where it is erupted, cooling to form rhyolite. The rhyolite may form a plug, preventing gases from escaping from the magma beneath until the pressure builds up enough that the volcano violently explodes, shattering the volcanic dome. Volcanic domes often form on stratovolcanoes, such as the one shown below on Mt. Saint Helens after the 1980 eruption.

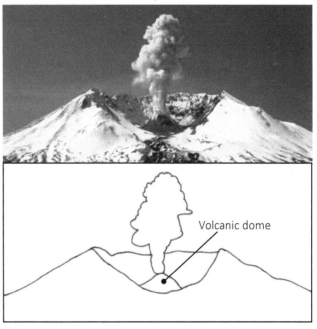

## Check

☐ Describe the key features of the four types of volcanoes.
☐ Compare the lava compositions and gas content of the four types of volcanoes.
☐ Compare and contrast shield volcanoes and stratovolcanoes in terms of shape, size, and eruption style.

# 7.5 Volcanoes and Plate Tectonics

**Key Concept:** Different plate tectonic settings result in different magma compositions, volcano types, and eruption styles. Divergent plate boundaries may form a variety of lava compositions, which result in a variety of volcano types and eruption styles **❶**. Convergent plate boundaries with subduction tend to form explosive stratovolcanoes from intermediate and felsic lava **❷**. Hotspots under the ocean form peacefully erupting mafic lava, which piles up to create islands of shield volcanoes **❸**. Hotspots under the continent, however, may form a variety of magma compositions, which result in a variety of volcano types and eruption styles **❹**.

## ❶ Divergent plate boundary

At a divergent plate boundary that splits continental lithosphere, as shown below, the magma that initially forms is mafic. However, intermediate and felsic lava may erupt explosively to form stratovolcanoes due to contamination by felsic crust and fractional crystallization as minerals form as the magma cools (see 6.6). At a divergent plate boundary that splits mafic ocean crust, the mafic magma remains mafic. The lava erupts peacefully, creating new ocean crust that pulls apart and forms ocean ridges.

Composition: mafic, sometimes intermediate and felsic
Volcano type: shield volcano, sometimes stratovolcano
Eruption style: peaceful, sometimes explosive

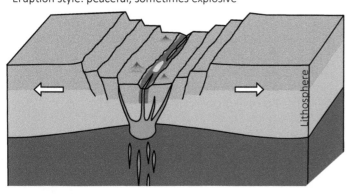

**Example volcanoes:**
The East African Rift is a divergent plate boundary that typically forms intermediate stratovolcanoes such as Mount Nyiragongo and Mt. Kilimanjaro. Iceland formed where a hotspot is directly beneath a divergent plate boundary in the ocean, and it is made up primarily of mafic shield volcanoes.

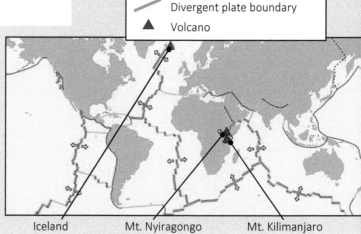

Iceland          Mt. Nyiragongo          Mt. Kilimanjaro

## ❷ Convergent plate boundary

Magma formed by subduction is initially mafic, but by the time it erupts it has generally become intermediate or felsic composition because of contamination and fractional crystallization. In the diagram, oceanic lithosphere subducts under continental lithosphere to form explosive stratovolcanoes. Subduction under another ocean lithosphere results in the same processes and explosive stratovolcanoes.

Composition: intermediate and felsic
Volcano type: stratovolcano (most)
Eruption style: explosive (most)

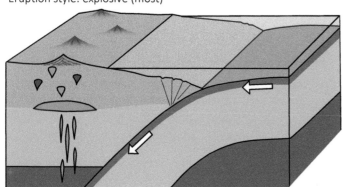

**Example volcanoes:**
The Ring of Fire is the circle of volcanoes around the Pacific Ocean where the oceanic plate is subducting. It includes many of the world's well-known stratovolcanoes. These volcanoes erupt explosively, often with deadly results (see 7.9).

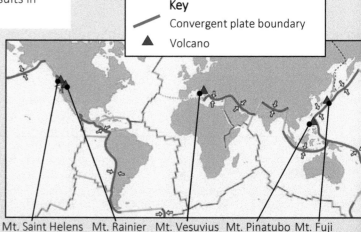

Mt. Saint Helens   Mt. Rainier   Mt. Vesuvius   Mt. Pinatubo   Mt. Fuji

# 3 Hotspot under oceanic lithosphere

At a hotspot in the ocean, the initially formed magma has a mafic composition, and it remains mafic when it erupts, similar to divergent plate boundaries in the ocean. These peaceful eruptions result in large shield volcanoes.

Composition: mafic
Volcano type: shield volcano
Eruption style: peaceful

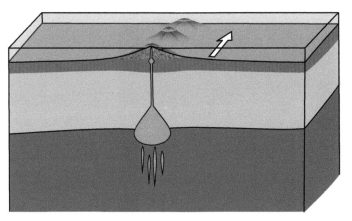

## Example volcanoes:

Volcanic islands that are not near plate boundaries form as a result of hotspots. These hotspots often form chains of volcanic islands as the plate moves over the hotspot. For example, the shield volcano Kilauea on the Big Island of Hawaii has been erupting basalt continuously since 1983.

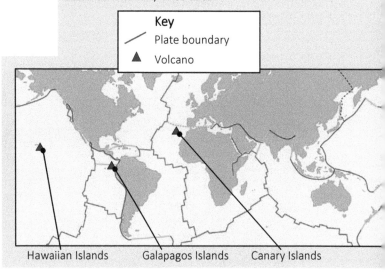

Key
— Plate boundary
▲ Volcano

Hawaiian Islands       Galapagos Islands       Canary Islands

# 4 Hotspot under continental lithosphere

At a hotspot under a continent, the initially formed magma is mafic, but a variety of lava compositions may erupt. Magma pools up beneath the thick continental lithosphere and may erupt peacefully as large amounts of mafic composition lava. However, if the mafic magma is contaminated or undergoes fractional crystallization, it may erupt explosively with a felsic composition.

Composition: mafic, intermediate, and felsic
Volcano types: shield volcano or stratovolcano
Eruption styles: peaceful or explosive

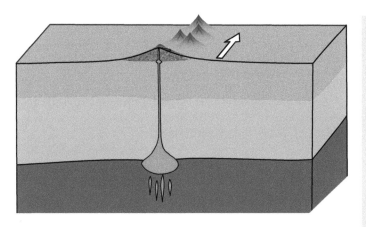

## Example volcanoes:

Magma pools under the crust, building up in volume, so continental hotspots often result in large eruptions. For example, a large amount of mafic lava can erupt by spreading out over a large area, forming flood basalts, such as the Columbia River Flood Basalts. In contrast, a large amount of felsic lava may erupt so explosively that it forms a caldera, such as what happened in the past couple million years to form the calderas in Yellowstone National Park.

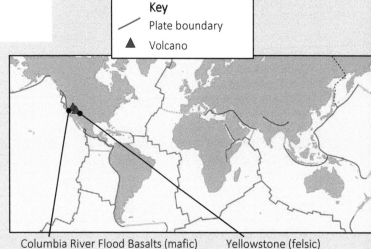

Key
— Plate boundary
▲ Volcano

Columbia River Flood Basalts (mafic)       Yellowstone (felsic)

# Check

☐ For four different plate tectonic settings, compare the composition of lava, volcano type, and eruption style.
☐ Locate one example volcano that forms at each plate tectonic setting.

# 7.6 DATA AND DIAGRAMS: Volcanoes

**Key Concept:** Viewing landscapes allows geologists to make observations about landforms, which allow them to **interpret how they were formed.** Geologists first make observations about what geologic features are seen **1**. Next, they apply to their observations their knowledge of how features form and change over time. They can then make interpretations of how a landscape formed, which can lead them to formulate hypotheses to test, including interpretations of the history of an area, resources present, and potential hazards. Tips on how to interpret a landscape are below **2**. Use the questions to practice making observations and interpreting landscapes **3**.

## 1 How to view the landscape

Make observations about what is seen, including observations about the size, shape, color, and patterns of the features in the landscape. To convert observations into interpretations about the formation of the landscape, determine which observations are critical and which details are not relevant.

## 2 An example of what you might interpret

The observation of the shape of the landform is critical, and the observation of the four people is not relevant to the geologic history of the area. A key interpretation of the landform in this photograph is that it is a volcano.

## 3 Questions

**1. Which of the following is an observation, not an interpretation, of the photograph?**
a. The area does not have many plants.
b. The area is cold and desert-like.
c. The area gets a lot of snow in winter.
d. These are all observations.

**2. What are key geologic observations that can be used to identify the type of volcano pictured?**
a. Steep slopes and intermediate size
b. Dark soil and eroded sides
c. White snow that does not reach the bottom

**3. Based on your observations, what type of volcano is pictured?**
a. Shield volcano
b. Cinder cone
c. Stratovolcano
d. Lava dome

**4. Based on your interpretation and geologic knowledge, predict the type of eruption generally expected from this volcano.**
a. Peaceful eruption
b. Explosive eruption
c. It is impossible to predict eruption style.

**5. Based on your interpretation and geologic knowledge what is a logical conclusion about how the volcano would have looked in the distant past when it first started forming?**

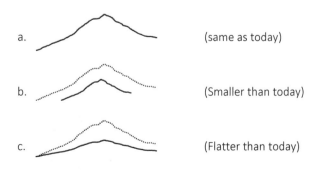

# 7.7 – 7.11 Volcano Hazards

In this section, you will learn about volcanic hazards and how geologists interpret past eruptions and predict future ones.

## Frequently Used Terms

The terms listed here are used repeatedly throughout this section, so by learning them before you read this section, you can focus your mental energy on the concepts presented.

**deposit** Anything that has been erupted from a volcano and left behind, such as pyroclasts and lava, creating a record of the eruption.

**hazard** A potential event that has the possibility to negatively impact people; volcanic hazards generally involve lava, volcanic gases, and pyroclasts erupting out of a volcano.

**lahar** A volcanic mudflow created when ash and other pyroclasts mix with water from sources such as rivers, melted glaciers, or rain.

The magma beneath Yellowstone National Park heats water in the ground. The hot water and steam come out of the ground at geysers. If the magma erupts in the future, it will have a major impact on people.

# 7.7 Hazards from What Erupts from Volcanoes

**Key Concept:** **Lava, volcanic gases, and pyroclasts can erupt out of a volcano.** The primary hazards, or potential dangers, associated with volcanic eruptions depend on what erupts from the volcano, which in turn depends on the magma composition. As magma rises to near Earth's surface under the volcano, gases dissolved in the magma escape out, and at the surface both lava **1** and volcanic gases erupt **2**. The eruption of volcanic gases may blast the lava into pyroclasts, such as ash and volcanic bombs **3**. Volcanic deposits are what erupt from a volcano and settle on Earth, and they can help geologists determine what past eruptions were like.

## 1 Lava

Lava is what we call magma after it comes out of a volcano. Mafic composition lava flows are more common than felsic composition lava flows. This difference is because the high viscosity and dissolved gas content of felsic lava frequently results in it exploding rather than flowing (see 7.3). Intermediate and felsic composition lava flows move very slowly and are much thicker.

**What deposits does lava form?**
Flowing lava glows orange, but it cools into solid basalt, andesite, and in some cases rhyolite rock, depending on its composition. Lava flows can be many shapes, from long and skinny, like the one shown here, to dome-shaped. The edges of a lava flow cool faster than the center, resulting in smaller minerals along its margins.

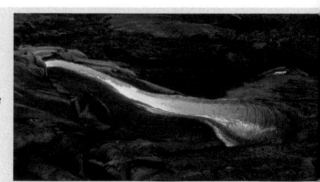

**What are hazards from lava?**
Lava is not very dangerous to people. Few people are killed by lava because it is generally slow enough for people to get out of its way. However, lava flows bury and destroy property as shown in this photo from Kilauea, Hawaii in 2018.

## 2 Volcanic Gases

Volcanic gases bubble out from magma as it rises to the surface because there is less pressure nearer the surface. In addition, water in the ground can be heated to form steam, which also comes out of the volcano as a volcanic gas. Most gas emitted by a volcano is water vapor (steam), with some carbon dioxide and a smaller amount of sulfur gases. Felsic composition magmas generally contain more dissolved gases than mafic composition magmas.

**What deposits do volcanic gases form?**
Most volcanic gases do not leave solid deposits, as they tend to stay in gas form and become part of the atmosphere. In some cases, sulfur gases may leave bright yellow solid sulfur deposits, as can be seen around the gas vent in this photo.

**What are hazards from volcanic gases?**
Volcanic gases are rarely dangerous to people. Most gases disperse in the atmosphere, or are composed of harmless gases like the steam shown in the photo of Mt. Martin in Alaska. There are unusual cases where volcanic gases concentrated in a small area during a volcanic eruption, suffocating nearby people and animals.

# 3 Pyroclasts

Pyroclasts are pieces of solidified lava that form when lava is shattered due to explosively expanding gas bubbles. Pyroclasts are more common with felsic and intermediate composition lava because these lavas have a high dissolved gas content and high viscosity which prevents the volcanic gases from easily bubbling out. Pyroclasts are named based on their size, shape, and composition. For example, dust- to sand-sized pieces are called ash (left photo), gravel- to boulder-sized pieces are called volcanic bombs, and mafic pieces are called cinders (right photo).

### What deposits do pyroclasts form?

Pyroclasts such as ash, cinders, or volcanic bombs may be deposited in layers and may fuse together due to their immense heat, as seen in this outcrop in New Zealand. The size and thickness of the pyroclasts in each layer gives clues about the style of eruption. Large volcanic bombs do not travel far from a volcano, but small pyroclasts, such as ash, may be carried by the wind thousands of kilometers (thousands of miles) from the volcano.

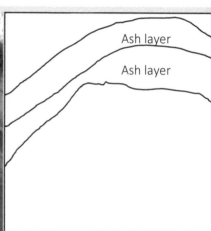

Ash layer

Ash layer

### What are hazards from pyroclasts?

The danger from pyroclasts depends largely on size. Large volcanic bombs are generally only dangerous to people on the volcano, but small ash fragments can be carried high in the atmosphere within a tall column of hot gas and ash, called an eruption column (left photo Mt. Mayon, Philippines). When ash in an eruption column eventually falls, it can collapse buildings with its weight, cause breathing difficulties, destroy plane engines, and bury property like the cars and buildings (right photo Rabual, Papua New Guinea). A particularly large eruption column can carry ash high enough to circle Earth, reflecting sunlight away from Earth's surface, causing global temperatures to cool (see 7.11). Pyroclasts are most directly dangerous in the form of pyroclastic flows and lahars, described next in 7.8.

## Check

☐ Describe three things that can come out of a volcano when it erupts.
☐ Discuss the hazards related to the eruption of pyroclasts, gas, and lava flows.
☐ Relate magma composition to what comes out of a volcano.
☐ Summarize different types of deposits formed by volcanic eruptions.

# 7.8 Hazards from Pyroclastic Flows and Lahars

**Key Concept:** Some of the most dangerous aspects of a volcanic eruption are pyroclastic flows and lahars because of their speed and unpredictable nature. Lava flows, volcanic gas, and pyroclasts individually do not tend to be dangerous to nearby people. However, pyroclastic flows are a combination of pyroclasts and volcanic gases that suddenly flow down a volcano **1**. Lahars are a mixture of water and pyroclasts that form a mudflow on the slope of a volcano **2**. Both leave distinctive deposits that can give clues about how dangerous past volcanic eruptions may have been.

## **1** Pyroclastic flow

A pyroclastic flow is a fast-moving cloud of very hot ash and volcanic gases that surges quickly down the side of a volcano, as shown in this photo of Mt. Saint Helens. Pyroclastic flows form when the density of the ash and gases is greater than the density of the surrounding air, so gravity pulls the ash and gas down the side of the volcano, instead of allowing them to rise in an eruption column. Pyroclastic flows are a hazard related to volcanoes with intermediate and felsic composition magma because of the high amount of ash and gases erupted.

### What deposits do pyroclastic flows form?

Pyroclastic flows result in layers of ash, generally felsic or intermediate in composition. The high temperatures in a pyroclastic flow sometimes cause the ash particles to weld together and mimic a rhyolite or andesite lava flow in texture. Geologists identify and map the locations of pyroclastic flow deposits, such as these in New Mexico, in order to make interpretations about the size of past eruptions. This information can be used to hypothesize about the potential danger of future eruptions. For example, a volcano with multiple and widespread ash layers nearby indicates an explosive past and potentially explosive future.

### What are hazards from pyroclastic flows?

Pyroclastic flows are extremely dangerous because they are unpredictable and move faster than 100 km/hr (60 miles per hour). Not only can the flows destroy buildings, as shown in the photo of Mt. Merapi in Indonesia, but the ash and gas can cause suffocation and burns, and may engulf people, entombing their bodies. The high density of pyroclastic flows along with their speed causes them to destroy buildings and infrastructure more efficiently than an equivalent amount of wind.

## 2 Lahar

A lahar is a volcanic mudflow made up of ash and water. Lahars can occur when volcanic eruptions melt snow and ice on the volcano, when ash mixes with streams, and when rain falls on loose ash deposits at some time after an eruption. Lahars often flood valleys to levels much higher than typical stream water levels, ripping up vegetation, rocks and other debris as can be seen in this photo from Nevado Del Ruiz in Colombia, described below.

### What deposits do lahars form?

Lahars result in a layer of mud made of ash, other pyroclasts, and sharp-edged igneous rock pieces shattered during the eruption. The high speed and density of a lahar allow it to carry large objects, such as boulders and trees. As with pyroclastic flow deposits, identifying and mapping lahar deposits allows geologists to interpret past eruption hazards. For example, towns built on multiple layers of lahar deposits in a valley should plan for future lahars. The lahar deposit shown in this photograph is a 2,500 year old lahar from Mt. St. Helens.

### What are hazards from lahars?

Lahars are very dangerous because they tend to flow faster than 80 km/hr (50 miles per hour) and are hard to predict because they may occur during an eruption or during a rain storm days to months after an eruption. This photo shows damage when there was a small eruption of Nevado Del Ruiz in 1985 that melted a glacier on the volcano, forming a lahar. The entire village of Armero was buried or destroyed and 25,000 people were killed. The high density of the ash-water mixture causes lahars to cause more destruction than an equivalent amount of water. Many people live in valleys near volcanoes, and in some locations they have set up lahar warning systems to trigger an evacuation alert if a lahar is detected roaring down their valley.

## Check

☐ Compare the compositions and formation of pyroclastic flows and lahars.
☐ Discuss why pyroclastic flows and lahars are dangerous to people.
☐ Describe the types of deposits that help geologists to determine where pyroclastic flows and lahars have happened in the past.

# 7.9 Measuring the Size of a Volcanic Eruption

**Key Concept:** Volcanic eruptions can be ranked by the amount of pyroclasts that erupt. The Volcanic Explosivity Index (VEI) helps geologists compare the sizes of different volcanic eruptions by comparing the volume of erupted pyroclasts. It uses a scale from 1 to 8, with each increase of one number on the VEI indicating 10 times more pyroclasts, a more intense eruption, and a taller eruption column. A VEI of 0-1 indicates a peaceful eruption with no eruption column **1**. If an eruption is explosive, but the volume of pyroclasts ejected is less than 1 cubic kilometer, it is ranked as a VEI 2-4 **2**. Eruptions with a VEI of 5 or 6 are fairly rare and can cause minor global consequences **3**. The largest eruptions are ranked 7 and 8 and have considerable local and global consequences, often sending enough ash into the atmosphere to cool global temperatures **4**.

## **1** Volcanic Explosivity Index 0-1

These eruptions are peaceful, with some spattering of lava but generally no eruption column. Damage to the surrounding area is primarily related to the lava, which flows over or around whatever it encounters. VEI 0-1 eruptions usually result from mafic composition lava, generally forming shield volcanoes at hotspots and divergent plate boundaries.

**Example volcano:**
Kilauea, Hawaii, has been erupting continuously for decades. Although the lava is shown here fountaining during the eruption from Kilauea in Hawaii, it is a still considered to be a peaceful eruption because of the lack of an eruption column of pyroclasts.

Volume of erupted pyroclasts is less than 0.001 cubic km

## **2** Volcanic Explosivity Index 2-4

These eruptions are explosive, with an eruption column that can reach up to 25 kilometers (16 miles or 82,000 feet) high, which is over twice the height that commercial airplanes fly. The eruption column height indicates the intensity of the eruption. Damage to the surrounding area is related to the pyroclasts, through ash fall, pyroclastic flows, and lahars.

**Example volcano:**
The eruption of Mount St. Helens in Washington in 1980 that killed 57 people was a VEI 4. The blast from the eruption knocked down trees 27 kilometers (17 miles) away. It caused pyroclastic flows and lahars, and ash caused darkness up to 400 kilometers (250 miles) away. Mount St. Helens erupted 1 cubic kilometer of ash, which is equivalent to 100 Empire State Buildings full of ash.

Volume of erupted pyroclasts is between 0.001 cubic km and 1 cubic km

## ❸ Volcanic Explosivity Index 5-6

These eruptions are explosive, with an eruption column that reaches over 25 kilometers (16 miles) high, above the height where clouds and rain quickly remove the ash. Direct damage to the area surrounding the volcano is due to the pyroclasts, through ash fall, pyroclastic flows, and lahars. Damage can also be caused indirectly by volcanic gases and ash injected high enough in the atmosphere where they block sunlight and cool temperatures globally.

**Example volcanoes:**
Mount Vesuvius in Italy erupted in 79 AD (VEI 5) with pyroclastic flows that buried the city of Pompeii and many of its inhabitants.

In 1991 the eruption of Mount Pinatubo in the Philippines (VEI 6, shown) was successfully predicted and tens of thousands of people were evacuated, saving their lives. The huge eruption column can be seen in the photo. A typhoon hit during the eruption, resulting in abundant lahars and heavy, wet ash fall that collapsed roofs.

Volume of erupted pyroclasts is between 1 cubic km and 100 cubic km

## ❹ Volcanic Explosivity Index 7-8

These rare supervolcano eruptions are extremely explosive and occur every few thousand years. The eruptions are so explosive they will often destroy the volcano during the eruption. Damage to the area surrounding the volcano is directly related to the force of the explosion and pyroclasts, and the substantial amount of volcanic gases and pyroclasts injected high into the atmosphere result in indirect damage from global cooling.

**Example volcanoes:**
When Mount Tambora in Indonesia erupted in 1815 (VEI 7, over 100,000 people were directly killed by pyroclastic flows and a tsunami and indirectly killed by famine because the amount of ash ejected into the air caused global temperatures to cool so crops around the world died.

The hotspot beneath Yellowstone National Park caused an eruption 640,000 years ago (VEI 8), leaving a huge caldera 50 km (30 miles) across. An ash layer 1 cm (0.4 inches) thick fell as far away as what are now the cities of Chicago, St. Louis, and Los Angeles.

**Volume of erupted pyroclasts is greater than 100 cubic km**

## Check

☐ Describe eruption characteristics with different Volcanic Explosivity Index numbers.
☐ Give examples of four volcanoes that had a range of different VEIs, and explain what their differences were.

# 7.10 Interpreting Past Volcanic Eruptions

**Key Concept:** Geologists study volcanic eruption deposits to learn more about the timing and style of past volcanic eruptions. To help keep people living near volcanoes safe, it is important to identify the volcanoes that are mostly likely to erupt in the near future by studying their eruption history. Dates are determined for past eruptions to identify the frequency with which the volcano erupted **1**. The types of volcanic deposits and their extent are identified and mapped by geologists to determine the potentially most hazardous future eruptions **2**. Earthquake data from past eruptions can also help geologists make models that help to understand patterns associated with future volcanic eruptions **3**.

## **1** Determining timing of past eruptions

There are thousands of volcanoes in various states of activity around the world, and geologists prioritize continuously monitoring the volcanoes that are most likely to impact human life. In order to help predict which are the most likely to erupt again, one thing geologists determine is how frequently volcanoes have erupted in the past.

Geologists use carbon-14 dating of plants buried during an eruption to determine the age of the eruptions up to 50,000 years ago.

Historical records and counting tree rings are useful tools for dating more recent eruptions.

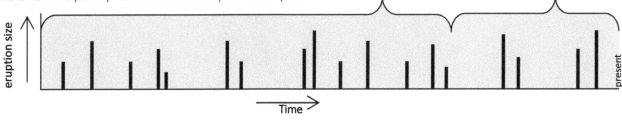

## **2** Determining past eruption style and extent

In addition to identifying active volcanoes, geologists also identify which volcanoes had the largest and most explosive eruptions in the past. To do this, geologists look for deposits left behind by hazards such as pyroclastic flows and lahars and create maps of the areas these hazards covered. Volcanoes tend to have reoccurring eruption styles because the magma source and composition remain relatively the same over time.

This map of Mount St. Helens shows the location of volcanic deposits from the 1980 eruption. These areas are potentially dangerous for future eruptions. Deposits that cover a larger area generally indicate a more explosive eruption.

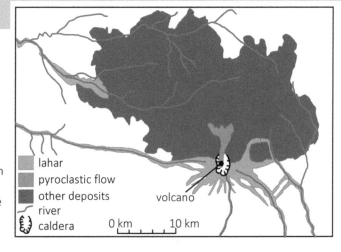

## **3** Past eruptions characterize future eruptions

Geologists studying earthquakes that occurred in past volcanic eruptions have identified a pattern. Many weeks before an eruption, small movements occur deep beneath the volcano indicating a deep magma chamber is filling with magma. A couple of weeks before the eruption nearby faults move, and explosions caused by groundwater turning to steam may occur. Earthquakes continue to get shallower, more frequent, and larger as magma moves toward the surface. Careful monitoring of volcanoes allows geologists to identify these patterns of past eruptions to understand magma movement and the processes that happen in a volcano.

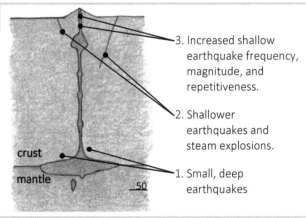

3. Increased shallow earthquake frequency, magnitude, and repetitiveness.

2. Shallower earthquakes and steam explosions.

1. Small, deep earthquakes

## Check

☐ Describe how geologists learn how a volcano erupted in the past and may erupt in the future.
☐ Explain what geologists do to reduce the risk to people from volcanic hazards.

# 7.11 Predicting Volcanic Eruptions

**Key Concept:** Potentially hazardous volcanoes are monitored for warning signs that they may erupt. Volcanic eruptions cannot be exactly predicted, but geologists can determine when a volcano is becoming active by watching for particular warning signs. For example, signs that indicate magma is moving underneath a volcano, which may result in an eruption, include small earthquakes **1**, tilting of the ground due to swelling of the magma chamber **2**, and changing volcanic gases **3**. Geologists use different techniques to collect these data, which often requires them to be near an active volcano. Once geologists determine an eruption is likely, then an evacuation is ordered that follows previously created evacuation plans.

## 1 Earthquakes

A warning sign a volcano may erupt is an increase in the size and frequency and decrease in depth of earthquakes. These earthquakes are caused by magma pushing its way to the surface and breaking rocks, which causes detectable tremors. To measure earthquakes, geologists set up seismometers around a volcano like the one shown in the photograph. These seismometers detect the shaking of the ground to determine where below the surface the magma is moving.

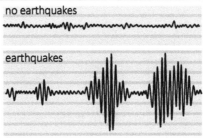

Volcanoes with no earthquake activity, shown in the top seismogram, are less likely to erupt compared to volcanoes that have increased earthquake activity, shown in the bottom seismograms.

## 2 Tilting

A warning sign a volcano may erupt is a slight change in the shape of a volcano. When magma fills and expands the magma chamber, the sides of the volcano may deform and swell. To measure this deformation, geologists set up tiltmeters and GPS stations (shown) on the sides of the volcano. The tiltmeters precisely measure the angle of the ground, and the GPS stations help create models of the ground surface deformation.

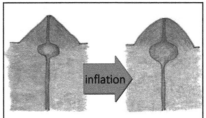

The inflating magma chamber can move and tilt the slopes of the volcano, as shown exaggerated in the second drawing of a volcano with bulging sides.

## 3 Volcanic Gases

A warning sign a volcano may erupt is a change in the amount or type of volcanic gases—such as carbon dioxide and sulfur gases—coming out of a volcano. This change occurs because gases bubble out of magma as pressure decreases as it rises to the surface. To measure volcanic gases, geologists hike or helicopter to the active volcano to collect the gases. In some cases they can set up permanent sampling equipment.

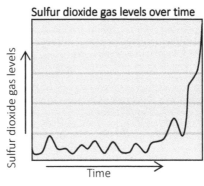

Sulfur dioxide gas levels over time

This graph shows how sulfur dioxide gas levels might increase as an eruption nears.

## Check

☐ Describe three warning signs that a volcano may soon erupt.
☐ Explain three ways that volcanoes are monitored to determine if they will soon erupt.

## End of Chapter Questions: Student Debates

For each of the following questions, determine which student you agree with and explain why.

**1. Two students are discussing what you would see if you could cut through a volcano.**

**Student 1:** There would be layers of lava flows or pyroclasts making up the entire volcano.

**Student 2:** The volcano had to start from a mountain, so there would be a core of metamorphic rock with layers of lava flows or pyroclasts on top of that other rock.

**2. Two students are discussing the locations of volcano types.**

**Student 1:** Different volcano types tend to match with different plate boundaries. For example, stratovolcanoes tend to occur at convergent plate boundaries with subduction.

**Student 2:** Different volcano types generally depend on the climate. For example, shield volcanoes tend to occur in hot climates because the hotter magma flows quickly.

**3. Two students are discussing which part of volcanic eruptions tend to be the most dangerous to people nearby.**

**Student 1:** The pyroclasts tend to be the most deadly because when flowing quickly, they can knock down, suffocate, and burn whatever is in their path.

**Student 2:** The lava flows tend to be the most deadly because they usually move downhill fast enough and without warning that people cannot escape.

**4. Two students are discussing how geologists identify eruptions in the past.**

**Student 1:** Geologists look for deposits left behind by eruptions, such as solidified lava or ash.

**Student 2:** Geologists only know a volcano erupted if they can find records written by someone who saw it erupt.

**5. Two students are discussing how geologists predict volcanic eruptions.**

**Student 1:** Volcanoes erupt suddenly and with little warning, so even with monitoring equipment, eruptions cannot be predicted.

**Student 2:** Eruptions cannot be predicted years in advance, but monitoring equipment can identify increased activity that that indicates a likely eruption in the short term.

## End of Chapter Questions: Short Answer

Using your own words or sketching and labeling a diagram, answer the following questions.

6. Explain how the composition of magma affects the types of igneous rock formations that result. Support your answer with examples.

7. Imagine you are on a road trip with your friends, and you take this photo. Explain to your friends how this landscape formed.

8. Draw a table to compare and contrast at least 5 separate aspects of stratovolcanoes and shield volcanoes. Things to consider include shape, magma viscosity, composition, plate boundary, and volcanic hazards.

9. Two towns are built near two different volcanoes. Town A is more frequently and severely damaged by eruptions than Town B. Hypothesize at least three distinct explanations why there is a difference.

10. A friend wants to buy a house near either Kilauea in Hawaii or Mt. St. Helens in Washington and asks your advice. Make and justify a recommendation comparing and contrasting the pros and cons of living near each volcano. It might be helpful to make a chart. (See 7.5 for location maps)

11. Imagine you took this photo. Write a hypothesis explaining hazards people in the area need to prepare for. To test your hypothesis, describe three types of data you could collect and what each observation would tell you about your hypothesis.

12. It is your job to create an evacuation plan for an area near a volcano. Explain how you would identify what hazards are likely, what areas need to be evacuated, and when an evacuation should be called.

**Hints:** For each question, see the sections listed here for information relevant to answering it.

**1.** (7.2) **2.** (7.4, 7.5) **3.** (7.7, 7.8) **4.** (7.7, 7.8, 7.10) **5.** (7.11) **6.** (7.1, 7.2, 7.3, 7.4) **7.** (7.1, 7.2, 7.3, 7.4, 7.5) **8.** (7.2, 7.3, 7.4, 7.5, 7.6, 7.7, 7.8) **9.** (7.3, 7.4, 7.7, 7.8) **10.** (7.3, 7.4, 7.7, 7.8, 7.9, 7.10) **11.** (7.4, 7.5, 7.6, 7.7, 7.8, 7.10) **12.** (7.4, 7.7, 7.8, 7.10, 7.11)

# Chapter 8:
# Sedimentary Rocks

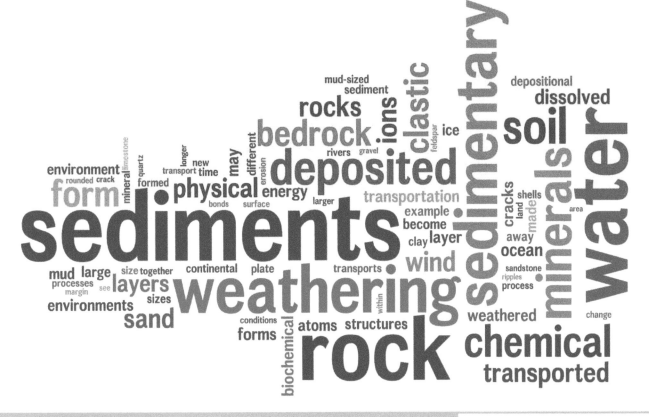

## Chapter Objectives

When you are finished reading this chapter, you should be able to …

• explain how chemical and physical weathering break down rock, describe factors that influence weathering, and relate weathering to the resulting types of sediments (8.1–8.6).

• explain how soil forms and erodes and the factors that influence each process (8.1–8.4, 8.6–8.7).

• relate the characteristics of sediments and sedimentary rocks to the environment in which the sediments were deposited (8.7–8.15).

• compare depositional environments and relate them to the plate tectonic setting (8.13–8.15).

• summarize the steps involved in creating sedimentary rocks, starting from sediments and ending with the resulting rock (8.7–8.9, 8.12).

# 8.1 – 8.6 Weathering, Sediments, and Soil

In this section, you will learn how bedrock breaks down into sediments through weathering and how soil forms as a result.

## Frequently Used Terms

The terms listed here are used repeatedly throughout this section, so by learning them before you read this section, you can focus your mental energy on the concepts presented.

**atom** The smallest particle into which elements, such as carbon or iron, can be divided; atoms bond together to form minerals.

**bedrock** The rock that makes up the solid component of Earth's crust; every place on Earth has bedrock underneath it, sometimes exposed at the surface where you can see it and sometimes deep beneath soil, sediments, and buildings.

**chemical sediments** Minerals that have precipitated out of water.

**clastic sediments** Pieces of rock created by the weathering of bedrock.

**dissolve** The process of separating ions from a solid mineral and surrounding them with water molecules by breaking the bonds between atoms.

**erosion** The initial movement of sediments away from the soil or bedrock from which they weathered; after rock is eroded, the sediments are transported.

**ion** An atom that has gained or lost negatively charged electrons, resulting in a negative or positive charge on the atom.

Soil, such as the soil on this farm, is vital for plant growth. Soil forms over thousands of years from weathered rock and dead plants.

# 8.1 Physical Weathering of Rock

**Key Concept:** Physical weathering breaks bedrock into pieces. Bedrock is the rock that makes up all of Earth's crust, and weathering is the process by which it is broken down. Physical weathering (discussed here) and chemical weathering (discussed next in 8.2) are the two components of weathering that work together to turn rock into sediment as part of the rock cycle. Physical weathering happens when processes cause cracks in bedrock to enlarge to the point of breaking the bedrock into pieces, called clastic sediments. Some physical weathering occurs across a large area as a result of decreased pressure on the bedrock **1**. Other physical weathering processes are more localized, such as when plant roots break rock apart **2** or when water in cracks in rock expands as it freezes, wedging the cracks farther apart **3**.

## **1** Decreased pressure

One physical weathering process that affects bedrock at a large scale is the formation of cracks due to decreasing pressure on bedrock when overlying bedrock is eroded away. This photo showing slabs of bedrock breaking off the surface of Half Dome in Yosemite National Park is an example.

 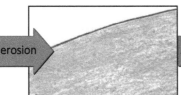 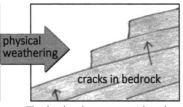

Deep bedrock is under pressure from the weight of the overlying bedrock.

Some bedrock erodes away, decreasing the pressure on the now less-deep bedrock.

The bedrock can expand and crack because of the decreased pressure, breaking it into clastic sediments.

cracks

## **2** Living Organisms

Another physical weathering process is when plants and animals break rock into smaller pieces, such as when tree roots enlarge cracks as the roots grow. You may have seen results of this process as tree roots form cracks in sidewalks or in rocks as in this photo.

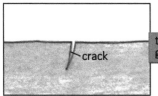 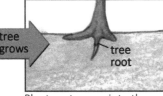 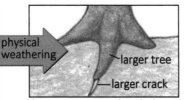

This bedrock has a small crack.

Plant roots grow into the crack and enlarge it.

The growing roots break the bedrock into clastic sediments.

cracks

## **3** Ice

A final example of a physical weathering process is when cracks enlarge as water within them expands as it freezes to form ice, wedging rock apart as shown in the photo. This process when water repeatedly freezes and enlarges cracks is called frost wedging.

 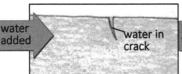 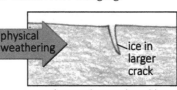

This bedrock has a small crack.

Water gets in the crack and expands when it freezes.

Ice enlarges the crack and breaks the bedrock into clastic sediments.

crack

**Check**   Before you continue, you should be able to answer each check without looking at the page.

☐ Describe the steps involved in three processes of physical weathering.
☐ Generalize how solid bedrock becomes clastic sediments.

# 8.2 Chemical Weathering of Rock

**Key Concept:** Chemical weathering changes the arrangement of the atoms in minerals in bedrock. While physical weathering breaks a rock into pieces, chemical weathering breaks or rearranges bonds between atoms in minerals, usually where water reaches bedrock. A common type of chemical weathering is when the minerals forming bedrock dissolve in water **1**. It also occurs when atoms in minerals form new bonds, such as with oxygen, which happens as minerals rust **2**, or turn into other minerals **3**. Chemical weathering results in dissolved ions or minerals that have a different composition than the original rock. 8.3 discusses how chemical and physical weathering each increases the effectiveness of the other.

## **1** Minerals dissolve

Some minerals can chemically weather by dissolving in water as bonds between atoms in a mineral break. This process results in the atoms separating from the mineral and becoming ions surrounded by water molecules. Calcite and halite are examples of minerals that dissolve easily in water because they have weak bonds between atoms that break easily. The resulting dissolved ions may become chemical sediments, as described in 8.7. The photos show small and large caves formed by chemical weathering.

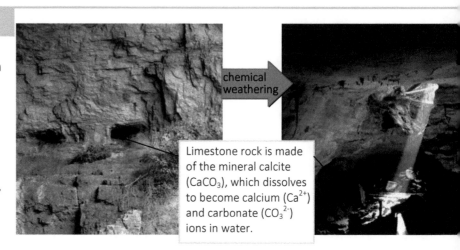

Limestone rock is made of the mineral calcite ($CaCO_3$), which dissolves to become calcium ($Ca^{2+}$) and carbonate ($CO_3^{2-}$) ions in water.

## **2** Minerals rust

Minerals that contain iron atoms are chemically weathered by exposure to oxygen in air or water. The iron atoms that were part of the original mineral structure break apart from that mineral and combine with oxygen to form new minerals. You may be familiar with the result of this process if you have seen iron nails that have turned into rust. The photo on the left shows freshly cooled basalt, while the photo on the right shows basalt with iron that has rusted.

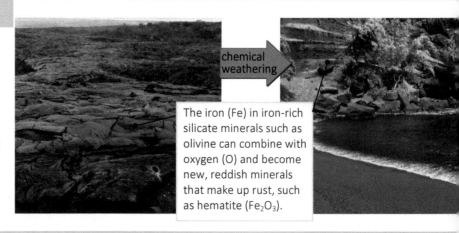

The iron (Fe) in iron-rich silicate minerals such as olivine can combine with oxygen (O) and become new, reddish minerals that make up rust, such as hematite ($Fe_2O_3$).

## **3** Minerals change into clay minerals

A final example of a chemical weathering process is when some atoms in certain minerals are dissolved and the remaining atoms rearrange, turning the original minerals into clay minerals. Clay minerals form at the wet and relatively low pressure and temperature conditions at Earth's surface. The photo on the left shows fresh feldspar minerals, while on the right the feldspar is becoming chemically weathered.

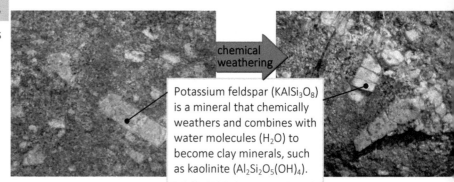

Potassium feldspar ($KAlSi_3O_8$) is a mineral that chemically weathers and combines with water molecules ($H_2O$) to become clay minerals, such as kaolinite ($Al_2Si_2O_5(OH)_4$).

## Check

☐ Describe three processes of chemical weathering.
☐ Generalize how solid bedrock changes when undergoing chemical weathering.
☐ Summarize the role of water in chemical weathering.

# 8.3 DATA AND DIAGRAMS: Physical and Chemical Weathering

**Key Concept:** Time-sequence diagrams can show how rock changes over time. This diagram shows granite bedrock weathering into clastic sediments, clay minerals, and dissolved ions 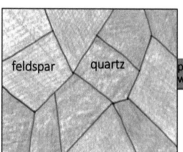. Weathering of granite may take many hundreds of years. Therefore, to create a diagram like this, geologists examine many different examples of granite that have been exposed to various amounts of weathering and compare what the minerals in the rocks look like. Tips on how to read this diagram are below **2**. Use the questions to practice interpreting time-sequence diagrams **3**.

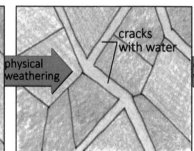
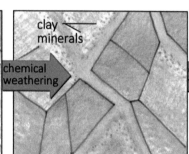
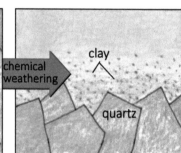

| | | | |
|---|---|---|---|
| The rock granite is made up of many minerals, such as potassium feldspar and quartz. Initially the rock is not weathered. | Physical weathering forms cracks in the rock, allowing water to move into the interior of the rock. | The water chemically weathers the potassium feldspar, turning it into clay minerals and dissolved ions. Clay minerals are not as strong as potassium feldspar, so the chemical weathering weakens the rock further. | Chemical and physical weathering continue, resulting in the granite becoming clastic sediments (physically weathered quartz and feldspar and new clay minerals) and dissolved ions. |

## 1 How to read the diagram

Figure out what is changing from diagram to diagram. A combination of physical weathering and chemical weathering breaks the granite bedrock apart or changes the composition of parts of it over time.

## 2 An example of what you might interpret

In the third panel, the mineral potassium feldspar chemically weathers into clay minerals, but this could only happen after physical weathering formed cracks that allowed water to enter the bedrock, as shown in the second panel.

## 3 Questions

**1. What does the diagram show?**
a. How sediments come together to form granite
b. How granite is weathered by chemical and physical weathering
c. How granite is extremely stable and resistant to weathering

**2. Which mineral in the diagram is most quickly chemically weathered?**
a. Quartz
b. Clay minerals
c. Potassium feldspar

**3. How does chemical weathering help speed up physical weathering?**
a. Chemical weathering causes minerals to become weaker, so the cracks in the rock can become larger.
b. Chemical weathering causes cracks in the rock to be wedged open, so more weathering can happen.
c. Chemical weathering causes acid rain, which makes rocks break down faster.

**4. Why does potassium feldspar within the rock weather into clay only after cracks form due to physical weathering?**
a. Chemical weathering of potassium feldspar requires water, which enters along the cracks.
b. Chemical weathering of potassium feldspar requires longer periods of time.
c. Physical weathering of potassium feldspar is what makes the clay.

**5. If the granite was in an environment with very little chemical weathering, how would that affect the physical weathering?**
a. Physical weathering would continue and not be affected.
b. Physical weathering would slow down.
c. Physical weathering would completely stop.

**6. How does the process of rock weathering as shown relate to the observation that many sand grains are made of quartz?**
a. The mineral quartz is resistant to chemical weathering.
b. The mineral quartz is created in the form of sand grains.
c. The mineral quartz dissolves in water.

# 8.4 Factors That Influence Weathering

**Key Concept:** The amount that rock weathers is dependent on factors such as climate, internal structure, rock type, and time. You may think of bedrock as permanent, but all rock at Earth's surface is weathering. However, it does not weather equally everywhere. Hot, humid climates cause rock to weather faster than dry or cold climates **1**. Rock with internal cracks **2** and rock with less stable minerals **3** will also undergo a quicker rate of weathering. Regardless of the conditions, the longer that rock is exposed to processes that cause weathering, the more it will be weathered **4**.

|  | Less weathering | More weathering |
|---|---|---|

## 1 Climate

The climate of an area is the long-term average of weather conditions, including rainfall, humidity, and temperature. The climate affects the rate of weathering because water causes many physical and chemical weathering processes. In addition, high temperatures speed up how quickly bonds between atoms break, increasing chemical weathering. Therefore, cooler and drier climates tend to have rock that is less weathered than hotter and wetter climates.

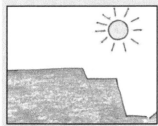 

Limestone in a cold, dry climate is barely weathered. / Limestone in a hot, wet climate is very weathered.

## 2 Bedrock structure

The structure of bedrock is described by the thickness of the layers of rock that composes it, as well as the number of cracks within it. The rock structure affects the rate of weathering because water flows more easily between layers of rock and along cracks. This water comes into contact with more rock surface and increases both chemical weathering and physical weathering. Therefore, rock with few layers and cracks tends not to weather as easily as rock with layers or cracks.

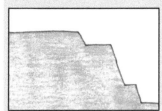 

A large layer of sandstone is barely weathered. / Sandstone with layers and cracks is very weathered

## 3 Bedrock type

Different rocks are comprised of different types of minerals, which affects the rates of weathering because some minerals weather faster than others. For example, minerals with weak bonds between the atoms, such as calcite or clay minerals, tend to result in more chemical or physical weathering. Other minerals have strong bonds between the atoms, such as quartz, and tend to be more resistant to weathering. Therefore, rock made up of resistant minerals tends to not weather as easily as rock with more weakly bonded minerals.

Sandstone made up of the stable mineral quartz is barely weathered. / Limestone made up of calcite is very weathered in wet climates.

## 4 Time

The longer rock is exposed at the surface, especially to water, the more chemical and physical weathering occurs. Each of these weathering processes takes a long time to occur (usually hundreds to many thousands of years), so if a rock has only recently been exposed to weathering, such as a new lava flow or newly uncovered bedrock, it will not have experienced much weathering.

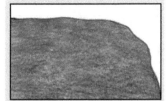 

Young basalt lava is barely weathered. / Old basalt lava is very weathered.

## Check

☐ Explain how climate, rock structure, rock type, and time affect how much weathering occurs.
☐ Describe a type of bedrock and location that would have low rates of weathering and another that would have high rates of weathering.

# 8.5 Soil Formation

**Key Concept:** **Soil forms from weathered bedrock, and the amount and type of soil depends on a variety of factors.** Soil is all around you, and it is made up of physically and chemically weathered rock, organic matter, water, and air **❶**. Soil forms very slowly, although the conditions that affect the rate of weathering (described previously in 8.4) also affect the characteristics of soils that form. Soil forms in layers with different characteristics **❷**. The bottom layer is in the first stages of weathering from the bedrock directly beneath it, and the top layer is the most well developed.

## ❶ How soil forms

Soil is the loose layer at Earth's surface composed of weathered rock, organic matter made of decomposing plants and animals, water, and air. Unlike sediments that were deposited in an area, soil forms in place. Processes that affect soil formation include physical weathering, chemical weathering, transportation of clay minerals and ions through the soil by water, and addition of organic matter.

### Factors that affect soil formation
Climate affects soil formation because warmer and wetter climates generally have faster weathering and more plants. Bedrock type affects the characteristics of the resulting soil because different minerals react differently to weathering. Sloping ground may cause weathered sediments to erode away more quickly. Finally, the longer the time that soil has had to develop, the thicker the soil will be.

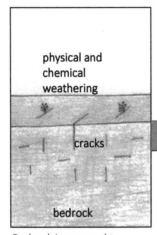 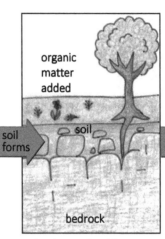 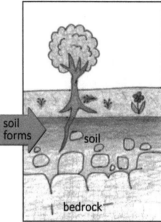

Bedrock is exposed to weathering at the surface and along cracks. Physical weathering creates clastic sediments and chemical weathering creates clay minerals and ions.

A thin layer of soil forms through continued weathering of bedrock and the addition of organic matter. Layers begin to develop because organic matter is added to the top, and water carries tiny clay minerals and ions down.

Over thousands of years, the processes of weathering, adding organic matter, and transporting ions and clay minerals continue and form a thick, well-developed soil, often with clear layers.

## ❷ Soil horizons

Soil tends to form with layers because different soil-forming processes affect different depths. These layers are called soil horizons, and may be simple, as shown in this photo, or may have more sub layers. The soil horizon at the top is the topsoil, which is essential for plant growth. The climate, type of bedrock, slope of the ground, and time for soil development all affect the presence, thickness, and characteristics of these layers.

**Topsoil:** This is the layer most changed from the original bedrock. It is the best for plants because it has the most nutrients from decomposing organic matter, as indicated by its dark color. It is a valuable resource, but is the first soil horizon to erode away during soil erosion.

**Subsoil:** This layer is beneath the topsoil. It has partially weathered bedrock but little organic matter, as indicated by its light color.

**Bedrock:** The unweathered bedrock beneath the soil layers is the rock that has weathered to form the soil.

## Check

☐ Explain how soil forms.
☐ Discuss how climate, type of bedrock, slope of ground, and time affect soil formation.
☐ Explain why there are layers of soil with different characteristics.

# 8.6 Soil Erosion

**Key Concept:** **Wind and water erode soil, so slowing them down helps to reduce soil erosion.** As most farmers know, it is important to preserve soil because it takes so long to form. Soil can be removed, or eroded away, by water and wind, in a process called soil erosion **1**. Methods to reduce soil erosion are designed to protect the soil by preventing water and wind from moving the soil. These techniques include covering the ground, slowing down water that runs over the soil during rainstorms, and reducing wind speed **2**. You may have seen some of these methods at farms or near construction sites to prevent exposed soil from eroding away.

## **1** Causes of soil erosion

Soil forms slowly over thousands of years at Earth's surface, but flowing water and blowing wind can quickly remove it. For example, water can erode deep gullies when it carries away soil (left photo), and dust storms can occur when wind carries soil particles into the air (right photo).

## **2** Reducing soil erosion

Soil is essential for plant growth but takes a long time to form, so it is important to reduce soil erosion. Techniques include slowing or stopping moving water and wind.

### Ground cover
Ground cover prevents wind or water from eroding the topsoil. To add ground cover, farmers leave stalks and roots in place after harvest (left), or people plant vegetation to hold the soil in place (right).

### Reduce wind speed
Slower-moving wind cannot blow away as much soil as fast-moving wind. To reduce wind speed, farmers can plant tall plants, such as trees (left) or taller crops such as corn (right), to protect soil around shorter crops.

### Reduce water speed
Slower-flowing water cannot carry away as much soil as fast-moving water. To reduce water speed, people create horizontal barriers, such as staking down coconut fiber logs (left), plowing contours around hills, or creating steps in hill sides (right) to prevent rain water from being quickly channeled downhill and carrying soil away.

## Check

☐ Explain what may cause soil to erode.
☐ Describe six methods to reduce soil erosion, and explain why each method works.

# 8.7 – 8.11 Forming Sedimentary Rocks

In this section, you will learn the processes that turn sediments into sedimentary rock and how geologists classify sedimentary rock.

## Frequently Used Terms

The terms listed here are used repeatedly throughout this section, so by learning them before you read this section, you can focus your mental energy on the concepts presented.

**biochemical sedimentary rock** Sedimentary rock formed from sediments created when organisms remove ions that are dissolved in water and bond them together to form minerals; an example is limestone.

**chemical sedimentary rock** Sedimentary rock formed when ions that are dissolved in water bond together to form minerals; an example is rock salt.

**clastic sedimentary rock** Sedimentary rock formed from clastic sediments that have been compacted and cemented together; examples are sandstone and shale.

**deposit** When sediments that were being transported are no longer moving and are left in place; deposition tends to happen when there is not enough transportation energy to continue moving the sediment.

**precipitate** When ions that are mixed with water molecules bond together with other ions and become large enough that they are no longer dissolved in water and separate from the water molecules as solid minerals; "undissolve."

**rounding** A description of the shape of the sediment, where angular sediments have pointy or jagged edges or corners, and well-rounded sediments are more shaped like a sphere with rounded edges.

**sorting** A description of the variety of sediment sizes in one location; poorly-sorted sediments have a wide range of sediment sizes, whereas well-sorted sediments are all the same size (e.g., all sand).

**transport** The movement of sediments; most sediments are transported by water (as rivers and coastal waves), but some are transported by air (as wind) and ice (as glaciers).

The pyramids of Giza in Egypt were constructed of a rock called limestone. Through observations of the rock and the fossils within it, geologists interpret that approximately 40 million years ago, the desert in which the limestone was quarried was a tropical ocean.

# 8.7 Types of Sediments

**Key Concept:** **Sediments are categorized based on how they are formed.** Physical weathering of bedrock results in the formation of clastic sediments. These are solid pieces of rock can be seen, though to do so may require a microscope. Clastic sediments are further described by their size **1**. Recall from 8.2 that chemical weathering by water forms ions. These dissolved ions can precipitate out of the water on their own as chemical sediments or aided by organisms as biochemical sediments **2**. Each of these sediment types forms a different category of sedimentary rock.

## 1 Clastic sediments

Clastic sediments are pieces of rock formed by physical weathering. You could mimic the creation of clastic sediments by taking a rock hammer and pounding on rock until pieces break off. In nature, clastic sediments are created when bedrock is broken into pieces through physical weathering, as discussed in 8.1. Clastic sediments are classified by their size, ranging from the size of large boulders, to gravel, to sand, to tiny mud-sized sediments. The rocks they may eventually form, clastic sedimentary rocks, are classified by these same sediment sizes (see 8.11).

In each particle of mud in this microscopic image, there are millions of billions of atoms ($1 \times 10^{15}$, or 1,000,000,000,000,000).

Large sediment size ◄──────────────────────► Small sediment size

 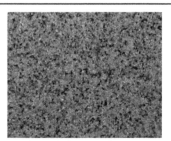 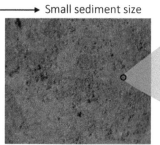

Gravel-sized clastic sediments are larger than 2 mm diameter, the thickness of a quarter.

Sand-sized clastic sediments are smaller than gravel but larger than the width of a human hair (0.06 mm).

Mud includes both silt-sized and clay-sized sediments. Silt is smaller than sand but larger than bacteria (0.002 mm). Clay is smaller than silt, with individual clay-sized sediments requiring a microscope to see.

## 2 Chemical and biochemical sediments

Chemical weathering creates dissolved ions in water, and chemical and biochemical sediments result when dissolved ions combine to form new minerals that precipitate out of water. You could mimic the creation of chemical sediments by letting salt water evaporate and the dissolved ions form new salt minerals. Other chemical sediments, specifically called biochemical sediments, form when animals, such as clams and coral, remove the dissolved ions from water to build shells. These chemical and biochemical sediments are the building blocks of chemical and biochemical sedimentary rocks (see 8.11).

Salt minerals (left) are examples of chemical sediments precipitated as water evaporates. Shells (right) are examples of biochemical sediments.

## Check

☐ Explain how physical sediments and chemical and biochemical sediments form.
☐ Describe what physical sediments and chemical and biochemical sediments look like.

# 8.8 Sediments Change During Transportation

**Key Concept:** Sediments become more rounded and sorted as they are transported. After sediments form, they are moved, or transported, from their original location by flowing water, blowing wind, or flowing ice. An environment with a higher transportation energy transports larger sediments **1**. Clastic and biochemical sediments change as they are transported, getting more rounded and better sorted as they move **2**. Once the transportation energy is not high enough to continue to move sediments, they fall and are deposited, retaining the characteristics acquired during transportation **3**. Observations of these characteristics are used by geologists to learn about how sediments were transported.

## 1 Transportation energy

Water, wind, and ice have different amounts of energy to transport sediments, called transportation energy, which is what determines the size of clastic sediments they can move. Fast, turbulent water, like the river in the photo or like waves at a beach, has a high transportation energy, so it can move large sediments. Water that flows slowly, such as water in wetlands or swamps, has low energy, and only the smallest mud-sized sediments are transported. In contrast to water, wind has a low transportation energy, so it generally cannot pick up and transport sediments larger than sand. Although ice flows slowly, it has a high transportation energy and can carry sediment larger than gravel.

## 2 Rounding and sorting

As clastic and biochemical sediments are transported, the shape and size distribution of the sediments change depending on the transportation energy and distance traveled. Sediments tend to begin with an angular shape with a variety of sediments sizes. They become rounded and sorted by size as they are transported over a longer distance.

### Rounding
Sediments transported by water or wind often rub together and wear away jagged edges until they are smooth and well-rounded. The amount of rounding depends on how much the sediments interact with each other, which increases with increasing transportation energy and transportation distance.

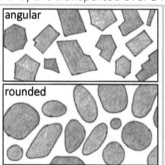

### Sorting
Well-sorted sediments have a similar size because the transportation energy causes only a particular sediment size to be transported and deposited. Poorly sorted sediments with a wide range of sizes tend to be deposited after short distances or in high-energy environments.

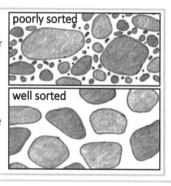

## 3 Transported sediments

Examples of the characteristics of sediments that have been transported different distances by water with different transportation energies are given below.

Sediments start off angular and poorly sorted, including boulder-, gravel-, sand-, and mud-sized.

After a short distance, sediments are more rounded but poorly sorted, ranging from gravel- to mud-sized.

With a longer distance, sediments are well-rounded and better sorted, with gravel- to sand-sized.

After a long distance and a constant transportation energy, sediments are well-rounded, well-sorted, and sand-sized.

## Check

☐ Explain how the characteristics of sediments are described.
☐ Describe the changes in sediments from when they initially form to when they have been transported a large distance.

# 8.9 Transporting and Depositing Sediments

**Key Concept:**  Sediments are deposited after they are transported by water, wind, and glacial ice.  Sediments are transported until the transportation energy is no longer enough to carry the sediments, and they are then deposited in that environment. The method of transportation affects the type and size of sediments that are deposited and where they are deposited. Water transports clastic sediments and biochemical sediments of a variety of sizes in addition to dissolved ions **1**. Wind transports only smaller-sized clastic sediments **2**, while glacial ice transports clastic sediments of all sizes **3**. The characteristics of deposited sediments are retained if they become a sedimentary rock, so geologists can make observations of sedimentary rocks to learn more about the geologic history and past environments of an area.

## **1** Water

Most sediments are transported and deposited by water. Water transports clastic sediments, biochemical sediments, and dissolved ions. The dissolved ions change very little during transport by water. However, as previously described in 8.8, clastic and biochemical sediments may become rounded and sorted. Where the water slows down, the transportation energy is too low to move the sediments, so they are deposited by the water.

This high-energy stream transports and deposits gravel and sand.

This low-energy stream transports and deposits sand and mud.

This medium-energy beach transports and deposits sand.

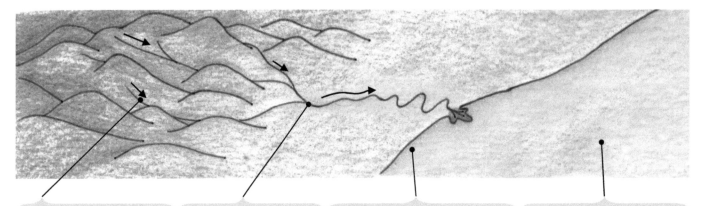

Steep streams are high-energy environments, so they can transport clastic sediments from boulder-sized to mud-sized. Generally the largest sediments are deposited in this environment because the water is moving fast enough to carry away smaller sediment sizes.

Gently sloping streams are lower energy environments because the water is calm with very little turbulence. The water typically transports and deposits sand-sized and mud-sized sediment.

Near shore, currents move sediments of a variety of sizes (from gravel-sized to mud-sized) depending on the energy of the waves. Many beaches are made of well-sorted sand because the ocean waves can transport sand, but the mud-sized sediments continue to be swirled in the water and carried out to sea.

The deep ocean and lakes have water that is barely moving. Large gravel- and sand-sized sediments are deposited near the shore. Away from the shore in the deep ocean, the nearly still water can only transport and deposit the smallest mud-sized sediments.

## 2 Wind

Wind transports clastic sediments, mostly sand- and mud-sized (called dust when in the air). Wind is good at sorting sediments by size because a particular strength wind will not be able to move pieces that are too large and will easily keep tiny pieces suspended in the air. This process results in sediments of about the same size being deposited in a given location. Wind rubs sediments against each other, resulting in rounded sediments.

These sand dunes are made up of rounded and well-sorted sand-sized sediments transported and deposited by the wind.

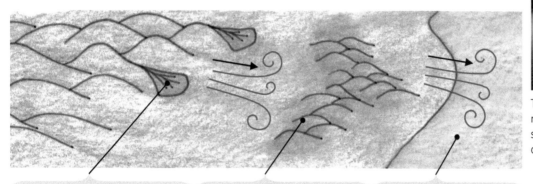

Wind does not have a high enough transportation energy and larger sediments are left behind.

Sand-sized sediments are moved by wind along the ground and deposited as sand dunes in this environment.

Mud-sized sediments are carried away from this environment by wind.

## 3 Ice

Ice that makes up glaciers slowly flows downhill over land. Glacial ice transports and deposits clastic sediments of all sizes, from large boulders to mud-sized, because the solid but slowly moving ice can move all sediment sizes equally. Sediments do not rub together during transport while frozen within the glacier, so they are not rounded and are instead angular when they are deposited.

These sediments deposited by the glacier in the background are generally not rounded and have a large range of sizes, from gravel to mud.

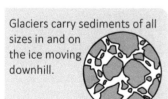 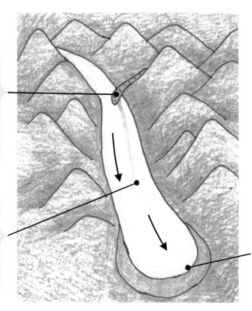

Glaciers scrape sediments of all sizes from the bedrock, and landslides with sediments of all sizes add sediments to the glacier.

Glaciers carry sediments of all sizes in and on the ice moving downhill.

Sediments of all sizes and shapes are deposited together by the glacier ice when it melts.

## Check

☐ Compare and contrast water, wind, and ice in terms of the type and size of sediments they transport.
☐ Explain how sediments are changed during transportation b water, wind, and ice.

# 8.10 Sediments Become Sedimentary Rock

**Key Concept:** Sediments become sedimentary rock through several processes. In most cases, to become rock, clastic and biochemical sediments need to be buried after they have been transported and deposited in a location. Burial compacts the sediments, and minerals cement them together to form solid rock, a process called lithification **1**. As a result of these processes, the layer of sediments is transformed into a layer of sedimentary bedrock. In comparison, chemical sedimentary rock forms when the concentration of ions in water becomes too great and they precipitate out to form rock **2**. The processes that form sedimentary rock are different than the processes that form metamorphic or igneous rock, although at first glance they may appear the same.

## **1** Lithification

Deposited sediments are buried as additional sediments are deposited on top. Over time, clastic and biochemical sediments may turn into rock, a process called lithification. Sediments are compacted by the weight of the overlying sediments, which helps the separate sediments combine to become solid rock. In addition, sediments can be cemented together by minerals precipitated from water underground.

**Compaction**
Sediments are compacted during lithification.

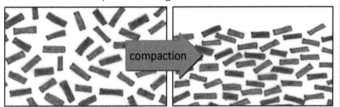

Deposited sediments are randomly oriented and will compact from the pressure of the overlying sediments.

Mud-sized sediments, in particular, compact considerably because the sediments align and take up less space.

**Cementation**
Sediments are cemented together during lithification.

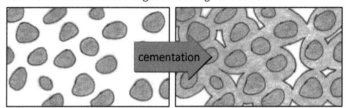

Loose deposited sediments allow water to move through them and precipitate dissolved ions, forming minerals.

Sand-sized sediments cement as calcite or quartz minerals fill in the empty spaces between them.

### Sedimentary rock

Once clastic and biochemical sediments are lithified as a single unit through compaction and cementation, they are considered a sedimentary rock. Sediments that are not lithified will remain as sediments. The photo on the left shows loose sand particles, so they are sediments. The sand particles on the right have been cemented together, so it is a sedimentary rock.

### Comparing sedimentary rock and metamorphic rock

The formation of sedimentary rock and metamorphic rock both require burial with increased temperature, but there are important differences. Sedimentary rock usually forms at temperatures below 150°C (300°F), which, in comparison, is slightly lower than the temperature to bake cookies. Above 150°C, some minerals begin to change into new minerals that are stable at that higher temperature. As the minerals change identity, the rock metamorphoses, so it is no longer considered sedimentary rock. Metamorphic rock tends to form deeper within Earth's crust, where there are higher pressures and temperatures. There is a gray area, though, between sedimentary rock and the beginnings of metamorphic rock.

# ❷ Chemical sediments

Chemical sedimentary rocks do not go through the same process of lithification. When dissolved ions precipitate out of water as chemical sediments, they are immediately considered sedimentary rock because they are already a single unit and do not need to be compacted and cemented.

## Precipitation
Chemical sediments are precipitated out of water.

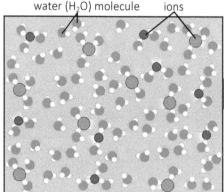
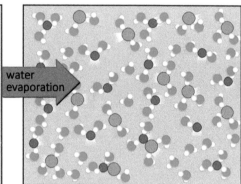
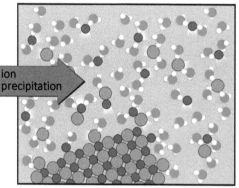

Ions dissolved in the ocean are dispersed among water molecules and are not visible, even under a microscope.

As water evaporates, the ions become concentrated in the ocean water. In the absence of water molecules keeping the ions apart from each other, some begin to bond together.

When the ions bond together to form new minerals, they are chemical sediments and form a chemical sedimentary rock.

## Sedimentary rock
Once ions precipitate as layers of chemical sediments, they are considered to be sedimentary rock. As described on the next page, a common sedimentary rock formed through evaporation this way is formed from the mineral halite. The photo on the left shows water with dissolved ions. The right photo shows the salt crystals that formed from dissolved ions and are now a sedimentary rock.

## Comparing sedimentary rock and igneous rock
Chemical sedimentary rock and igneous rock both start from liquid and end with solid, but the process is quite different. Sedimentary rock forms from the ions dissolved in water, not the water itself. The bonds between ions form minerals because there are no longer enough water molecules between them. In comparison, igneous rock forms from all of the atoms making up the liquid magma, not just some of them. The bonds between atoms form minerals when the temperature of magma cools.

# Check

- ☐ Explain how clastic and biochemical sediments change into sedimentary rock.
- ☐ Explain how chemical sedimentary rock forms.
- ☐ Compare the formation of sedimentary rock with the formation of metamorphic rock and igneous rock.

# 8.11 Identifying Sedimentary Rocks

**Key Concept:** The processes that form clastic, biochemical, and chemical sedimentary rocks result in unique and identifiable characteristics. The processes of formation are also the basis for categorizing sedimentary rocks. Clastic sedimentary rock, such as sandstone, is made up of clastic sediments **1**. Biochemical sedimentary rock, such as limestone, forms predominantly from biochemical sediments created as living organisms create bonds between dissolved ions to make their shells **2**. Chemical sedimentary rock, such as rock salt, is made up of chemical sediments, without the help of living organisms **3**.

## 1 Clastic sedimentary rocks

Clastic sedimentary rocks form from clastic sediments. The rocks are classified primarily by the size of the sediment comprising them, which gives geologists clues about how the sediments were transported and deposited. The minerals present and the level of rounding and sorting can give additional naming descriptions to the rock (e.g., quartz sandstone).

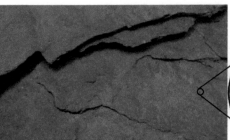

Shale (mudstone) is made up of mud-sized clastic sediments that cannot be seen without a microscope.

Sandstone is made up of sand-sized clastic sediments. The microscope used changed their colors to make them distinct.

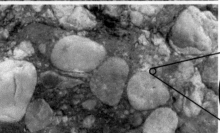

Conglomerate is made up of rounded gravel-sized and smaller clastic sediments. Angular sediments form breccia.

## 2 Biochemical sedimentary rocks

Most biochemical sedimentary rocks form when biochemical sediments, such as shells, are compacted and cemented. These rocks are classified primarily by composition. Coal, however, forms when plant matter buried under sediment decays and, over millions of years, becomes rock.

Limestone is made up of calcite shells or skeletons. Additional naming descriptions depend on the size and number of shells.

Chert is made up of microscopic shells made of quartz.

Coal is made up of primarily carbon atoms (its use as a fuel is described in 5.8).

## 3 Chemical sedimentary rocks

Chemical sedimentary rocks form when dissolved ions precipitate out of water as chemical sediments without the help of living organisms. These rocks tend to be composed of a single mineral and are classified primarily by composition. When the ions precipitate out due to evaporation of the water, they form a group of chemical sedimentary rocks called evaporites, such as rock salt.

Rock salt is made up of the mineral halite.

## Check

☐ Explain how each of the three categories of sedimentary rocks form.
☐ List and describe one characteristic each of clastic, chemical, and biochemical sedimentary rocks.

# 8.12 – 8.15 Depositional Features and Environments

In this section, you will learn how geologists use sedimentary rocks and the clues within to interpret what Earth was like in the past.

## Frequently Used Terms

The terms listed here are used repeatedly throughout this section, so by learning them before you read this section, you can focus your mental energy on the concepts presented.

**depositional environment** An environment where sediments are deposited over time, rather than eroded away; different depositional environments have distinctive combinations of sediments and sedimentary structures.

**sedimentary structures** Structures and shapes in sedimentary rocks that give clues to the environments in which they were deposited.

These dinosaur bones at Dinosaur National Monument in Utah are in sedimentary rock. Geologists have interpreted that the rock formed from sand- and mud-sized sediments deposited in a river valley where and when dinosaurs roamed.

Chapter 8: Sedimentary Rocks     Section 3

# 8.12 Sedimentary Structures

**Key Concept:** Sedimentary structures within sedimentary layers give clues about the depositional environments.

After sediments are created and transported, they are deposited, generally in a layer, depending on the environment **1**. If the conditions in the environment change, a different layer may form on top, reflecting the new conditions during deposition. Fossils within sedimentary rocks can help geologists determine the past environmental conditions by indicating what organisms lived in the environment at that time **2**. The conditions in the environment result in sedimentary structures within the layer. Some sedimentary structures may modify sediments after they were initially deposited, such as ripples forming at the top of a layer **3**, and other sedimentary structures, like graded beds **4** and cross-bedding **5**, form as the layers are deposited.

## **1** Layers

Sediments tend to form a horizontal layer throughout the environment in which they are deposited. Each layer of sediments deposited under similar conditions is called a bed. Beds are usually a centimeter to a meter (an inch to several feet) thick and can extend many kilometers (miles) across. If the conditions change, then new sedimentary layers, or beds, begin forming on top. Conditions may change for many reasons, such as changing climate and rising or falling sea level.

After sediments were deposited in layers and turned into rock millions of years ago, the Colorado River eroded the layers to form the Grand Canyon.

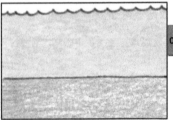
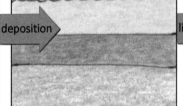
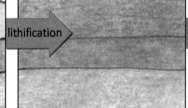
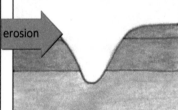

Sand deposited at a beach forms a horizontal layer of sand.

Sea level rises, and mud is deposited in muddy seas. Next limestone shells are deposited in clear seas.

After being buried deep enough, the sediment layers are lithified to become sedimentary rock.

A stream erodes a canyon through the once-continuous layers, so they can be seen on either side.

## **2** Fossils

Fossils are the preserved evidence—usually remains or tracks—of ancient living organisms. Fossils indicate the types of organisms that once lived in a particular area at a given time in the distant past. This information can help scientists determine the environmental conditions. For example, the fossilized trilobite and rock type in the photo indicate the environment was a shallow ocean.

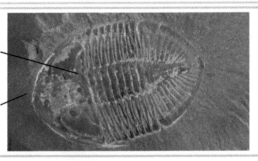

The hard parts of the trilobite were replaced by minerals.

The sediment in which the trilobite died, turned into rock.

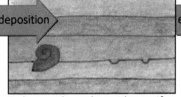

Animals lived on the ocean floor millions to hundreds of millions of years ago.

The animals die and their soft parts decay, leaving behind shells, bones, and tracks in the sediments as evidence they lived.

Sediments bury the evidence. If the sediments lithify, the tracks become rock and the shells and bones may be replaced by new minerals, forming fossils.

After hundreds to millions of years, erosion of the overlying layers exposes the fossils for people to find.

## 3 Ripples

Ripples form in deposited sediments when water flows or wind blows over sediments, such as at a beach, desert, or stream. If these ripples are buried, they may be preserved when the sediments become sedimentary rock. Ripples can indicate the direction and speed of the flow of water or wind in the past.

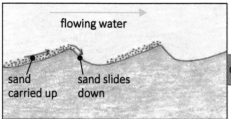

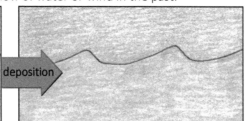

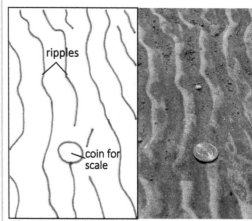

Sand is carried up one side of a ripple and collapses down the other side.

Another sedimentary layer is quickly deposited on top, preserving the ripples.

These ripples show the water was flowing to the photographers left.

## 4 Graded beds

In graded beds, the layer contains large sediments on the bottom, with subsequently smaller and smaller sediments toward the top of the layer. This change in sediment size indicates that the water transporting the sediments slowed down. As the transportation energy was reduced, the smaller sediments took longer to be deposited. An underwater landslide or a flooding stream could create graded beds.

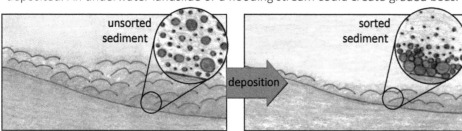

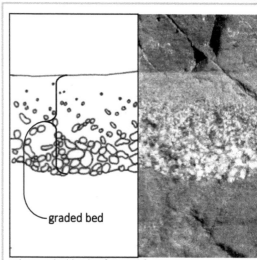

Large and small sediments are transported in the fast-moving water.

Large sediments settle to the bottom faster than smaller sediments.

This graded bed is formed from light colored sediment.

## 5 Cross-bedding

Cross-bedding is a sedimentary bed within which there are tilted and curved thin layers. Cross-bedding in a bed indicates it formed from migrating sand dunes such as in a desert (see 16.15) or from water forming ripples. The size and direction of cross-bedding can indicate the size of dunes and direction of the wind.

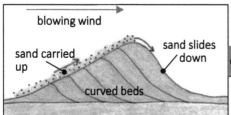

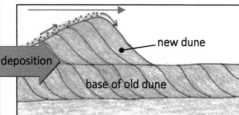

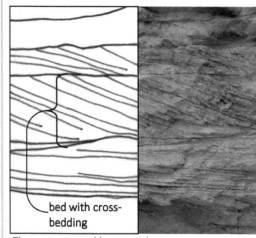

Sand blown up one side of a dune is deposited on the other side, preserving tilted layers within the horizontal bed.

Wind blows another dune into the area, depositing another layer with cross-bedding on the previous one.

There are several layers with cross-bedding in this photo.

## Check

☐ Explain why sedimentary rock forms as layers.
☐ Describe five sedimentary structures within sedimentary rocks.
☐ Explain how each sedimentary structure forms and relate that to what it says about the history of the rock.

# 8.13 Sedimentary Rocks and Plate Tectonics

**Key Concept:** Vast areas of sediments are deposited in environments created by processes related to plate tectonics. These environments where abundant sediments are deposited are called depositional environments. Many depositional environments results from processes happening at plate boundaries or along continental margins ❶. For example, abundant sediments are weathered from mountains formed at convergent plate boundaries, which are then transported away from the mountains and deposited. Sediments are deposited in rift valleys formed as divergent plate boundaries split continents apart. In addition, abundant sediments are deposited in the shallow ocean on continental margins ❷.

## ❶ Plate boundaries

Convergent and divergent plate boundaries create environments where large amounts of sediment are deposited. After a divergent plate boundary has created an ocean, a large amount of sediments are also deposited on the continental margin on the edge of the ocean where the continental crust is covered by shallow ocean water.

### Convergent plate boundaries
Mountain formation at convergent plate boundaries (see 3.9 and 3.10) and the resulting weathering of the exposed bedrock forms abundant sediments. These sediments are transported down the slopes of the mountains and deposited on the continent or on the active continental margin. Some of the sediment continues into the deep ocean trench formed by subduction.

### Divergent plate boundaries
Divergent plate boundaries on the continents pull the lithosphere apart, causing it to thin. The resulting rift valley (see 3.8) is a lower area where sediments are deposited.

### Passive continental margins
A divergent plate boundary can rift a continent apart to create an ocean. The resulting passive continental margin does not have a plate boundary (see 3.1).

## ❷ Locations of sediment deposition

The different plate boundaries create depositional environments where large amounts of sediments may be deposited over long periods of time as the areas are depressed. Below is an overview relating them to plate tectonics; specific depositional environments are described in 8.14 and 8.15.

| Key |
|---|
| ░ Sediments |

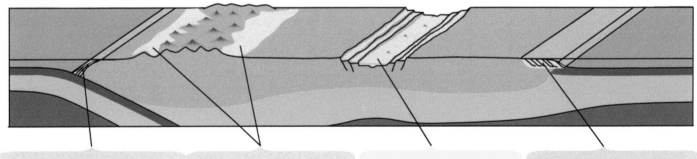

### Active continental margin
Sediments eroded from volcanoes and mountains are transported by rivers and glaciers. These sediments are deposited in a variety of depositional environments along the shore, such as deltas and beaches, offshore on the continental margin, and in the deep ocean. The initially flat layers of sediments may be bent and broken if they are squeezed between the plates.

### Next to mountains
Sediments are transported down the slopes of mountains. The weight of the mountains slowly pushes down the continental lithosphere, creating a lower area next to them. Rivers and glaciers deposit sediments in the resulting depositional environments, with the thickest layers near the mountains.

### Rift valley
Sediments are deposited in low-lying rift valleys on continents. Sediments eroded from the sides of the valley are transported by rivers, where they are deposited on the valley bottom, which is often a depositional environment of a river or lake.

### Passive continental margins
Sediments from the continent are eroded and transported, usually by rivers, and are often deposited along the beach or in the ocean at the continental margin as thick layers covering continental lithosphere. The weight of this sediment pushes down the lithosphere, lowering the passive margin and allowing more sediment to be deposited.

## Check
☐ Describe four locations where abundant sediments are deposited.
☐ Summarize three ways that plate tectonics play a role in creating locations where abundant sediments are deposited.

# 8.14 Depositional Environments in the Ocean

**Key Concept:** **Sediments are deposited in a variety of environments in the ocean.** Sediments originate from weathered rock and are transported. They are then deposited in a wide variety of depositional environments, both in the ocean and on land. Although most sediments originate on land, they are moved downhill because of gravity, and most are eventually deposited in the ocean. Each environment tends to have consistent conditions, so each has typical sediments and sedimentary structures. As a result, after the sediments turn into sedimentary rocks, it is possible for geologists to "read" those rocks to determine the past depositional environment. Depositional environments in the ocean include reefs **1**, the shallow ocean of continental margins **2**, and the deep sea **3**. Depositional environments on land are discussed in 8.15.

## 1 Reefs

Reefs are areas of coral and other organisms that live just below the surface of warm, shallow oceans. Organisms, such as the coral shown in the photo, build reefs by removing dissolved ions in ocean water to build their shells, made of calcite. These organisms can only grow where clastic sediments, such as sand and mud, are not present because they block sunlight and bury them.

> **Example sediments:** shells
> **Related rock:** limestone
> **Sedimentary structures:** fossils

## 2 Continental margin

The continental margin is the shallow part of the ocean that is next to the edge of the continent, above the continental lithosphere. The ocean you can see from most beaches, as shown in the photo, is above the continental margin. A large amount of mud-sized sediment from land is deposited on the continental margin, in quieter water beyond the beach. If the water is clear, with no clastic sediments like mud, then sediments are frequently shells.

> **Example sediments:** mud, sand
> **Related rocks:** shale, sandstone
> **Sedimentary structures:** graded beds, ripples

## 3 Deep sea

The floor of the deep sea is the part of the ocean that is above oceanic lithosphere, far from the continent. Dust blown by the wind and mud carried out to sea slowly sink to the bottom of the ocean. Microscopic skeletons of single-celled organisms that live near the ocean's surface also sink to the bottom after they die.

> **Example sediments:** mud, microscopic shells
> **Related rocks:** shale, limestone, and chert
> **Sedimentary structures:** microscopic fossils

## Check

☐ Describe three environments in the ocean where sediments are deposited.
☐ Compare and contrast the typical sediments deposited in three depositional environments in the ocean.

# 8.15 Depositional Environments on Land

**Key Concept:** Sediments are deposited in a variety of environments on land. As with depositional environments in the ocean (discussed in 8.14), sediments deposited on land tend to have consistent sediment types and structures in each depositional environment, allowing geologists to use observations of the resulting rock to determine what the area was like in the past. In most depositional environments on land, such as in rivers **1**, deltas **2**, beaches **3**, swamps **4**, lakes **5**, and desert lakes **6**, sediments are deposited by water. In other depositional environments on land, such as in desert dunes **7** and glaciers **8**, sediments are deposited by wind or ice.

## 1 Rivers

Rivers are surface water that flows downhill in channels. As the water moves, it transports a variety of sediments, depending on the transportation energy. Sediments transported by a river tend to become well rounded, as shown by the boulders and cobbles in the photo. The flowing water often creates ripples, and floods form layers with graded beds.

> **Example sediments:** Mud, sand, gravel
> **Related rocks:** Shale, sandstone, conglomerate
> **Sedimentary structures:** Graded beds, ripples

## 2 Deltas

Deltas, such as the one shown, are areas of flat land formed when sediments are deposited by rivers as they flow into oceans or lakes and the water slows down. The sediments were transported by rivers, so they tend to be well-rounded. Deltas form in a variety of shapes depending on factors such as the amount of sediments, the amount of river water, and the waves in the ocean.

> **Example sediments:** Mud, sand, gravel
> **Related rocks:** Shale, sandstone, conglomerate
> **Sedimentary structures:** Graded beds, ripples

## 3 Beaches

Beaches, such as the one shown, are shorelines made of sediments, typically sand or sometimes gravel (see 15.7). They form where ocean waves transport and deposit sediments. Mud-sized sediments are transported away by the wind or water, leaving well-sorted, well-rounded sand on the beach.

> **Example sediments:** Sand
> **Related rock:** Sandstone
> **Sedimentary structures:** Ripples, fossils

## 4 Swamps and Wetlands

Swamps and wetlands, such as the one shown, are land areas frequently underwater because water pools on flat, low-lying ground. The low-energy environment transports mostly mud-sized sediment. If plants die and do not decompose before they are buried, they may eventually turn into coal.

> **Example sediments:** Mud, plant remains
> **Related rocks:** Shale, coal
> **Sedimentary structures:** Plant fossils

## 5 Lakes

Lakes are bodies of water on land formed where water pools. Water generally enters and leaves by rivers. When river water flows into a lake, the water slows down, and the sediments settle to the bottom. Most lakes, such as the one shown, are freshwater, but closed lakes that are not drained by rivers often become salty as the dissolved ions remain in the lake (see desert lakes to the right).

**Example sediments:** Mud
**Related rock:** Shale
**Sedimentary structures:** Thin layers

## 6 Desert lakes

Desert lakes are lakes in a desert where most water leaves through evaporation, not through a river. Water containing mud and dissolved ions temporarily fills the lake and initially deposits mud. As the water evaporates, the dissolved ions remain behind and precipitate out as chemical sediments, forming layers of salts, such as the halite that can be seen as white in the photo (see 16.16).

**Example sediments:** Salts, mud
**Related rocks:** Evaporites (e.g. rock salt), shale
**Sedimentary structures:** Thin layers

## 7 Desert dunes

Sand dunes, such as those shown, are hills of sand-sized sediments that are transported and then deposited by wind (see 16.16). They are found in deserts or other areas with abundant sand-sized sediments and little flowing water to transport them. Wind transports sand up the sides of the dunes, rounding the sand grains.

**Example sediments:** Sand
**Related rock:** Sandstone
**Sedimentary structures:** Cross-bedding

## 8 Glaciers

Glaciers are huge bodies of slow-moving ice on land, commonly found in cold areas on mountains or near Earth's poles (see 16.8). As the ice that makes up glaciers slowly flows, it transports angular sediments of all sizes generally without rounding them. It deposits them where the ice melts, as can be seen in this photo.

**Example sediments:** Mud, sand, gravel
**Related rocks:** Conglomerate, breccia
**Sedimentary structures:** None

## Check

☐ Describe eight environments on land where sediments are deposited.
☐ Compare and contrast the typical sediments and their rounding and sorting characteristics deposited in eight depositional environments on land.

# End of Chapter Questions: Student Debates

For each of the following questions, determine which student you agree with and explain why.

**1. Two students are discussing how to make mud.**

**Student 1:** If you add water to sand and let it sit for a long time, it will turn into mud.

**Student 2:** Mud is made up smaller particles like clay-sized sediments, so you would need to add water to dust.

**2. Two students are discussing what the large sediments in a conglomerate tell you.**

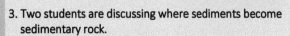

**Student 1:** The large sediments indicate the sediments were deposited in a high-energy environment, such as a stream.

**Student 2:** The large sediments indicate that the processes to lithify the sediments into rock happened very slowly.

**3. Two students are discussing where sediments become sedimentary rock.**

**Student 1:** It is possible to dig to where sediments become sedimentary rock, such as where sandstone layers are forming under a desert.

**Student 2:** Most sedimentary rocks form too deep to dig to, since they need to be buried to form.

**4. Two students are discussing how this fossil formed.**

**Student 1:** This animal died, was buried by sediments, and both the animal remnants and sediments turned into rock.

**Student 2:** This animal lived on sedimentary rocks. When it died, it became a part of the sedimentary rock and is on the rock's surface.

**5. Two students are discussing sedimentary rocks can tell you about the current conditions of an area.**

**Student 1:** Sedimentary rocks don't tell you about what an area is like today because they formed from sediments that are millions of years old and Earth has changed since then.

**Student 2:** Sedimentary rocks tell you what an area is like today because the sediments that formed the rock, like sand or mud, are still being deposited on Earth's surface today.

**6. Two students are discussing where sediments are deposited in the ocean.**

**Student 1:** The type of sediment that is deposited in the ocean varies from place to place.

**Student 2:** Sediments are deposited throughout the ocean, with the same types of sediments deposited everywhere.

# End of Chapter Questions: Short Answer

Using your own words or sketching and labeling a diagram, answer the following questions.

7. Identify two types of chemical and/or physical weathering that occur in the environment in which you live. Explain why those types of weathering occur.

8. You have been hired to create a monument that will last one million years. You need to make two decisions: the location and the rock type. Explain each of your decisions.
Location: Florida (climate: hot and wet), New York (climate: warm and wet), Arizona (climate: hot and dry)
Rock type: marble (mineral: calcite), quartzite (mineral: quartz), basalt (mineral: iron rich silicates and feldspars)

9. Two towns are built on land with different amounts of soil. Town A has more soil than Town B. Hypothesize at least three distinct explanations for why there is a difference.

10. A friend with no geology experience calls you to help her identify a sedimentary rock. Identify three questions you would ask her about the sedimentary rock over the phone. Explain what information you would learn from each question.

11. Imagine you took this photo. Write a hypothesis explaining how the sediments got there. To test your hypothesis, describe three observations you could make by visiting the landscape and what each observation would tell you about your hypothesis.

12. Draw a table to compare and contrast four separate aspects of the geologic environments of a lake in a forest and in a desert. Include the amount and type of weathering, the method of sediment transportation, the sizes of sediments deposited, and the eventual rock that might form.

13. Imagine you are on a trip and take this photo of a sedimentary rock. Explain how this rock formed and what the area was like in the past.

14. Draw a table to compare and contrast at least five separate aspects of clastic, biochemical, and chemical sedimentary rocks. Things to consider include the type of initial weathering to produce the sediments, type of sediments, processes to form the rock, example rocks, and depositional environments.

**Hints:** For each question, see the sections listed here for information relevant to answering it.
**1.** (8.7) **2.** (8.8, 8.9, 8.11) **3.** (8.11, 8.12) **4.** (8.12) **5.** (8.8, 8.9, 8.10, 8.12) **6.** (8.14) **7.** (8.1, 8.2, 8.4) **8.** (8.1, 8.2, 8.3, 8.4) **9.** (8.1, 8.2, 8.4, 8.5, 8.6) **10.** (8.7, 8.1) **11.** (8.8, 8.9, 8.12, 8.15) **12.** (8.1, 8.2, 8.4, 8.9, 8.11, 8.15) **13.** (8.2, 8.7, 8.9, 8.10, 8.11, 8.13, 8.14) **14.** (8.1, 8.2, 8.7, 8.9, 8.10, 8.11, 8.14, 8.15)

# Chapter 9:
# Metamorphic Rocks and Deformation

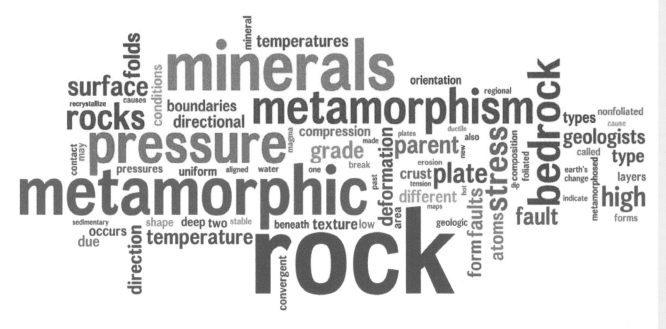

## Chapter Objectives

When you are finished reading this chapter, you should be able to …

• identify metamorphic rocks using the characteristics of metamorphic texture and composition, and relate them to metamorphic grade and the minerals within (9.1–9.4).

• connect the causes of metamorphism with the resulting rocks and different plate boundaries (9.3, 9.5–9.7).

• compare and contrast rock deformation by folding and faulting, including at which plate tectonic environment (9.8–9.12).

# 9.1 – 9.5 Forming Metamorphic Rocks

In this section, you will learn the causes of metamorphism and how geologists describe and identify metamorphic rocks.

## Frequently Used Terms

The terms listed here are used repeatedly throughout this section, so by learning them before you read this section, you can focus your mental energy on the concepts presented.

**bedrock** The rock that makes up the solid component of Earth's crust; every place on Earth has bedrock underneath it, sometimes exposed at the surface where you can see it and sometimes deep beneath soil, sediments, and buildings.

**directional pressure** Pressure on rock that pushes more in one direction than another; often the direction of greatest pressure is caused by two tectonic plates moving towards each other.

**foliated texture** A metamorphic texture in which flat or long minerals in a rock are aligned nearly parallel to each other.

**metamorphic grade** The amount rock has metamorphosed; low grade metamorphic rock has been slightly metamorphosed while high grade metamorphic rock has undergone significant metamorphism due to high pressures and temperatures.

**metamorphic rock** The rock type that forms from a preexisting rock when its minerals change shape or composition, generally under high pressure and temperature.

**metamorphism** The processes that cause bedrock to transform into metamorphic rock, which involve changing the minerals or the texture, usually due to high pressure and temperature.

**nonfoliated texture** A metamorphic texture in which minerals in rock are not aligned parallel with each other.

**parent rock** The original rock before it was metamorphosed.

**recrystallize** To break the bonds between atoms making up minerals and bond them again into a specific, orderly pattern, forming new minerals without melting.

**texture** The size, shape, and orientation of minerals in a rock; it does not describe how a rock feels when you touch it.

**uniform pressure** Pressure on rock that pushes equally in all directions.

This statue of Abraham Lincoln is made of the metamorphic rock marble, a rock commonly used for sculptures.

# 9.1 Metamorphism

**Key Concept:** Metamorphism of bedrock depends on the parent rock and the metamorphic grade. In the rock cycle, metamorphic rocks form from any rock that reaches the metamorphic conditions of high pressure and temperature. The process of metamorphosing rock transforms the original bedrock, called the parent rock, by changing the minerals or mineral arrangement due to the extreme conditions. This process happens very slowly, usually over millions of years. One factor that affects the metamorphic rock that forms is the composition of the parent rock **1**. A second factor is the extent to which rock metamorphoses, called the metamorphic grade, which is controlled by the temperature and pressure reached **2**.

## 1 Parent rock

The initial rock before it is metamorphosed is called the parent rock, which may be igneous, sedimentary, or metamorphic. Its composition affects the resulting metamorphic rock.

### Parent rock
The atoms that make up the minerals in the parent rock reconfigure to make up the minerals in the new metamorphic rock. Therefore, different parent rocks, each with a particular proportion of atoms, will metamorphose into different metamorphic rocks with that particular proportion of atoms (see 9.4 for examples). The example parent rock shown is the sedimentary rock sandstone, which is composed of sand-sized sediments made up of the mineral quartz.

### Metamorphic rock
Metamorphic rock forms when the atoms in the minerals of the parent rock reconfigure and create new minerals. Although the metamorphic rocks are made from the same atoms, the resulting mineral arrangement looks different than the parent rock's because of conditions they were exposed to during metamorphism. The example shown is quartzite, which is the metamorphic rock that forms when sandstone is metamorphosed. It is also composed of the mineral quartz, but with a different mineral arrangement.

## 2 Metamorphic Grade

Bedrock, which makes up Earth's crust, is metamorphosed under high pressures and temperatures, although hot water may also play a role (see 9.2). Pressure and temperature increase with depth in Earth's crust. They affect the extent to which rock metamorphoses, called the metamorphic grade. The same parent rock can become different metamorphic rocks if it reaches different metamorphic grades. This pressure-temperature graph shows pressure and temperature conditions for different metamorphic grades, with pressure increasing downward, as it does within Earth.

### Low grade metamorphic rock
There are relatively low pressures and temperatures near Earth's surface, approximately 10 km (6 miles) down. At this depth, the minerals begin to change just enough from the parent rock for the rock to become a low grade metamorphic rock.

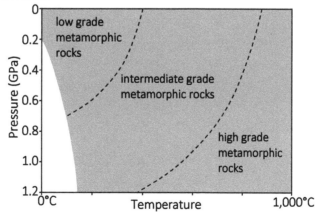

### High grade metamorphic rock
Deep in Earth's crust, high pressures and temperatures create high grade metamorphic rocks. The minerals are significantly changed from the parent rock, so the metamorphic rock is changed significantly from

## Check
Before you continue, you should be able to answer each check without looking at the page.

☐ Summarize how parent rocks relate to metamorphic rocks.
☐ Explain how pressure and temperature relate to metamorphic grade.

# 9.2 Causes of Metamorphism

**Key Concept:** Factors that cause rock to metamorphose are high pressure, high temperature, and sometimes hot water. To metamorphose rock, the conditions need to change enough so the bonds between atoms that form minerals in the parent rock are no longer stable, so they change without melting. High pressure on rock causes the atoms in the original minerals to recrystallize into new minerals **1**. High temperatures increase the rate that atoms rearrange, creating minerals that are stable at high temperatures **2**. Hot water also increases the rate that atoms recrystallize, but it can also change the composition of minerals by adding or removing atoms **3**. Although discussed separately, these three factors work together to cause bedrock to metamorphose.

## **1** Pressure

As the parent rock experiences increasing pressure, some minerals become unstable. The bonds between atoms in the minerals break and recrystallize into new minerals during metamorphism to adjust to the new, more compact conditions. There are two types of pressure that cause metamorphism: uniform and directional. Uniform pressure results as pressure increases with depth below Earth's surface, and directional pressure may be added due to compression at convergent plate boundaries.

### Uniform pressure

Uniform pressure is pressure on a rock that pushes the same in all directions. Uniform pressure is caused by the weight of overlying bedrock that compresses bedrock beneath it evenly. Therefore, it happens below the surface throughout Earth's crust. With enough pressure, the rock metamorphoses.

The arrows illustrate uniform pressure on the bedrock. They are all the same size because the pressure is the same in all directions.

Bedrock experiences uniform pressure as it is buried deep beneath the surface.

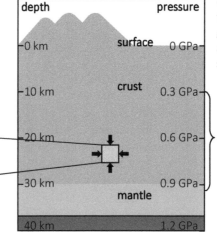

The pressure within Earth increases 0.1 gigapascals for every 3 kilometers (2 miles) of depth. To help understand the amount of pressure, 0.2 gigapascal is equivalent to about 1,000 elephants standing on your chest.

Bedrock typically metamorphoses during burial at pressures of 0.3-1 gigapascal, equaling depths of 10-30 km (6-19 mi).

### Directional pressure

Directional pressure is pressure on a rock that is greater in one direction than in others. All underground rock experiences uniform pressure. However, where rock has added pressure in one direction more than others, such as at a plate boundary, it is also under directional pressure.

The arrows illustrate directional pressure on the bedrock. The larger arrows indicate a larger pressure in the horizontal direction, adding to the uniform pressure.

Bedrock undergoes directional pressure in addition to uniform pressure where it is at a plate boundary.

Directional pressure occurs at convergent plate boundaries, where bedrock experiences additional compression horizontally as two plates come together. Even with the additional directional pressure, only the bedrock deep underground has enough pressure to metamorphose. Therefore, the required depths for metamorphism are the same as for uniform pressure.

# ❷ Temperature

As the parent rock experiences increasing temperatures, some bonds between atoms that form minerals become unstable. The minerals recrystallize through metamorphism into new minerals to adjust to the new conditions. There are two causes of increased temperature that cause metamorphism: deep burial within the crust and magma. Temperature increases with deep burial because temperature increases with depth below Earth's surface, but additional heat may also be added to the solid rock by nearby magma.

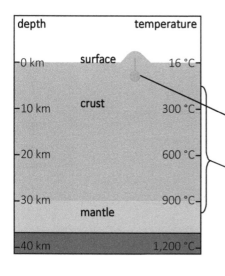

The temperature within Earth increases 30°C (54°F) for every kilometer (0.6 miles) depth for typical continental crust. To help understand the temperature, 450°C (840°F) is the temperature of bedrock at depths of approximately 15 km (9 miles). This temperature is much hotter than what is needed to bake cookies, which is 190°C (375°F).

Although most rock metamorphoses because of deep burial within the crust, magma can heat nearby shallow bedrock to temperatures high enough to metamorphose it.

Rock typically metamorphoses at temperatures between 150°C (300°F) and 1000°C (1800°F). Lower temperatures are not high enough for bonds between atoms to change to recrystallize the minerals. Higher temperatures would result in melting.

# ❸ Hot water

An increase in temperature and pressure is required to metamorphose rock. However, the presence of hot water in bedrock can help atoms break and reform bonds to recrystallize the minerals and facilitate metamorphism. Hot water can also flow through bedrock dissolving away atoms in some places and depositing them elsewhere, changing the rock composition. Hot water may come from some minerals as they change into new minerals during metamorphism, releasing water. The composition of the metamorphic rock in the photo was changed when atoms carried by hot water along cracks formed the white quartz minerals.

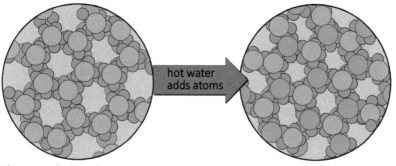

The original mineral is exposed to high pressures and temperatures, but it does not metamorphose under dry conditions because water helps atoms break and reform bonds.

Hot water present helps the mineral recrystallize to adjust to the extreme conditions. It also adds new atoms into its changed mineral structure, giving it a slightly different composition.

# Check

☐ Explain the three causes of metamorphism.
☐ Describe how each cause of metamorphism changes the atoms and minerals in rock.
☐ Identify two causes of increased pressure and two causes of increased temperature on bedrock.

# 9.3 Metamorphic Rock Characteristics

**Key Concept:** Metamorphic texture and composition give clues about how rock formed during metamorphism.

Metamorphic texture is a description of the arrangement of minerals within the rock, such as their size, shape, and orientation. It can indicate whether the pressure during metamorphism was uniform pressure or directional pressure **1**. The overall composition of the rock and minerals present gives clues about the parent rock **2**. Taken together, the characteristics of texture and composition are important because geologists analyze them to learn about the metamorphic processes and determine the plate tectonic conditions in the past.

## **1** Metamorphic texture

Metamorphic texture is a description of the size, shape, and orientation of minerals in a metamorphic rock. It is described as either foliated or nonfoliated. The formation of either foliated or non-foliated textures depends on the shape of the minerals that recrystallize as well as whether the pressure applied during metamorphism was directional or uniform. Foliated textures form only when there are flat or long minerals under directional pressure.

|  | **Directional pressure** Directional pressure causes minerals to grow perpendicular to the direction of greatest pressure. | **Uniform pressure** Uniform pressure allows minerals to grow in all directions equally, without constraining them in a particular direction. |
|---|---|---|
| **Flat or long mineral shapes** Minerals with one or two sides longer than others, such as muscovite and biotite mica, will grow more easily in a direction perpendicular to the direction of greatest pressure.  | **Foliated metamorphic texture** Metamorphic rock with foliated texture has minerals that are aligned mostly parallel to each other. It is formed when directional pressure causes long or flat minerals to rotate or to grow more easily perpendicular to the direction of greatest pressure. 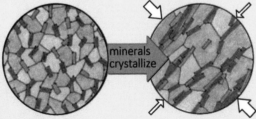 | **Nonfoliated metamorphic texture** Metamorphic rock with nonfoliated texture has minerals that are randomly oriented and not aligned. It can form in rock with flat or long minerals under uniform pressure because the minerals can grow in all directions equally. 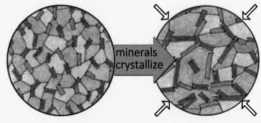 |
| **Minerals with all sides similar in shape** These minerals, such as quartz and calcite, do not have one side that is longer than others and cannot be aligned in a particular orientation, just as cubes or marbles cannot be aligned parallel to each other.   | **Nonfoliated metamorphic texture** Metamorphic rock with nonfoliated texture forms in rock under directional pressure if it is made up of minerals that are similar in shape from all sides, because these minerals cannot be aligned. 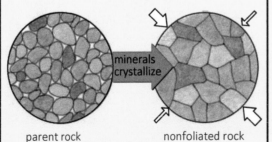 | **Nonfoliated metamorphic texture** Metamorphic rock with nonfoliated texture forms if the rock is made up of minerals that are similar in shape from all sides and under uniform pressure. 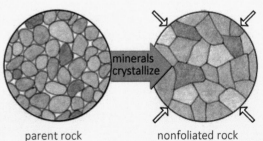 |

# ❷ Metamorphic rock composition

The atomic composition of a metamorphic rock is largely the same as its parent rock, but the arrangement of the atoms in minerals may be different because the minerals recrystallize. Recrystallizing means that the bonds between atoms break and reconnect without the minerals melting. When the original minerals in the parent rock formed, the particular configuration of atoms was stable because the atoms bonded into arrangements that were ideal for those specific conditions. If the conditions change, such as an increase in pressure and temperature, that arrangement may no longer be ideal, and the mineral becomes unstable. The atoms remain the same, so geologists can examine the minerals present in a metamorphic rock and make inferences about the parent rock, as shown in the examples.

### Example: same atoms, different minerals form
Parent rocks composed primarily of silicate minerals will result in metamorphic rocks also composed of silicate minerals because the composition remains high in silicon and oxygen atoms. However, the specific silicate minerals often change because the original arrangement of silicon and oxygen atoms may not be stable under metamorphic conditions. These silicate minerals recrystallize to form different silicate minerals with atoms in an arrangement that is stable under the new conditions.

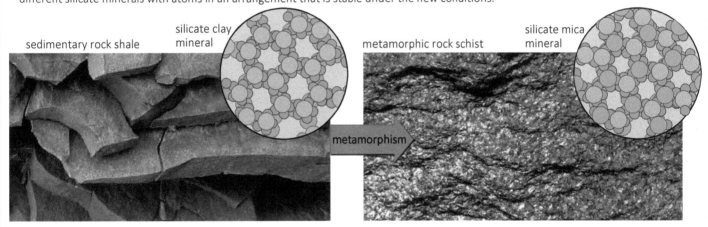

sedimentary rock shale · silicate clay mineral · metamorphism · metamorphic rock schist · silicate mica mineral

### Example: same atoms, same minerals form
Parent rocks composed of primarily carbonate minerals will result in metamorphic rocks also composed of carbonate minerals because the composition will remain high in carbon and oxygen atoms. Some carbonate minerals, like calcite, are stable under a range of metamorphic conditions because the arrangement of the carbon and oxygen atoms is ideal through the variety of conditions. Recrystallizing often causes these minerals to grow into larger carbonate minerals.

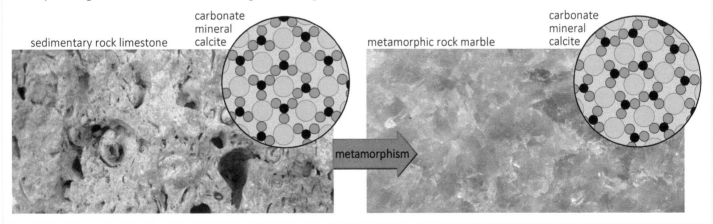

sedimentary rock limestone · carbonate mineral calcite · metamorphism · metamorphic rock marble · carbonate mineral calcite

# Check
☐ Describe the two key characteristics of metamorphic rocks and define each term.
☐ Explain what the metamorphic texture and the rock composition tell us about the history of a metamorphic rock in terms of type of pressure and type of parent rock.

# 9.4 DATA AND DIAGRAMS: Minerals and Metamorphic Grade

**Key Concept:** Diagrams can show how individual characteristics relating to a single variable can change as that variable is altered. This diagram shows how certain minerals, called index minerals, are stable at a small range of metamorphic grades, while other minerals are stable at a large range of metamorphic grades. Index minerals can help geologists pinpoint the temperature under which a parent rock metamorphosed **1**. To create a diagram like this, geologists in labs have observed the minerals present in different rocks that they have heated and compressed at different temperatures and pressures. Tips on how to read this diagram are below **2**. Use the questions to practice interpreting this type of diagram **3**.

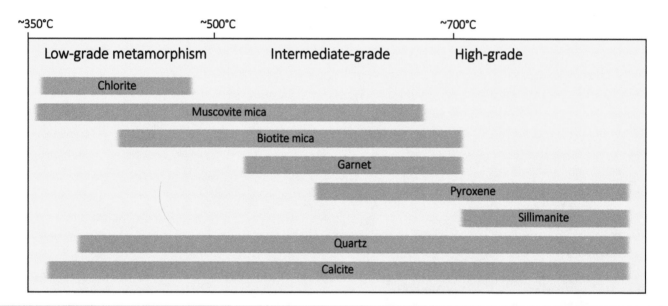

## **1** How to read the diagram

Determine what the variable is. In this case, the horizontal axis indicates increasing metamorphic grade and temperature, while the vertical component does not have a meaning. The characteristic affected by the variable is shown by the horizontal gray bars, which represent the range of grades and temperatures in which a mineral is found to be stable.

## **2** An example of what you might interpret

Garnet is stable at intermediate to high metamorphic grades and approximately 500° to 700°C (900° to 1300°F).

## **3** Questions

**1. What does the diagram show?**
a. The time it takes minerals to form in different metamorphic rocks.
b. The metamorphic rocks that are stable at different temperatures.
c. The temperatures at which different minerals melt into magma.
d. The minerals that are stable at different metamorphic grades and temperatures.

**2. If you find a rock with both muscovite mica and garnet, what metamorphic grade is that rock?**
a. Low grade
b. Intermediate grade
c. High grade
d. It is impossible to tell

**3. What does the length of the horizontal mineral lines mean?**
a. The range of metamorphic grades at which they are stable.
b. The size of the minerals that form at different metamorphic grades.
c. The locations of minerals within rock at different metamorphic grades.

**4. Which of the following minerals is least useful for determining the temperature at which a rock metamorphosed?**
a. Chlorite
b. Garnet
c. Quartz

**5. Which of the following minerals is an index mineral, helping to identify the metamorphic grade of a rock in which it occurs?**
a. Chlorite
b. Calcite
c. Quartz

# 9.5 Identifying Metamorphic Rocks

**Key Concept:** Metamorphic texture and types of minerals are used to identify metamorphic rock. The texture of a metamorphic rock is the first clue to its identity, and it is divided into the two categories of foliated and nonfoliated. Foliated metamorphic rocks have aligned minerals, and they are further subdivided based on the size, orientation, and type of minerals. The type of foliation is typically dependent on, and therefore indicates, the metamorphic grade **1**. Nonfoliated metamorphic rocks are classified based primarily on the type of minerals that make up the rock **2**. The characteristics of metamorphic rock give clues about the rock's formation, the parent rock, and therefore geologic history of the area.

## **1** Foliated metamorphic rocks

Metamorphic rocks with foliated textures have minerals that are aligned, but the specific type of foliation is defined by the size, orientation, and types of minerals. The type of foliation is used to name foliated metamorphic rocks. A low grade metamorphic rock retains many of the characteristics of the parent rock, whereas a high grade metamorphic rock is substantially different.

## **2** Nonfoliated metamorphic rocks

Nonfoliated texture is one in which the minerals are not aligned in a metamorphic rock. Nonfoliated metamorphic rocks are classified primarily by the types of minerals, since the texture of the rock varies little due to the lack of foliation. The mineral types and identifying characteristics generally do not change as the metamorphic grade increases.

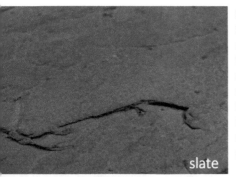
slate

Slate has slaty foliation. Slaty foliation forms when clay and mica minerals that are too small to be seen are aligned and result in a rock that breaks into flat layers. Slate forms from the parent rock shale at a low metamorphic grade.

schist

Schist has schistose foliation. Shistose foliation forms when visible mica minerals are aligned. Schist may also contain some larger minerals. It is typically metamorphosed from the parent rock shale at an intermediate grade.

gneiss

Gneiss has gneissic foliation. Light-colored bands of quartz and feldspar alternate with dark bands of iron-rich silicate minerals, such as biotite, pyroxene, and amphibole. It forms from the parent rocks granite or shale at a high metamorphic grade.

Quartzite is made up of the mineral quartz. It is nonfoliated because the shape of quartz minerals is equal in all directions. Quartzite is typically metamorphosed from the parent rock quartz sandstone.

quartzite

Marble is made up of the mineral calcite. It is nonfoliated because the shape of calcite minerals is similar in all directions. Mica minerals may form bands in marble. Marble is typically metamorphosed from limestone, and mica minerals indicate parent clay minerals in the form of mud.

marble

Hornfels is made up of randomly-oriented silicate minerals. The minerals are usually small, may be flat or long, and often include mica, quartz, and feldspar. Hornfels is nonfoliated because it forms under uniform pressure. It is typically metamorphosed from the parent rocks shale or basalt.

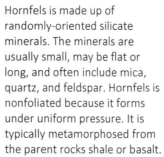
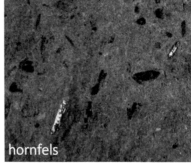
hornfels

## Check

☐ Name six metamorphic rocks and describe their texture and composition.
☐ Explain why rock texture is important in identifying foliated metamorphic rocks.

Ch 9: 2nd section
# 9.6 – 9.7 Metamorphism

In this section you will learn how metamorphism is related to plate tectonics and how geologists interpret metamorphic conditions from the past.

## Frequently Used Terms

The terms listed here are used repeatedly throughout this section, so by learning them before you read this section, you can focus your mental energy on the concepts presented.

**contact metamorphism** Metamorphism that occurs when the temperature of the parent rock increases due to contact with nearby magma.

**high pressure metamorphism** Metamorphism that occurs at particularly high pressure relative to the temperature; it occurs in the subducting plate at a convergent plate boundary with subduction.

**regional metamorphism** Metamorphism that occurs across a broad region due to an increase in temperature and pressure, which happens at convergent plate boundaries.

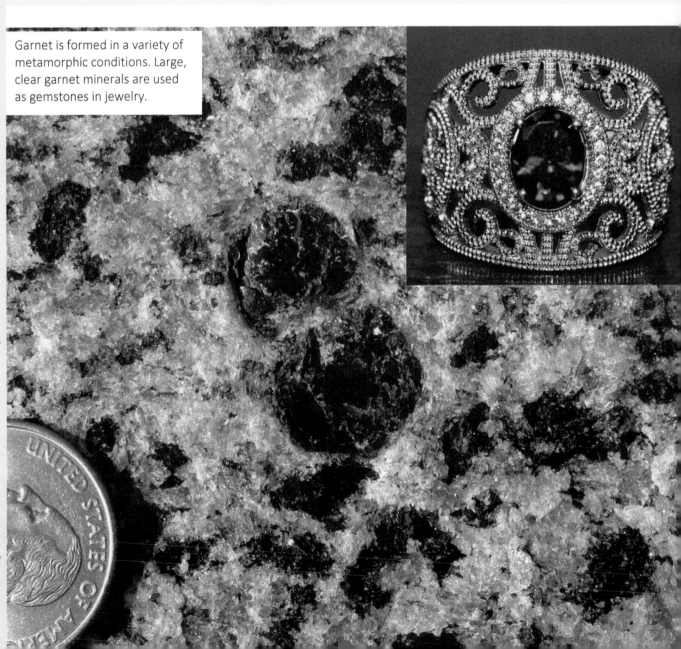

Garnet is formed in a variety of metamorphic conditions. Large, clear garnet minerals are used as gemstones in jewelry.

# 9.6 Types of Metamorphism

**Key Concept:** The unique combinations of metamorphic pressures and temperatures result in different types of metamorphism. There are three major types of metamorphism: contact metamorphism, regional metamorphism, and high pressure metamorphism **1**. Each type is characterized by a unique combination of pressures and temperatures. To determine the particular combination of temperatures and pressures under which a rock metamorphosed, geologists use a variety of techniques like making maps, experimenting with rocks, and modeling with computers **2**. These techniques allow geologists to identify the conditions required for metamorphism, helping them to reconstruct the geologic history of an area.

## **1** Metamorphic type, pressure, and temperature

Different combinations of pressure and temperature under which rock metamorphoses are related to the type of metamorphism. These different conditions are found in distinct locations of a pressure-temperature graph, as indicated by the dashed lines showing metamorphic types.

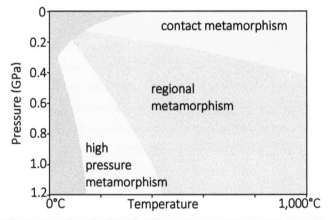

### Contact metamorphism
Rock recrystallizes in high temperature but comparatively low pressure metamorphic conditions. This relationship occurs where magma that was created elsewhere intrudes into the parent rock. It increases the parent rock's temperature and bakes it under uniform pressure. It is called contact metamorphism because the parent rock comes in contact with magma but does not melt. Rock is generally low or intermediate grade and is nonfoliated.

### Regional metamorphism
Rock recrystallizes where temperature and pressure both increase equally to cause metamorphism. This relationship occurs across a broad region due to deep burial of the parent rock, such as where mountains form due to directional pressure. The forming mountains add thickness to the crust, increasing temperature and adding weight that increases the pressure on the bedrock in the entire region beneath the mountains. Rock is generally low, intermediate, or high metamorphic grades and is foliated.

### High pressure metamorphism
Rock recrystallizes in high pressure but comparatively low temperature metamorphic conditions. This relationship occurs where rock is quickly moved to extreme depths during subduction, so the pressure is very high, but the rock takes time to heat up. Rock is generally low or intermediate grade and is foliated.

## **2** Techniques for determining types of metamorphism

It is impossible to directly study the process of metamorphism because metamorphic rocks form deep within Earth. Therefore, geologists use a variety of techniques to learn more about the conditions under which metamorphic rocks form and make the connections with plate tectonics discussed next in 9.7.

### Laboratory experiments
To identify the temperatures and pressures at which certain minerals form, geologists run lab experiments. For example, they may apply high temperatures and pressures to rocks and identify the recrystallized minerals that form. The resulting data allow geologists to create graphs like the one in 9.4, which lists minerals and the conditions at which they form.

### Computer modeling
In some cases, replicating the pressures and temperatures at which rocks form is not practical or possible in a lab. Geologists create computer models to determine what minerals are stable together and under what conditions. They can then compare the rocks and minerals they find in nature to the modeled conditions to learn how those rocks formed.

### Maps
Geologists create geologic maps of the locations and types of metamorphic rocks. These maps can be used to examine how the metamorphic rock types relate to each other and to other rock. For example, maps can show how regionally metamorphosed rocks cover a large region, with the highest metamorphic grade rocks surrounded by lower metamorphic grade rocks.

## Check

☐ Compare and contrast the pressure and temperature required for regional, contact, and high-pressure metamorphism.
☐ Summarize three ways geologists learn the conditions under which metamorphic rocks formed.

# 9.7 Metamorphism and Plate Tectonics

**Key Concept:**  **Most metamorphic rock forms at convergent plate boundaries.** All three major types of metamorphism (contact, regional, and high pressure) occur near convergent boundaries with subduction because the related environments include mountains, volcanoes, and subducting plates **1**. In contrast, only regional metamorphism occurs at continent-continent convergent plate boundaries because of the large region of mountains **2**. While some contact metamorphism may occur at divergent plate boundaries **3**, transform plate boundaries do not have the pressure and temperature conditions to metamorphose large areas of rock. Rarer types of metamorphism can occur under unusual circumstances, such as when a meteor strikes the Earth.

## **1** Convergent Plate Boundaries with Subduction

Convergent plate boundaries cause different types of metamorphism to occur in different locations. Geologists study clues about the types of metamorphism produced in these areas by examining the metamorphic characteristics of grade, texture, and mineral composition. These rocks form deep within Earth's crust. Therefore they are primarily studied after erosion has removed the overlying bedrock, and they are exposed at Earth's surface.

### Contact metamorphism
Contact metamorphism, which takes place next to magma, occurs at convergent plate boundaries with subduction because magma forms due to melting caused by the subducting plate. The magma moves upwards into the overlying bedrock, coming in contact with it and metamorphosing it. There is primarily uniform pressure on the bedrock because the magma does not add pressure in a particular direction.

• Metamorphic characteristics: low to intermediate grade, nonfoliated
• Common rocks produced: hornfels

### Regional metamorphism
Regional metamorphism occurs at convergent plate boundaries with subduction because the plates move towards each other, causing a large amount of pressure over a broad area. The mountains add thickness to the crust, adding weight that increases the uniform pressure throughout the entire region beneath the mountains. The thickened crust also increases the temperature, since temperature increases with depth in Earth's crust. Directional pressure is added due to the compression from the converging plates.

• Metamorphic characteristics: low to intermediate grade, foliated (if flat minerals are present)
• Common rocks produced: slate, schist, gneiss, marble, quartzite

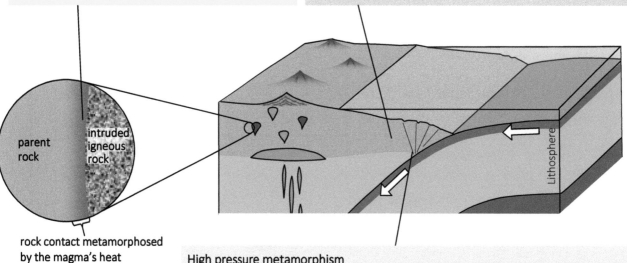

parent rock

intruded igneous rock

rock contact metamorphosed by the magma's heat

Lithosphere

### High pressure metamorphism
High pressure metamorphism occurs only at convergent plate boundaries with subduction because it is the only location where rock is pushed beneath the crust to extreme depths and therefore extreme pressures. Although regional and contact metamorphism at this type of plate boundary can affect any parent rock, high pressure metamorphism primarily metamorphoses the sediments and sedimentary rocks that were deposited on and then subducted with the oceanic lithosphere.

• Metamorphic characteristics: intermediate grade, foliated
• Common rocks produced: schist

## ❷ Continent-continent convergent plate boundaries

At convergent plate boundaries with two continental lithospheres, the primary cause of metamorphism is the high pressure and temperature caused by the massive mountain range. Eroded ancient mountains expose the deeply-formed metamorphic rocks, allowing geologists to collect samples and make maps to learn more about the processes that happen deep in these mountains.

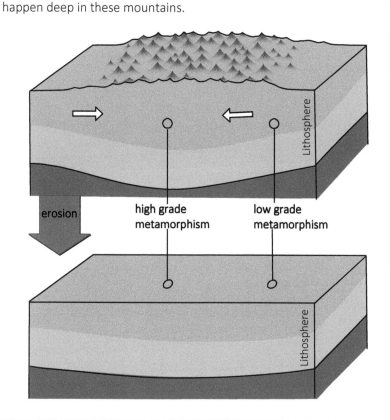

### Regional metamorphism

Regional metamorphism occurs at continent-continent convergent plate boundaries because of the extensive high pressures and temperatures created by the converging plates. The converging plates create a large amount of directional pressure, and the crust thickened by the formation of mountains creates high pressures and temperatures on the rock buried beneath the tall mountains. These factors tend to cause higher grades of metamorphism than convergent plate boundaries with subduction because, in this situation, there is no subduction to help relieve the pressure.

• Metamorphic characteristics: low to high grade, foliated (if flat minerals are present)
• Common rocks produced: slate, schist, gneiss, marble, quartzite

### After erosion

If geologists identify a large region with high grade metamorphic rocks surrounded by low grade metamorphic rocks, this indicates that the area had undergone regional metamorphism at a convergent plate boundary.

## ❸ Divergent plate boundaries

At divergent plate boundaries there is very little metamorphism because the pressure is low. The plates move apart, and the oceanic crust is relatively thin, resulting in the deepest crustal rocks being relatively shallow. However, magma does heat up the surrounding basalt crust. These areas are difficult to study, as they are generally in the bottom of the ocean. In a few situations, part of the ocean crust is preserved on land, so geologists can study the rocks (see 15.2).

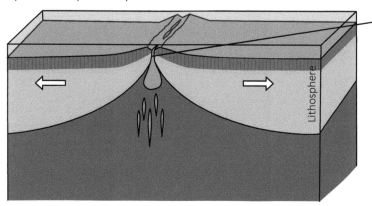

### Contact metamorphism

Contact metamorphism occurs as the two plates move apart and create magma. The magma then moves up through the oceanic lithosphere, coming in contact with the rocks that make up the plates. In this situation, the rocks are also changed by circulating ocean water that is heated by the magma.

• Metamorphic characteristics: very low grade, nonfoliated
• Common rocks produced: basalt (this is an igneous rock, but it forms at high temperatures from molten rock, so it is stable under those hot conditions and does not metamorphose from the nearby magma)

## Check

☐ Summarize what types of metamorphism occur in different plate tectonic environments.
☐ Describe the rocks that would be formed at different tectonic environments.

Ch 9: 3<sup>rd</sup> Section

# 9.8 – 9.13 Deformation of Rock

In this section you will learn what features form as bedrock deforms because of added stress and why those features form. You will also study how geologists learn about conditions that caused deformation of bedrock in the past, especially at plate boundaries.

## Frequently Used Terms

The terms listed here are used repeatedly throughout this section, so by learning them before you read this section, you can focus your mental energy on the concepts presented.

**bedrock structure** The feature in the bedrock, such as a fold or fault, that results from deformation.

**brittle deformation** Deformation that breaks an object under stress, such as shattering a glass.

**compression stress** Stress caused by bedrock being pushed together.

**deformation** A change in shape of rock due to stress.

**dip** The direction and amount that rock layers or a fault are tilted downward.

**ductile deformation** Deformation that changes the shape of an object under stress but does not break it, such as squeezing playdoh.

**fault** A broken surface within rock, like a crack, where the two sides have moved relative to one another.

**fold** A bend or curve in rock that was initially flat.

**shear stress** Stress caused by bedrock sliding sideways or being skewed.

**stress** Pressure exerted on rock that may cause metamorphism on the atomic scale or deformation on the large scale.

**tension stress** Stress caused by bedrock being pulled apart or stretched.

Rock breaks along faults in the same way that crayons may break. In other situations rock bends for similar reasons that a crayon may bend.

# 9.8 Metamorphism Compared to Deformation

**Key Concept:** Metamorphism changes the minerals in bedrock while deformation changes the overall shape of the rock.

As studied in the previous sections, metamorphism occurs at relatively high pressures and temperatures, and it changes the rock type because it causes minerals throughout the rock to change, creating new metamorphic rock **1**. In contrast, deformation of bedrock occurs at slightly lower temperatures. It changes the shape of the bedrock through stress affecting its orientation but not the type of minerals composing it. There are two main styles of deformation: folding and faulting. When bedrock forms folds, it does so by bending **2**. When bedrock forms a fault, it is breaking **3**. Studying the rock type and deformation style gives geologists clues about the types and locations of plate boundaries in the past.

|  | **1 Metamorphism** | **2 Deformation: Folds** | **3 Deformation: Faults** |
|---|---|---|---|
|  | High pressure and temperature changes the mineral structures of rock due to stress. | Moderate pressure and temperature change the shape of rock by folding due to stress, but the types of minerals stay the same. | Moderate pressure and temperature change the shape of rock by folding due to stress, but the types of minerals stay the same. |
| **Relative stress required** | High stress from uniform or directional pressure | Moderate stress from directional pressure | Moderate stress from directional pressure |
| **Relative temperature required** | High | Moderate | Low |
| **Rock type** | Changes any rock (the parent rock) into a metamorphic rock | Typically affects sedimentary rocks, but can affect any rock without changing the type | Can affect any rock without changing the type |
| **Requires erosion to see** | Yes, because it happens very deep in the crust | Yes, because it happens deep in the crust | Sometimes, because it happens from Earth's surface down to moderate depths |
| **Scale affected by stress** | Stress affects minerals on the atomic and microscopic scale | Stress affects the orientation of rock on the microscopic to visible scale | Stress affects the relative location of rock on the visible scale |
| **Occurs during metamorphism** | -- | Yes, metamorphosing rocks may also form folds | No, metamorphosing rocks are generally too hot and deep to also form faults |
| **Used to determine the geologic history of an area** | Yes, metamorphic rocks indicate the area was at one time deep beneath the surface at temperatures and pressures that recrystallized minerals without melting. | Yes, folds indicate the area was at one time deep beneath the surface with directional pressures and temperatures high enough to bend the rock. | Yes, faults indicate the area was at one time under directional pressures high enough to cause the rock to break in reaction. |

## Check

☐ Summarize differences and similarities between metamorphism and deformation.
☐ Summarize differences and similarities between folds and faults.

# 9.9 Factors Influencing Rock Deformation

**Key Concept:** There are two primary factors that influence deformation: the direction of the stress and whether rock undergoes brittle or ductile deformation. Directional stress on a rock causes a rock to deform. Geologists describe this stress as compression (squeezing), tension (stretching), or shear (sliding) **1**. When bedrock is under stress, its environment, internal strength, and speed of deformation dictate whether it undergoes brittle deformation (it breaks) or ductile deformation (it bends) **2**.

## **1** Three types of directional stress

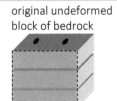

original undeformed
block of bedrock

Directional stress occurs where the stress on rock is stronger in one direction than another due to directional pressure. The direction of stress results from areas of rock moving toward each other, away from each other, or side-by-side in opposite directions. The result is bedrock deforming into different structures (see 9.10 and 9.11).

**Compression stress**
Compression stress pushes or squeezes rock together. The dots show how locations move closer together, shortening and thickening the block. It often occurs at convergent plate boundaries.

**Tension stress**
Tension stress stretches or pulls rock apart. The dots show how locations move further apart, lengthening and thinning the block. It often occurs at divergent plate boundaries.

**Shear stress**
Shear stress slides two sides of rock in opposite directions parallel to each other. The dots show how locations move side-by-side, changing the shape of the block. It often occurs at transform plate boundaries.

## **2** Ways bedrock can deform due to stress

Whether bedrock undergoes brittle or ductile deformation by breaking or bending as a result of directional stress depends on factors such as the depth of the rock, the rock type, and the speed of deformation.

| Factors | Brittle Deformation | Ductile Deformation |
|---|---|---|
| Several factors affect whether rock deforms in a brittle or ductile fashion. | Bedrock that is brittle breaks, forming a structure called a fault. A fault is the plane along which bedrock on either side moved due to stress. | Bedrock that is ductile bends, forming structures called folds. Folds are curved bedrock that bent due to compression stresses. |
| Depth | Rock in the top few kilometers of Earth's crust is cooler, which makes it harder. It tends to break as faults, just as cold butter is harder and more likely to break than warm butter. | Rock deeper in the crust is warmer, which makes it softer. It tends to fold without melting, just as warmer ice cream is softer and easier to scoop than very cold ice cream. |
| Rock type | Rock that is harder, such as igneous and metamorphic rock, tends to break as faults, just as uncooked pasta breaks. | Rock that is softer, such as many sedimentary rocks, tends to bend into folds, just as cooked pasta bends. |
| Speed of deformation | Rock that deforms quickly tends to break as faults, just as a piece of taffy breaks if it is pulled suddenly. This reaction is due to broken bonds between atoms that do not have time to reform before others break. | Rock that deforms slowly tends to bend into folds, just as a piece of taffy stretches if it is pulled slowly. This reaction is due to broken bonds between atoms that have time to reform before others break. |

## Check

☐ Describe the three different stress directions on rock.
☐ Discuss the three main factors that determine if a rock will break (brittle deformation) forming faults or bend (ductile deformation) forming folds.

# 9.10 Faults

**Key Concept:** The sides of a fault move in opposite directions depending on the type of stress on the bedrock. Faults form when bedrock breaks and moves as a result of brittle deformation. The sudden release of energy may be felt as an earthquake. Geologists use the angle of the fault and the direction of motion on either side to describe faults **1**. Different types of directional stress cause different types of faults. Compression stress causes reverse faults that shorten the crust **2**. Tension stress results in normal faults that lengthen the crust **3**. Shear stress results in strike-slip faults with the bedrock on either side sliding horizontally past each other **4**.

## 1 Describing faults

A fault is a break in bedrock along which the two sides have moved relative to one another. Faults form underground but sometimes reach the surface. Describing faults is important to geologists because it gives them information about the direction of stress at the time the fault formed. To discover this information, geologists study the fault's orientation and the motion of the two sides relative to that orientation.

**Fault orientation**
The orientation of the fault is both the map direction of the fault and the angle at which it dips, or tilts, down beneath the surface. Some faults dip so steeply that they are vertical.

**Footwall vs hanging wall**
The bedrock that is above, hanging over the fault, is called the hanging wall (HW). The bedrock beneath the fault is called the footwall (FW).

**Direction of motion**
The direction of motion along a fault can be horizontal, vertical, or both. If the bedrock breaks, but the two sides do not move, it is not a fault.

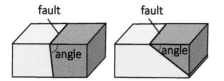

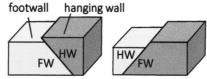

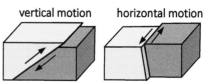

## 2 Reverse fault

A reverse fault occurs where the hanging wall moves up relative to the footwall because compression stress pushes the hanging wall above the footwall. Reverse faults where the dip is nearly horizontal have the special name of thrust faults. Reverse faults shorten the crust, as shown by the ruler in the diagram.

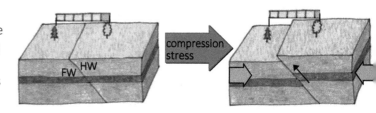

## 3 Normal fault

A normal fault occurs where the hanging wall moves down relative to the footwall. This motion happens because tension stress pulls the rock apart, and gravity causes the hanging wall to slide down along the footwall. Normal faults lengthen the crust. The name "normal" is a little deceptive, since it normally forms only where there is tension but not compression.

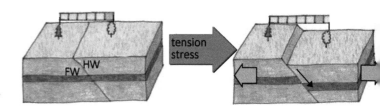

## 4 Strike-slip fault

In a strike-slip fault, shear stress causes the two sides of the fault to move, or slip, horizontally past each other. If you are on one side of the fault facing it, and the other side moves to your left, the fault is called a left-lateral strike-slip fault (as shown). If it moves to your right, it is called a right lateral strike-slip fault.

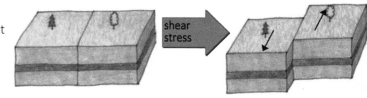

## Check

☐ Draw a fault and label the hanging wall and footwall.
☐ Draw a fault for each of the three types of stress (compression, tension, and shear), and indicate the direction each wall moves.

# 9.11 Folds

**Key Concept:** **Folds are structures that result when bedrock bends under compression stresses during ductile deformation.** Folds of all sizes form where compression stress deforms bedrock in a ductile way deep in Earth's crust. The initially flat bedrock layers bend, creating a series of folds, with some pointing up and others down **1**. They are only visible once the overlying bedrock has eroded away, and the shape of the landscape results from erosion of the folds. **2**.

## **1** Formation of folds

Folds form deep in Earth due to compression stress. For the folds to be visible at Earth's surface, erosion must remove the overlying rock to reveal the folds underneath.

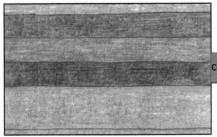
compression
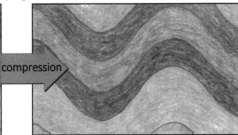
erosion
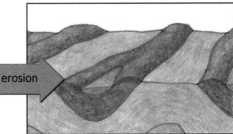

Flat sedimentary bedrock layers deep beneath Earth's surface are ductile because they are relatively hot.

The ductile sedimentary layers react to compressional stress by shortening to form a series of up and down folds.

Erosion exposes the folded sedimentary bedrock at the surface, allowing geologists to study it.

## **2** Folds in a landscape

The shape of the surface, or landscape, is a result of the erosion of bedrock, not the folding process deep in Earth. As weathering and erosion expose folded bedrock layers at the surface, the resistant layers erode more slowly than other layers, forming hills as the less resistant layers around them erode away.

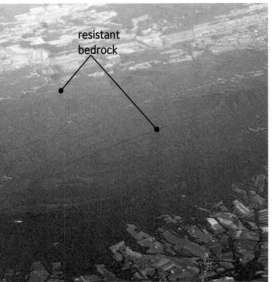

resistant bedrock

layers dip to right    layers dip to left    layers dip to right

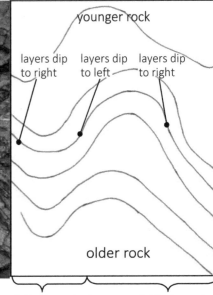

younger rock

layers dip to right    layers dip to left    layers dip to right

older rock

Resistant folded rock layers forms hills while the easily eroded rock layers forms the lower areas in Cumberland Valley, Pennsylvania.

A fold where the layers dip, or tilt, down towards the center is called a syncline.

A fold where the center of the fold points upward is called an anticline.

## Check

☐ Draw rock layers that have undergone folding and label synclines and anticlines.
☐ Describe how the erosion of folds may affect the shape of the surface.

# 9.12 DATA AND DIAGRAMS: Geologic Maps

**Key Concept:** Geologic maps use color and symbols to show the type and orientation of the bedrock, allowing geologists to interpret structures underground. Geologic maps are created by geologists to interpret the bedrock structures beneath the surface, which helps to determine the geologic history of an area **1**. To create a map like this, geologists find outcrops where bedrock can be observed at the surface, determine the type of rock, and measure the orientation of bedrock layers. They then use those relationships and knowledge of how different rocks form to make interpretations of their extent and orientation. Tips on how to read geologic maps are below **2**. Use the questions to practice interpreting geologic maps **3**.

### Making observations of landscapes to make geologic maps and cross-section interpretations

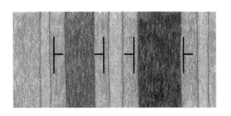

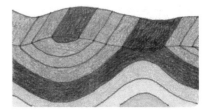

This landscape shows an area with sedimentary rock layers. Geologists make observations of the rock types and the orientation of the layers to create a geologic map.

The colors on this geologic map indicate each type of bedrock. The symbols indicate the orientation of sedimentary bedrock layers at the surface. The short line of the "T" shaped strike-and-dip symbol points in the downhill dip direction.

Based on the geologic map, geologists can make interpretations about the rock structures beneath the surface, such as anticline and syncline folds. Knowing there are folds in the area can help geologists figure out its history.

## **1** How to read the diagram

To understand each step, read the text beneath the diagram. As you do this, figure out how the text relates to the diagram and what information it is designed to communicate. In this case, observations of the landscape are used to create a geologic map, which is then used to create a cross-section interpretation.

## **2** An example of what you might interpret

For example, the symbols specify that the layers are tilted downward, or dip, to the west in some locations and to the east in other locations, indicating a series of folds.

## **3** Questions

**1. What do the diagrams show?**
a. The type of bedrock that can be seen at the surface.
b. The type of bedrock in the area, whether it is at the surface or is covered up.
c. The type of bedrock and its orientation that can be seen at the surface.
d. The type of bedrock and its orientation, whether it is at the surface or is covered up.

**2. If you look at the first diagram, you can see that if it rained on the surface at the pine tree on the left, the water would flow to the right. Use the geologic map or cross section to determine what direction the rocks in this location are dipping (tilted downward)?**
a. right       b. left       c. into the page       d. out of the page

**3. If you were walking along the surface, what color are the rocks at the center of the syncline and anticline?**
a. syncline: brown       anticline: yellow
b. syncline: red       anticline: brown
c. syncline: pink       anticline: red
d. syncline: blue       anticline: pink

**4. Which of these colored rocks is the oldest?**
a. red    b. purple    c. brown

**5. When looking at a geologic map, it is possible to determine the difference between a syncline and anticline by using the strike-and-dip symbols. It is also possible to determine the difference by using the ages of the rocks. If you were walking along the surface, where are the oldest rocks visible at the surface?**
a. Between the syncline and anticline
b. At the center of the syncline.
c. At the center of the anticline.

**6. Use the strike-and-dip symbols on the map below to determine what diagram best shows what is happening beneath the surface in this mapped area.**

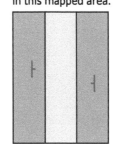
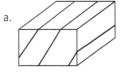
a.
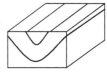
b.

c.

d.

# 9.13 Folds, Faults and Plate Tectonics

**Key Concept:** **Plate boundaries often determine the stress direction, which influences what types of structures form during deformation of bedrock.** At convergent plate boundaries, compression is the dominant type of directional stress, resulting in folds and reverse faults forming **1**. These folds often form in areas similar to those where metamorphism occurs. At divergent plate boundaries, tension stress results in normal faults **2**. At transform plate boundaries, shear stress results in strike-slip faults **3**. These relationships between bedrock deformation and type of plate boundary allow geologists to use observations of ancient folds and faults to determine the plate tectonic history of an area. This information helps geologists understand Earth's past and current processes and identify locations where there might be useful resources.

## **1** Convergent plate boundary

At all types of convergent plate boundaries, two plates come together so compression shortens the area. Reverse faults tend to form where rock undergoes brittle deformation, and folds tend to form deep underground where rock undergoes ductile deformation. This is the only plate boundary that forms wide-spread folds because folds form deep underground in locations with compression. Recall that these areas frequently also experience regional metamorphism, which occurs deeper in the crust, so metamorphism may occur in the same locations as folding (see 9.6).

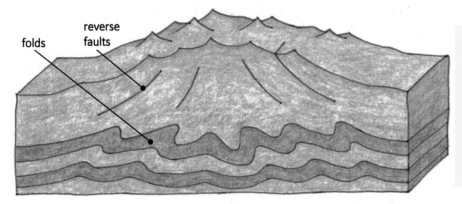

### Interpreting the past
Folds form at great depths, so by the time they are exposed at the surface, they indicate the stresses that formed in the distant past, millions of years ago. Faults, however, form at or near the surface and take less time to be exposed at the surface, so they may indicate stresses in the past or that are still occurring today.

Geologists in the Rocky Mountains in Canada observed this outcrop with folds and interpreted that this area was under compression in the past, and that erosion exposed the folds at the surface.

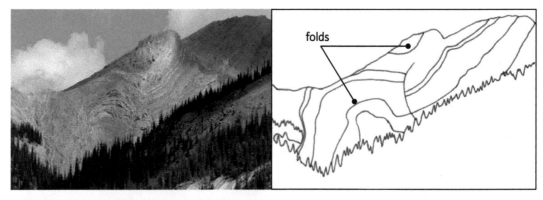

Geologists in Arches National Park observed this outcrop with a reverse fault and interpreted this observation to mean that this area was under compression in the past.

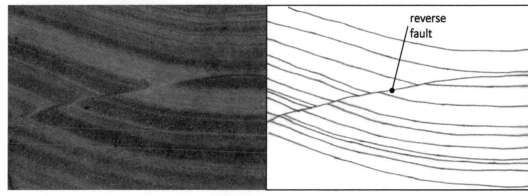

## 2 Divergent plate boundary

At a divergent plate boundary, two plates move apart, so tension stretches the area, resulting in the formation of normal faults near the surface. Compression is required for folding and regional metamorphism, so these areas do not experience much of either.

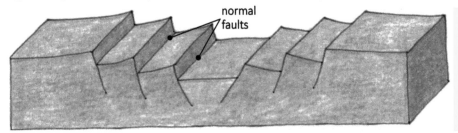

### Interpreting the past

Faults that break the surface indicate current stresses. Faults that formed in the distant past, millions of years ago, may be visible at the surface due to erosion and often indicate past plate movement, such as continents breaking apart.

Geologists observed this normal fault in Moab, Utah and determined that the area was under tension.

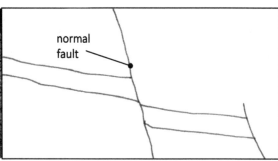

## 3 Transform plate boundary

At a transform plate boundary, two plates move past each other, so shear stresses cause strike-slip faults form. The tectonic plate motion causes movement on these faults to be consistently in the same direction over time. This means that a single fault will either always be a right lateral fault or a left lateral fault, as described in 9.10. Compression is required for folding and regional metamorphism, so these areas do not experience much of either.

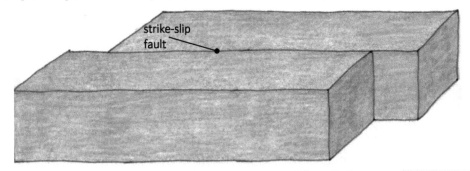

### Interpreting the past

Faults that break the surface indicate current stresses. However, faults that formed in the distant past, millions of years ago, may be visible at the surface due to erosion.

Geologists observed this active strike-slip fault in California and determined that the area is under shear stress. The stream once flowed straight, but the path has been moved by the fault.

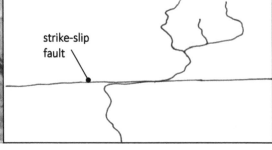

## Check

☐ Match the expected deformation of rock with each of the three types of plate boundaries.
☐ Explain how observations of folds and faults can be used to interpret the past.

## Chapter 9

# End of Chapter Questions: Student Debates

For each of the following questions, determine which student you agree with and explain why.

1. **Three students are discussing why minerals in metamorphic rocks are different sizes.**

   **Student 1:** The size of minerals often indicates how much a rock metamorphosed, with minerals growing larger in rock with a higher metamorphic grade.

   **Student 2:** The size of minerals often indicates how slowly the metamorphic rock cooled, with minerals growing larger when the rock cools slowly.

   **Student 3:** The size of minerals often indicates how much pressure the rock is under, with minerals growing larger when there is less pressure to confine them.

2. **Two students are discussing the temperature required to form metamorphic rocks compared to the temperature required to form igneous rocks.**

   **Student 1:** Metamorphic rocks form under conditions of high pressures and temperatures. So, the temperature to form metamorphic rocks is generally higher than for igneous rock.

   **Student 2:** Metamorphic rocks form below melting temperature, since melting results in igneous rocks. So, the temperature to form metamorphic rocks is generally lower than for igneous rock.

3. **Two students are discussing minerals in a rock sample they found.**

   **Student 1:** If you identify a rock, such as schist, there are many minerals that can commonly be found in it. You can't narrow down the minerals you'd expect to see before identifying them.

   **Student 2:** Schist only forms under certain metamorphic conditions. Minerals also form under certain conditions, so there are some minerals that are more likely to be in schist and others that cannot exist in a schist, and you can narrow down the ones you can expect.

4. **Two students are discussing the motion on most faults in the world.**

   **Student 1:** There is no typical motion on faults. The direction the sides of the fault slips depends on the stress in the area.

   **Student 2:** Actually, normal faults move the way that faults normally move. For most faults the hanging wall slips down the footwall.

5. **Two students are discussing why geologists give names to different types of faults.**

   **Student 1:** Geologists label faults with different names in order to put them into categories. These categories help geologists name a fault if they see a new one.

   **Student 2:** Geologists do more than that. They use how the different categories of faults form to make interpretations about the geologic history of an area.

# End of Chapter Questions: Short Answer

Using your own words or sketching and labeling a diagram, answer the following questions.

6. Two towns are built on metamorphic bedrock in two different areas. Town A has more biotite than Town B. Provide at least two distinct hypotheses for why there is a difference in the type of metamorphic bedrock.

7. A friend with no geology experience calls you to help her identify a metamorphic rock. List three questions you would ask her about the metamorphic rock over the phone. Explain what information you would learn from each question.

8. Make two observations about the minerals in this microscopic photograph of a rock. Identify a likely name for the rock, supporting your identification with interpretations of your observations.

9. You find a large area of marble bedrock. Create a story of the geologic history explaining how that area formed and changed over time. Include a minimum of three events.

10. Draw a table to compare and contrast at least three aspects of folds and faults. Things to consider include stress direction, type of deformation, and plate tectonic setting.

11. Imagine you are on a road trip with your friends, and you take this photo. Describe key observations of the bedrock, interpret why it looks the way it does, and explain the past plate tectonic environment that lead it to look this way.

12. Draw a table to compare and contrast at least three aspects of continent-continent convergent plate boundaries, convergent plate boundaries with subduction, divergent plate boundaries, and transform plate boundaries. Things to consider include type of metamorphism, presence of folds, and types of faults.

**Hints:** For each question, see the sections listed here for information relevant to answering it.

**1.** (9.3) **2.** (9.2) **3.** (9.4,9.5) **4.** (9.11) **5.** (9.11,9.12) **6.** (9.1,9.3,9.4,9.5) **7.** (9.3,9.4,9.5) **8.** (9.3,9.4) **9.** (9.1,9.2,9.3,9.4,9.5,9.6,9.7) **10.** (9.8.,9.0,9.10,9.11,9.13) **11.** (9.8,9.10,9.13) **12.** (9.6,9.7,9.8,9.11,9.13)

# Chapter 10: Earthquakes

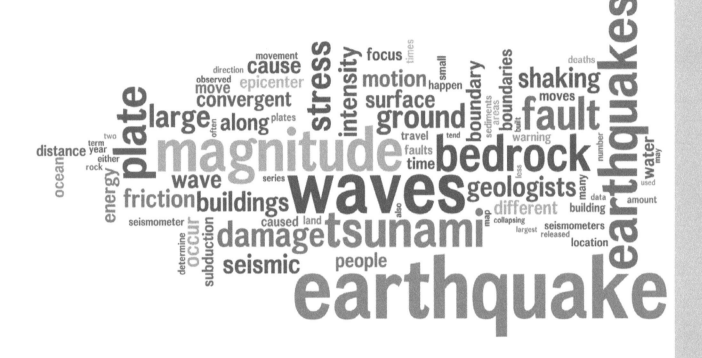

## Chapter Objectives

When you are finished reading this chapter, you should be able to …

• describe characteristics of earthquakes and explain why, how, and where they occur (10.1–10.5).

• apply knowledge of seismic waves to explain how to locate and warn for earthquakes (10.6–10.7).

• explain how earthquakes do damage and why some earthquakes do more damage than others (10.8–10.12).

• summarize the relationship between plate boundaries, earthquakes, and tsunami (10.3, 10.10, 10.12).

# 10.1 – 10.7 Understanding Earthquakes

In this section, you will learn how earthquakes work and how geologists describe and measure them.

## Frequently Used Terms

The terms listed here are used repeatedly throughout this section, so by learning them before you read this section, you can focus your mental energy on the concepts presented.

**deformation** A change in shape of rock due to stress.

**earthquake** The shaking felt when the bedrock making up Earth's crust on either side of a fault suddenly moves and releases energy.

**fault** A broken surface within rock, like a crack, where the two sides have moved relative to one another.

**friction** The resistance of a surface to movement; surfaces that are slippery have a low friction while surfaces that are rough tend to have a higher friction.

**magnitude** The measurement of the amount of energy released by an earthquake; the magnitude is the number most commonly heard in relaying the severity of an earthquake (such as magnitude 7.5).

**intensity** The measurement of the impact of an earthquake based on the amount of damage caused.

**offset** The distance the two sides of a fault move relative to each other.

**seismic wave** Waves of energy created when an earthquake occurs; they can travel through Earth's interior as body waves (P waves and S waves) or along its surface as surface waves.

**stress** Pressure exerted on rock that may cause metamorphism on the atomic scale or deformation on the large scale; the different stress directions are compression, tension, and shear.

Earthquakes can damage and destroy buildings, such as what happened to this building during the 2010 earthquake in Haiti.

# 10.1 Earthquakes and Faults

**Key Concept:** An earthquake occurs when bedrock on either side of a fault overcomes friction and the bedrock on each side moves suddenly. If you experienced an earthquake, you felt the ground shake because of the seismic waves, which are formed at a fault when the two sides of bedrock move. A fault is a break in the bedrock. The point where movement of bedrock begins along the fault is called the focus **1**. Stress on the bedrock causes it to deform, but it does not initially move because the force of friction opposes motion along a fault. Both stress and friction are essential to produce an earthquake **2**.

## 1 Faults and earthquakes

Sudden movement of bedrock on either side of a fault causes the shaking we call an earthquake. Seismic waves are released when motion begins on the fault at the focus. In this cross-section view of a normal fault, the movement began deep in the earth on the fault, at the focus.

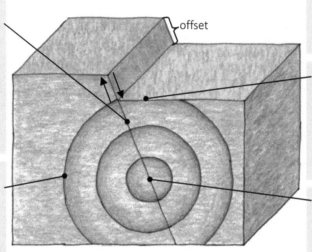

offset

**Fault**
The fault is the break where the two sides of bedrock moved in different directions causing an earthquake (see 9.10). The offset along the fault is the distance that the two sides moved relative to each other. Some faults can be seen at the surface, but many faults are so deep that they are not visible at the surface.

**Seismic waves**
Seismic waves are waves of energy released by an earthquake in the form of ground shaking. They spread out from where the bedrock moved along the fault. The motion of seismic waves is often shown as circles, as shown here, or arrows.

**Aftershock**
An aftershock is the name for smaller earthquakes that follow a larger earthquake. They occur on or near the same fault and result from the bedrock adjusting to the new position after an earthquake.

**Epicenter**
The epicenter is the point on the surface directly above the focus. The epicenter is often given in news reports of earthquakes because it can be located on a map and often has the worst damage.

**Focus**
The focus is the point on the fault where the bedrock on either side of the fault starts to move. The movement continues along the fault for some distance, similar to how a crack in a windshield spreads from where it starts.

## 2 Stress and friction

Stress on the bedrock near a fault and friction on the fault are both needed to cause an earthquake, as shown on the map view of a strike-slip fault to the right. Stress in bedrock is often caused by the constant motion of tectonic plates. Friction is caused by the rough bedrock on either side of the fault. When stress overcomes friction, as shown in 10.2, then an earthquake occurs as bedrock moves.

**Example:** In this example, the plates are moving in opposite directions, causing the bedrock on either side to bend due to stress. However, it has not yet moved along the fault because of friction.

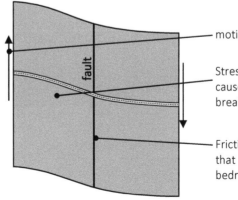

motion adding stress to bedrock

Stress on bedrock is the force that causes it to deform by bending or breaking.

Friction is the force along the fault that resists motion, preventing the bedrock from moving.

## Check
Before you continue, you should be able to answer each check without looking at the page.
- □ Draw a sketch to explain how the focus, epicenter, and seismic waves are related to a fault.
- □ Explain how stress and friction are related to a fault and the motion of bedrock.

# 10.2 How Faults Generate Earthquakes

**Key Concept:** Bedrock next to a fault moves when stress overcomes friction. Stress on the bedrock causes it to deform, and friction is the force opposing motion of the bedrock along a fault. An earthquake occurs when the force due to stress increases enough to overcome the friction force, and the bedrock on either side of the fault suddenly moves. This explanation of why earthquakes occur is called the elastic rebound theory **[1]**. As an earthquake occurs, the energy spreads out in the form of seismic waves which cause the ground to shake **[2]**. The shaking of the ground is recorded by seismometers, producing data that can be used to learn more about an earthquake **[3]**.

## **[1]** Elastic rebound theory

Both stress and friction are essential for producing an earthquake. Without stress, there would be no force to cause the bedrock to move, and without friction, bedrock at the fault would move continuously with the tectonic plates. Initially, bedrock undergoes elastic deformation by bending. Eventually, the bedrock cannot deform any further, and stress overcomes friction causing the bedrock to undergo brittle deformation by breaking as the bedrock on either side of the fault moves. This explanation is called the elastic rebound theory because bending is an elastic behavior, and the bedrock "rebounds" to undo the bending during the earthquake.

### Generating an earthquake

Initially, the road is straight. Plate tectonics will add stress by plates moving in a slow, continuous motion. The force of friction on the fault is greater than the stress on the bedrock.

*bedrock stressed*

The bedrock bends as the bonds between atoms in the rock are elastically compressed and stretched. The stored energy is shown by the bend in the road. Over time, the stress will become greater than the friction along the fault.

*earthquake*

During the earthquake, the bedrock rebounds into its original shape as shown by the straight road but shifts in position. This movement along the fault releases the stored energy as seismic waves.

*bedrock stressed*

The process continues as tectonic plates continue to move in the same direction, adding stress while friction prevents motion. A longer time between earthquakes means that more energy is stored, which could generate larger earthquakes.

### Analogy

Initially, the spring is not stretched. The person will add stress by pulling the spring in a slow, continuous motion. The force of friction between the brick and the ground is greater than the stress on the spring.

*spring stressed*

The spring stretches elastically, and the added stress results in stored energy. Over time, the stress will become greater than the friction between the brick and the ground.

*brick moves*

As the brick moves, the spring snaps back to its original shape, as shown by the unstretched spring, but the block shifts its position. This movement releases the energy stored in the stretched bonds between atoms in the spring.

*spring stressed*

The process continues, as stress is added while friction prevents motion. A longer time between when the brick moves means that more energy is stored, which could cause the brick to move a large distance.

# ❷ Seismic waves

Seismic waves are the waves of energy that are generated when a fault moves suddenly. They can be classified as either body waves that travel within and through Earth or surface waves that move along Earth's surface. Different types of body and surface waves are defined based on the motion of the bedrock relative to the direction the seismic wave is traveling. The two types of body waves, P waves and S waves, were also discussed in 2.6 because they help geologists learn about Earth's interior. Surface waves generate most of the shaking felt during an earthquake. A single earthquake results in P waves, S waves, and surface waves.

## P waves
P waves, one of the two types of body waves, travel through Earth causing the bedrock to compress in the same direction the waves are travelling.

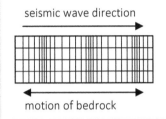

## S waves
S waves are also body waves, but they cause the bedrock they travel through to move perpendicular to the direction the waves are travelling.

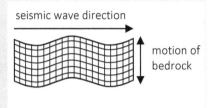

## Surface waves
Surface waves travel along Earth's surface, causing the most shaking and therefore doing the most damage. There are several types of surface waves: some cause a rolling motion along the surface and others cause side-to-side motion along the surface as the wave is traveling.

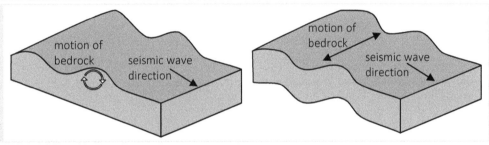

# ❸ Seismograms show ground motion

Seismometers are instruments that measure ground motion related to different seismic waves over time, and they record the data as a seismogram. Seismometers are now digital, but it is helpful to describe how they work using older technology.

## Seismometer
Before an earthquake, the drum of paper rotates and the pen draws a relatively straight line. During an earthquake, the ground moves the drum of paper, but the spring allows the weight and pen to remain still and continue to draw a line. The resulting wavy line is a record of the ground motion caused by different types of seismic waves generated by a single earthquake.

**P waves**
P waves are faster than other seismic waves, over 100 times faster than cars can drive, so it is the first seismic wave to be recorded by the seismogram. The P wave is sometimes heard as a boom or rattling windows.

**S waves**
The S wave is also a body wave and is the second seismic wave to arrive. The arrival of the S wave is sometimes felt as a quick, small, side-to-side jolt.

**Surface waves**
The surface waves travel along Earth's surface and are the last seismic waves to arrive because they are the slowest. They result in the greatest shaking and therefore do the most damage.

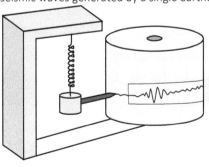
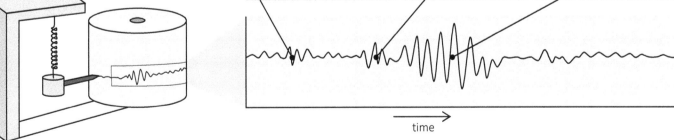

time

# Check

☐ Describe the conditions and events that lead to earthquakes.
☐ Explain why stress and friction are both necessary for an earthquake to happen.
☐ Compare P waves, S waves, and surface waves in terms of the motion of the bedrock compared to the direction of the wave and their arrival times at a seismometer.

# 10.3 Earthquakes and Plate Tectonics

**Key Concept:** **Different types of plate boundaries have different patterns of earthquakes.** Plate boundaries are locations where the movement of tectonic plates in different directions adds stress to the bedrock, resulting in earthquakes **1**. The processes that occur at divergent plate boundaries **2**, convergent plate boundaries with subduction **3**, continent-continent convergent plate boundaries **4**, and transform plate boundaries **5** result in earthquakes with different sizes, locations, and depths in the Earth. Although most earthquakes occur on faults at plate boundaries, some occur on faults in the interiors of plates, where small amounts of stress build up along faults that often formed at ancient plate boundaries.

## **1** World map of earthquakes

Earthquakes occur around the world where bedrock is under stress along and near plate boundaries as plates move relative to each other. The processes at the different types of plate boundaries results in earthquakes with different characteristics in regards to their size, location, and depth. For each of the plate boundaries labeled in the map, the observations and interpretations made by geologists are explained in detail below.

**Divergent:**
Narrow line of shallow-depth earthquakes.

**Convergent with subduction:**
Broad line of shallow-depth earthquakes near the boundary to deep earthquakes further away.

**Transform:**
Narrow line of shallow-depth earthquakes.

**Continent-continent convergent:**
Broad line of shallow- to medium- depth earthquakes.

| Key | |
|---|---|
| | Continent (land) |
| | Ocean |
| | Continental shelf (continent covered by ocean) |
| | Shallow earthquake (0 – 70 km) |
| | Intermediate earthquake (70 – 300 km) |
| | Deep earthquake (300 – 700 km) |

## **2** Divergent plate boundary

Earthquakes where plates move apart at divergent plate boundaries tend to have small magnitudes and shallow depths in the crust, and they occur right on the boundary. Most faults here are due to tensional stress.

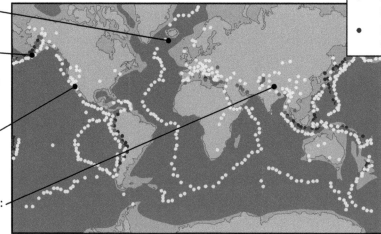

epicenter (at the surface)

focus (beneath the surface)

Lithosphere

**Observations and interpretations**

Geologists have observed that there are no large magnitude earthquakes here. Their interpretation is that large amounts of stress cannot build up to cause large magnitude earthquakes because rock is not strong under tensional stress.

Geologists have observed that epicenters of earthquakes occur along the plate boundary. They interpret this relationship to be because the plate boundary is narrow.

Geologists have observed that there are no deep earthquakes here. They interpret this relationship to be because the brittle lithosphere is thin, and the deep rock in the asthenosphere undergoes ductile deformation, which does not generate earthquakes.

# ❸ Convergent plate boundary with subduction

Earthquakes at convergent plate boundaries with subduction have small to very large magnitudes and shallow to very deep depths. This is because they occur along the subducting plate, which is angled beneath the surface, and in the overriding plate. Most faults here are due to compressional stress.

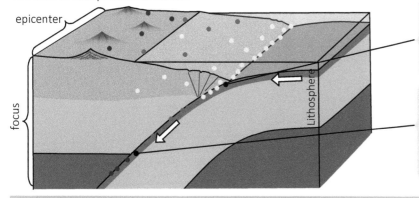

## Observations and interpretations

Geologists have observed that the largest magnitude earthquakes occur here. Their interpretation is that large amounts of stress can build up to cause these large magnitude earthquakes because rock is strong under compression.

Geologists have observed that the epicenters of shallow earthquakes are located along the plate boundary and the epicenters of deep earthquakes are located to one side of it. They interpret this relationship to be because the plate subducts at an angle.

Geologists have observed that the depth of earthquakes increases farther from the plate boundary. They interpret this relationship to be because earthquakes happen along the subducting plate. The deepest earthquakes occur in subducting lithosphere as long as it is cool enough to undergo brittle deformation.

# ❹ Continent-continent convergent plate boundary

Earthquakes at convergent plate boundaries have small to very large magnitudes and shallow to intermediate depths. Most faults here are due to compressional stress.

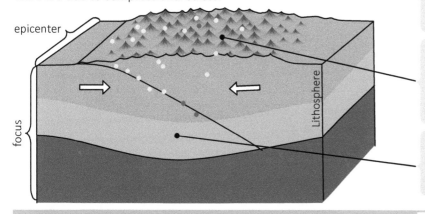

## Observations and interpretations

Geologists have observed that very large magnitude earthquakes can occur here. Their interpretation is that large amounts of stress can build up to cause these large magnitude earthquakes because rock is strong under compression.

Geologists have observed that the epicenters of shallow and intermediate earthquakes are scattered throughout the huge mountain range and are not exclusive to the plate boundary. They interpret this relationship to be because the entire mountain range is deforming.

Geologists have observed that there are no very deep earthquakes. Their interpretation is that there is no subducting plate to undergo brittle deformation in the surrounding asthenosphere.

# ❺ Transform plate boundary

Earthquakes at transform plate boundaries have small to large magnitudes and are mostly at shallow depths with a few reaching intermediate depths, along the plate boundary. Most faults here are due to shear stress.

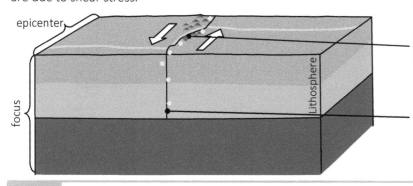

## Observations and interpretations

Geologists have observed that the largest magnitude earthquakes do not occur here. Their interpretation is that because rocks are stronger under compressional stress than under shear stress, not enough stress can build up to cause the largest magnitude earthquakes.

Geologists have observed that epicenters of earthquakes occur along the plate boundary. They interpret this relationship to be because the plate boundary is narrow and the fault along it is often vertical.

Geologists have observed that there are no deep earthquakes here. Their interpretation is that deep rock in the asthenosphere undergoes ductile deformation which does not generate earthquakes.

# Check

☐ Describe observations of the pattern and size of earthquakes at four types of plate boundaries.
☐ Explain why earthquakes occur in the patterns they do at four types of plate boundaries.

# 10.4 Measuring Earthquakes

**Key Concept:** **Earthquakes can be described in terms of magnitude or intensity.** Geologists determine an earthquake's magnitude, which is the amount of energy released by the earthquake, and they create a map of intensity, which describes how strongly people are affected by the shaking **1**. To measure the magnitude of earthquakes, geologists use a variety of instruments including seismometers to record the movement of the ground **2**. An earthquake's intensity is influenced by many factors and varies by location for each earthquake **3**.

## **1** How earthquakes are measured

A single earthquake will have one magnitude, but the intensity varies by location. To determine magnitude and intensity, geologists measure different aspects of the earthquake, so they use different strategies for determining each measurement.

| | How it is measured | What affects it | How geologists determine it |
|---|---|---|---|
| **Magnitude** Magnitude is how much energy is released by an earthquake. | It is measured by the moment magnitude scale, but in the past, geologists used the Richter scale. The numbers in the scales are nearly the same and are sometimes used interchangeably. | • The length of the section of the fault that moved—a longer section will cause a larger magnitude earthquake.<br>• Extent of offset along fault—a longer offset will cause a larger magnitude earthquake.<br>• Strength of the rock | The shapes and sizes of the waves on a seismogram allow geologists to interpret the length of the section of the fault that moved and the amount of offset. In some cases when the fault breaks at the surface, geologists can find the fault and map its length and offset. |
| **Intensity** Intensity is the effects of an earthquake related to how much the ground shakes at a given location. | It is measured by the Modified Mercalli scale. Instrumental intensity uses the same scale. | • The type of bedrock or sediment—soft sediments will shake more and have a higher intensity than solid bedrock.<br>• Quality of building construction—poorly built buildings will be damaged and result in a higher intensity.<br>• Distance from focus—close areas experience more shaking and a higher intensity. | People's experiences and amount of damage allow geologists to create maps of intensity. In addition, seismometer readings are used by computer models created by geologists to help create maps of how much the ground shakes in the areas around the fault. |

## **2** Magnitude

The energy released by earthquakes has a very wide range, so the magnitude scale covers this large range of sizes. Each increase of one magnitude releases about 30 times more energy. Therefore, one magnitude 7 earthquake releases the same amount of energy as about one million magnitude 3 earthquakes. Magnitude is the measurement of energy released, so it does not vary based on location and is the number given in the news to describe the size of an earthquake.

### Example Magnitudes

| Magnitude | Energy released (billions of joules) | Equivalent energy |
|---|---|---|
| 1 | 0.002 | Would power a small fridge for a week. |
| 3 | 2 | Would power a small American home for a week. |
| 5 | 2,000 | Would power an American shopping mall for a week. |
| 7 | 2,000,000 | Would power Washington, D.C. for a week. |
| 9 | 2,000,000,000 | Would power the entire United States for a week. |

# 3 Intensity

Following an earthquake, the United States Geological Survey (USGS) collects data to create maps of earthquake intensity. Intensity describes the effects of an earthquake, so it is measured in part by damage reports from people who experienced the earthquake, such as through the "Did You Feel It" website, and in part by computer models. See 10.9 for factors that influence intensity.

### Intensity Map

This map shows the instrumental intensity of shaking across the area caused by the 1989 Loma Prieta, California earthquake as determined from seismic recordings. The places that felt severe to violent shaking experienced more damage than the places that felt strong shaking.

| PERCEIVED SHAKING | Not felt | Weak | Light | Moderate | Strong | Very strong | Severe | Violent |
|---|---|---|---|---|---|---|---|---|
| INSTRUMENTAL INTENSITY | I | II-III | IV | V | VI | VII | VIII | IX |

### Simplified Modified Mercalli Scale

The Modified Mercalli Scale describes the shaking and damage for each intensity level. Shown here is a simplified version. Detailed descriptions can be found on the USGS website.

| Intensity | Shaking | Damage |
|---|---|---|
| I | Not felt | None |
| II – IV | Weak to light | None |
| V – VI | Moderate to strong | Light |
| VII – VIII | Very strong to severe | Moderate |
| IX – XII | Violent to extreme | Heavy |

This office in Menlo Park, CA experienced a strong intensity and had books and other items fell off shelves during the shaking caused by the 1989 Loma Prieta earthquake.

This house in Boulder Creek, CA experienced a severe to violent intensity and completely collapsed during the shaking caused by the 1989 Loma Prieta earthquake.

## Check

□ Discuss how the magnitude and intensity of an earthquake are different in terms of what they measure, how they are measured, and what affects them.

□ Explain how an earthquake will have one magnitude but many intensities.

# 10.5 DATA AND DIAGRAMS: Earthquake Size and Frequency

**Key Concept:** Line graphs with logarithmic scales can show the relationship between two variables when at least one variable occurs over a large range of values. A logarithmic scale is a scale where each number is ten times the previous number. It is used on the vertical y-axis below. Logarithmic axes allow a graph to show a characteristic with a huge range of values, such as from less than 1 to over a million **1**. To create a graph like this, geologists compiled information from a variety of earthquakes. Tips on how to read this graph are below **2**. Use the questions to practice interpreting logarithmic graphs **3**.

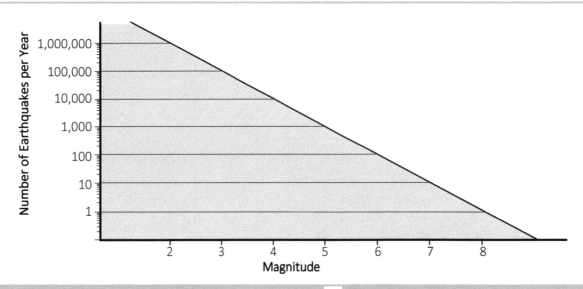

## **1** How to read the diagram

Examine the variables on the axes and their labels. The tick marks on the horizontal axis have equal values between them, but the intervals between tick marks on the vertical axis are not equal. Instead, each numbered point on the y-axis is ten times the previous number, indicating it is a logarithmic scale.

## **2** An example of what you might interpret

If you compare the magnitude of earthquakes to how many occur each year, you would see there are about 100 magnitude 6 earthquakes per year.

## **3** Questions

**1. What does the graph show?**
a. how many years there are between earthquakes of a particular magnitude
b. that earthquakes are getting smaller in magnitude over time
c. how many earthquakes occur each year at each magnitude
d. that the number of earthquakes each year is decreasing but that their magnitude is increasing

**2. Which part of the graph shows the largest increase in number of earthquakes per year between two tick marks?**
a. the top of the vertical axis
b. the bottom of the vertical axis
c. the left of the horizontal axis
d. the right of the horizontal axis

**3. Roughly how often do earthquakes with magnitudes of 7 happen?**
a. 10 times each year
b. 100 times each year
c. 1,000 times each year
d. 10,000 times each year

**4. How many more earthquakes of a magnitude 4 happen each year than earthquakes with a magnitude 6?**
a. approximately 1
b. approximately 100
c. approximately 10,000
d. approximately 1,000,000

**5. What relationship is shown by this graph?**
a. large magnitude earthquakes happen closer to the equator than smaller ones
b. earthquake magnitude decreases as time goes on
c. fewer earthquakes happen over the years
d. large magnitude earthquakes happen less often than small ones

# 10.6 Locating an Earthquake's Epicenter

**Key Concept:** Geologists use the arrival times of seismic waves at seismometers to determine the location of an earthquake's epicenter. Determining the epicenter of an earthquake that just occurred allows communities to react more effectively. The arrival times of P and S waves are used to determine the epicenter because of their different speeds **1**. The greater the distance a seismometer is from an earthquake, the greater the delay between the arrival times of the P and S waves. This time difference allows geologists to calculate the distance between the seismometer and an earthquake's epicenter **2**. To determine the exact epicenter geologists use the data from at least three different seismometers **3**.

## **1** Seismic waves

P waves travel at approximately 5 kilometers per second (11,000 miles per hour) through the bedrock making up the crust, followed by S waves, traveling at approximately half the speed of P waves. They both leave the focus of the earthquake at the same time, but it is the relationship between the speeds of P and S waves that is used to determine the location of the earthquake's epicenter.

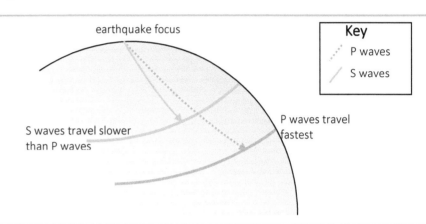

## **2** Arrival times indicate distance

P waves travel faster than S waves, so the difference in the time that they arrive at a particular seismometer increases as the waves move away from the epicenter. The length of time between when the P wave and S wave first arrive at a seismometer can be used to determine the distance to the earthquake's epicenter but not direction.

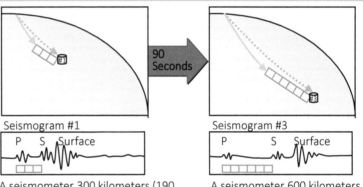

Seismogram #1

A seismometer 300 kilometers (190 miles) from the focus measures roughly 30 seconds between the initial P and S wave arrival times.

Seismogram #3

A seismometer 600 kilometers (370 miles) from the focus measures roughly 60 seconds between the initial P and S wave arrival times.

## **3** Locating the epicenter

To determine the location of the earthquake's epicenter, distances from at least three seismometers in different locations are needed in a process called triangulation. Only the epicenter's distance from the seismometer is known but the direction is not, so using a single seismometer means that the epicenter of the earthquake could be anywhere on a circle drawn around the seismometer at the calculated distance. Using three seismometers is required to narrow down the location to a single point.

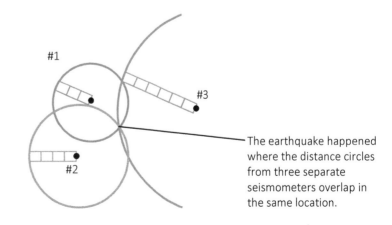

The earthquake happened where the distance circles from three separate seismometers overlap in the same location.

## Check

☐ Discuss the characteristics of seismic waves that allow them to be used to determine the distance of a seismometer from an epicenter.
☐ Explain how geologists use seismic data to locate earthquake epicenters.

# 10.7 Earthquake Warnings and Forecasts

**Key Concept:** Geologists give short-term earthquake warnings and determine long-term forecasts of earthquake likelihood.
People need to prepare for earthquakes. However, it is not possible to predict exactly when stress will overcome friction on a fault and cause an earthquake. To help react, very short term warnings can be given seconds before the ground starts shaking in some places if a seismometer network is set up to send out warnings **1**. Geologists also determine long term probabilities by considering how long it has been since the last earthquake and how often they tend to occur on a particular fault **2**.

## **1** Short term earthquake warnings

When an earthquake happens, nearby seismometers first detect the fast moving P waves. A computer model quickly assesses the danger posed by the approaching surface waves and sends out an alert. Short term warnings are different than predictions because the earthquake has already begun when the warning is sent out.

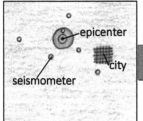 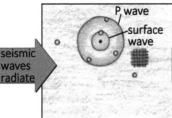 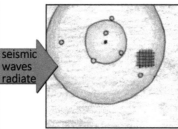 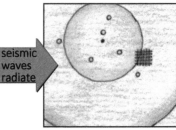

Seismic waves radiate from the focus when an earthquake begins.

Seismometers detect the P and S waves, and a computer analyzes the seismometer data.

An earthquake warning is sent out before surface waves hit the city.

Less than a minute later, when the surface waves hit people are more prepared.

**Benefits:** Seconds to a minute of warning is enough time for people to seek shelter, for surgeons to stop surgeries, for trains to slow down, and for other steps to occur to reduce damage and injuries.

**Drawbacks:** The warning is limited to a few of seconds to a minute. It cannot prevent a building from collapsing. It is expensive to put in place, so only a few places with advanced technology and abundant earthquakes, such as Japan and California, are implementing this type of warning system.

## **2** Long term earthquake forecasting

Geologists can determine where future earthquake hazards are most likely to exist based on the presence of faults, the history of earthquakes along those faults, and the slow motion of the bedrock nearby. This information is relevant because earthquakes tend to occur on faults along plate boundaries. Stress builds up on a fault over time, so if the bedrock on either side of a fault has not moved in a long time, the surrounding areas should prepare for the possibility of a large magnitude earthquake. This map of the United States shows the likelihood of experiencing a large earthquake. Notice that the West Coast, which is near a plate boundary, is more likely to experience worse earthquake hazards than the East Coast.

**Benefits:** A long term probability allows time for preparation. Buildings and bridges can be reinforced, emergency response plans can be made and tested, and individuals can create survival kits.

**Drawbacks:** Without immediate need, people may not prepare. Expensive preparations may be low priority or made and not needed. Areas with a low probability for earthquake hazards may not prepare but still experience an earthquake.

**Forecasting compared to predictions**
Long term earthquake forecasting is different than predictions because a forecast gives the likelihood it will happen in a given time. For example, a forecast geologists made for California in 2014 is "A magnitude 7 earthquake has a 93% chance of occurring in the next 30 years." A prediction, which is not made by geologists, is more specific, such as "A magnitude 6 earthquake will happen on August 10, 2022".

## Check

☐ Describe how the short term warning systems for earthquakes work.
☐ Explain what geologists look for and why to forecast future earthquakes.
☐ Explain how short term warnings and long term forecasts are different than earthquake predictions.

# 10.8 – 10.12 Earthquake Hazards

In this section, you will learn how earthquakes do damage and why that damage is worse in some areas than others.

## Frequently Used Terms

The terms listed here are used repeatedly throughout this section, so by learning them before you read this section, you can focus your mental energy on the concepts presented.

**hazard** A potential geologic event that has the possibility to negatively impact people.

**subduction-zone earthquake** An earthquake formed at a convergent plate boundary with subduction where ocean lithosphere descends into the asthenosphere; these plate boundaries tend to form the largest magnitude earthquakes which in turn often cause tsunami.

**tsunami** A series of large, broad ocean waves created by an underwater earthquake, volcanic explosion, or landslide.

This damage was caused by the tsunami in the Indian Ocean from the 2004 Sumatra, Indonesia earthquake.

# 10.8 Earthquake Hazards Overview

**Key Concept:** Ground motion and shaking from earthquakes can trigger collapsing structures, tsunami, landslides, and fires. When you think about earthquake damage, you probably think about shaking ground damaging buildings and other structures, but this is just one way earthquakes cause destruction **1**. Other hazards, or dangers caused by the ground shaking, can greatly affect people as well. Ground motion along a fault can cause tsunami (ocean waves rushing inland and out to sea) **2**, and the shaking ground can cause landslides (loosened slopes collapsing) **3** and fires (flames burning gas or other flammable objects) **4**.

## **1** Effects of ground shaking

Ground shaking is caused as seismic waves travel through bedrock, causing it to move. The effects of ground shaking include buildings, roads, and bridges being damaged or collapsing or objects within buildings falling because of the motion of the ground. Damage can also be caused by ground motion along the offset fault itself. See the detailed discussion in 10.9.

### Why does it happen?
Seismic waves, especially surface waves, cause the ground to move as they travel through bedrock as energy is released during an earthquake.

### How does it cause damage?
Buildings and other structures move so much that they break or items inside fall down. People are injured, not by the shaking of the ground, but by falling structures or objects. To prepare for shaking during an earthquake, people should build structures following strict building codes, such as using materials that can bend and not crumble and by designing buildings to withstand both vertical and horizontal shaking motions. To stay safe during ground shaking, people indoors should get under sturdy tables and move outside when the shaking has stopped. The buildings in the photo were destroyed by shaking during the 2010 Haiti earthquake.

## **2** Tsunami

Tsunami are a series of large, broad waves that are generated by underwater earthquakes, volcanic eruptions, or landslides. See the detailed discussion in 10.10-10.11.

### Why does it happen?
A large underwater earthquake, usually at a convergent plate boundary with subduction, moves a tremendous amount of water. The displaced water then spreads as waves across the ocean and onto land.

### How does it cause damage?
Water rushes inland and then back out to sea, destroying man-made and natural structures and drowning people and animals. To prepare for tsunami, people need to monitor ocean earthquakes and have evacuation plans. To stay safe during a tsunami, people should evacuate coastal areas after an earthquake or when a warning is sounded. The tsunami in the photo was caused by the 2011 Tōhoku Japan earthquake.

# ❸ Landslides

Landslides are the downhill movement of land, such as rock and soil. There are many different kinds of landslides. See the detailed discussion in 16.3-16.6.

### Why does it happen?

Shaking destabilizes slopes that would otherwise have remained stable. The friction holding the rock and soil in place is overcome by the shaking, and the destabilized rock and soil and everything on it move downhill. In places with water-saturated sediments, the shaking may cause the ground to act like a liquid because the shaking reduces the friction between the sediments, and the water in the pore spaces moves upwards. This resulting liquefaction may happen, even on flat land.

### How does it cause damage?

Land moves out from beneath buildings or crushes buildings lower down the slope. In places where liquefaction occurs, the buildings sink into the ground while it is acting like a liquid. To prepare for landslides, people should not build on or beneath steep slopes. To stay safe, people should evacuate landslide-prone areas after an earthquake. The landslide in the photo was a result of the 2010 Christchurch, New Zealand earthquake.

# ❹ Fires

Fires include flames burning buildings, other structures, gas, or other flammable objects.

### Why does it happen?

Flames or sparks from broken electrical wires, emergency candles, or cooking fires ignite leaking gas from broken pipelines or flammable objects. Most fires caused by earthquakes are caused by man-made objects.

### How does it cause damage?

Buildings are burned. People may be injured directly from the flames and smoke, or indirectly due to the collapse of structures that are burned and unstable. To prepare for possible earthquake-related fires, people should build gas lines so they do not break during an earthquake. To stay safe after an earthquake, people should turn off the gas to their home if they smell gas and avoid using candles or other open flames. The fire in this photo was a result of the 1995 Kobe, Japan earthquake.

## Check

☐ Identify the four main hazards of earthquakes and explain why they happen.
☐ Describe how people can work to avoid the danger of each of the four earthquake hazards.

# 10.9 Factors Influencing Intensity

**Key Concept:** The amount of damage caused by ground shaking during an earthquake depends on many factors.

Earthquake intensity, as discussed in 10.4, is frequently determined by the amount of damage that results from how much the ground shakes. Larger magnitude earthquakes tend to have a higher intensity **1**, although small magnitude earthquakes can still damage buildings that were not built following earthquake-resistant buildings codes **2**. Locations that are closer to the offset fault also tend to have a higher intensity **3**. Additionally, buildings on soft sediments, as opposed to solid bedrock, often experience more damage because the soft sediments can increase the shaking **4**. Soft sediments can also undergo liquefaction by behaving like a liquid when they contain water and are shaken.

## **1** Magnitude of earthquake

Large magnitude earthquakes cause more damage, and therefore have a higher intensity, all other things being equal. Both earthquakes shown here were beneath cities with strictly enforced building codes. The tremendous difference in damage was primarily due to the amount of energy released as measured by the earthquake magnitude.

**Small magnitude**
A small magnitude earthquake causes less damage. This collapsed chimney and other minor damage were caused by a medium-sized 5.6 magnitude earthquake in Oklahoma in 2011.

**Large magnitude**
A large magnitude earthquake causes more damage. This severe damage was caused by a large-sized 6.9 magnitude earthquake in Kobe, Japan in 1995.

## **2** Building construction

Strict and enforced building codes reduce the chances that buildings are damaged, reducing the impact of an earthquake. Strong building construction is one of the key ways to prevent damage and save lives in earthquake-prone areas. It uses a design and materials that provide flexibility without breaking. For example, brick and unreinforced cement crumble and collapse during shaking while wood or steel-reinforced structures are more likely to bend, but not crumble.

**Strong construction**
Buildings with strong construction sustain less damage. Many buildings, like this one, remained standing, and there were only 63 deaths after the magnitude 7.1 Loma Prieta, California earthquake in 1989, because California enforces strict building codes.

**Poor construction**
Buildings with weak construction sustain greater damage. A magnitude 7.0 earthquake in Haiti in 2010 caused complete collapse of buildings, like the one shown, and over 300,000 deaths because buildings were not built to strict building codes.

# 3 Distance from fault

Seismic waves spread out and their energy and resulting ground shaking decreases with distance, so more damage tends to occur closer to the offset section of the fault. Earthquakes with a focus close to the surface (shallow focus) tend to do more damage than deep-focus earthquakes because the energy is released nearer to structures.

### Large distance
Less damage occurs tens of kilometers (tens of miles) from the focus. Thirty-five miles from the epicenter of the 1994 Northridge, California earthquake, shaking was only severe enough to cause a few cracks in buildings.

### Short distance
Just 6 miles from the epicenter of the same 1994 Northridge earthquake, the ground shook enough to cause severe structural damage to buildings.

# 4 Ground type

Solid bedrock shakes less than ground made up of sediments, because soft sediments tend to amplify and prolong shaking, increasing the earthquake's intensity in those areas. This difference in shaking can be illustrated by jello on a plate, which represents sediments on solid bedrock. If you move the plate a tiny amount, the jello will jiggle and wobble much more than the small shake to the plate. Therefore, building on solid bedrock is another key way to prevent damage and save lives.

### Solid bedrock
Solid bedrock results in less damage. Other sections (not shown here) of this double-decker freeway were built on solid bedrock, so they did not collapse during the 1989 Loma Prieta, California earthquake.

### Soft sediments
Soft sediment and soft bedrock result in more damage. These sections of the double-decker freeway were built on soft mud, so they experienced more shaking during the 1989 Loma Prieta earthquake, which led to collapse, shown here.

### Liquefaction increases damage
When shaken, some sediments with water saturating and filling the spaces between them behave like a liquid. This behavior is called liquefaction. Anything that is built on this type of ground may sink into it while the ground temporarily behaves like a liquid during an earthquake. To prevent damage from liquefaction, builders avoid areas with water-saturated sediments or drain the water from the ground. These buildings were built on water-filled sediments and sank into the ground due to liquefaction during the 1964 Niigata, Japan earthquake.

## Check

☐ Discuss four factors that influence how much damage is caused by ground shaking.
☐ Relate each of these four factors to the intensity of an earthquake.

# 10.10 Tsunami

**Key Concept:** Most tsunami form when a large magnitude subduction-zone earthquake moves a large portion of the seafloor. Some people think that weather conditions can form huge ocean waves called tsunami, but tsunami are hazards most often caused by earthquakes. Large subduction-zone earthquakes cause a large portion of the seafloor to move up or down, generating a tsunami **1**. This water then moves away from the fault as a series of tsunami waves that spreads out like large ripples across an ocean **2**.

## **1** Generating tsunami

For a tsunami to form, a tremendous amount of water must be displaced. Therefore earthquakes that generate tsunami need to shift the seafloor up or down to displace the ocean water above it, and the earthquake must have a large magnitude to displace enough ocean water to form a tsunami. Geologists have determined that the location where these types of earthquakes happen is convergent plate boundaries with subduction. Large landslides, often caused by large magnitude earthquakes, may also displace enough water to form a tsunami.

### Before the earthquake
At a convergent plate boundary with subduction, the plates converge but friction prevents movement between the plates. Stress builds up and bends the seafloor bedrock downward.

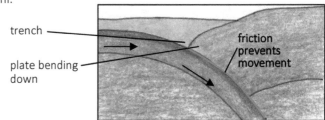

### During the earthquake
After enough stress has built up to overcome the friction, the bedrock on either side of the fault moves and releases the built-up energy as an earthquake. The top plate rebounds upward, pushing the ocean water above it. This vertical motion of the seafloor from a large magnitude earthquake is essential for generating a tsunami.

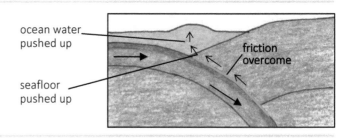

### After the earthquake
The bulge of water spreads in all directions as a series of tsunami waves, similar to ripples spreading from where a pebble is thrown in water. Some waves move toward land, and some travel across the ocean. The water rises and falls, resulting in a series of waves, each made up of a high peak and a low trough.

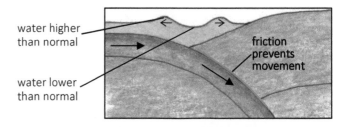

## **2** Map view of tsunami

The spreading out of the series of waves away from the plate boundary as described above is shown from a map perspective. The arrows indicate the tsunami radiates outward from the fault. The term tsunami refers to all of the waves in the series that travel away from the plate boundary.

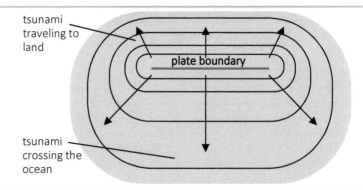

## Check

☐ Describe and sketch the steps involved in forming tsunami.

☐ Explain why each of the following criteria is necessary for an earthquake to generate a tsunami: large magnitude earthquake, vertical motion of the seafloor.

# 10.11 Tsunami Close to Land

**Key Concept:** Tsunami travel quickly across oceans, but people can be warned before water rushes onshore. In the open ocean, tsunami waves are so flat with a small wave height that they are not noticed by ships. However, when tsunami approach land they slow down and increase in wave height **1**. Tsunami are a series of high peaks and low troughs of waves, so when they hit the shore, the water alternately rushes ashore covering land and rushes out to sea exposing the seafloor **2**. Although tsunami cannot be prevented, preparations can save lives when they do occur **3**.

## **1** Tsunami approaching land

When tsunami get close to land, they change in behavior and appearance. As with wind generated waves (see 15.6), the friction with the shallower seafloor causes each wave in the series to slow down, shorten, and increase in height.

| Tsunami in the open ocean | Tsunami moving closer to land |
| --- | --- |
| • very fast: more than 800 km/hr (500 mph), as fast as a commercial airplane flies<br>• wide distance between waves: over 100 km (60 mi) apart<br>• flat wave: wave height less than 1 meter (3 feet) tall | • the speed slows to less than 80 km/hr (50 mph), as fast as cars on a freeway<br>• the distance shortens to less than 20 km (12 mi) apart<br>• the wave height increases up to 30 m (100 feet) tall |

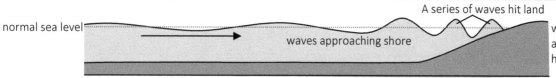

A series of waves hit land

normal sea level

waves approaching shore

waves drawn with an exaggerated height

## **2** Tsunami hitting land

The series of tsunami waves that hit the coast includes peaks above sea level and troughs below sea level that may be 10 minutes to over an hour apart.

**Experience on shore**
Either the peak or trough of a tsunami wave can hit the coast first. If the peak hits land first there is little warning for the people on the shore. If the trough arrives first, the sea level first drops, allowing people to escape to higher ground before the peak arrives. The first wave of a series may not be the biggest or travel the farthest inland.

The tsunami caused by the Sumatra, 2004 earthquake came ashore in Sri Lanka.

Minutes later, water was still rushing towards land. More waves followed.

## **3** Tsunami warning systems

Tsunami warning systems can save many lives, not by preventing tsunami, but instead by giving people enough time to evacuate the area.

1. Local governments prepare a plan with guidance from geologists and educate people in their communities.

2. Geologists at a tsunami warning center use seismometers to monitor large magnitude underwater earthquakes around the world.

3. If seafloor sensors detect an increase in water pressure after an earthquake, buoys send a signal to the tsunami warning center.

4. The tsunami warning center calculates tsunami motion and arrival times using data from multiple sensors.

5. A warning is given to people near the coast.

6. People follow clearly marked evacuation routes to higher ground (created in Step 1).

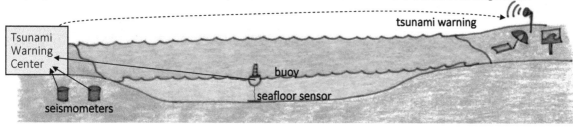

tsunami warning

Tsunami Warning Center

buoy

seafloor sensor

seismometers

## Check

☐ Summarize how tsunami change as they move from the open ocean to near the shore.
☐ Contrast what tsunami look like to people on a beach to what tsunami look like to people on a boat in the open ocean.
☐ Summarize what needs to be done to effectively save people's lives during a tsunami.

# 10.12 Major Earthquakes in Recent History

**Key Concept:** There is very little overlap among recent earthquakes with respect to highest magnitude, most deaths, and largest damage to property. Perhaps surprisingly, creating lists of the top 5 "worst" earthquakes results in very different lists depending on the criteria used. The largest earthquakes ranked by magnitude all occur at convergent plate boundaries **1**. However, the earthquakes with the largest number of deaths often occur in areas with a high population density and structures that are not built to earthquake building codes **2**. The earthquakes with the highest costs for recovering and rebuilding tend to occur where there are dense populations with high property values **3**. Each list is different than the others, and no earthquake is ranked in the top five on all three lists. However, looking at a map of the world, it is possible to see some relationships in the locations of these earthquakes **4**.

## **1** The five largest magnitude earthquakes since 1950

The magnitude of an earthquake is the measure of how much energy it releases. The largest-magnitude earthquakes are all subduction-zone earthquakes.

| Rank | Year | Location | Magnitude | Estimated Number of Deaths | Cause of Many of the Deaths | Recovery Cost (2015 billion US dollars) | Plate Boundary |
|------|------|----------|-----------|---------------------------|----------------------------|-----------------------------------------|----------------|
| 1. | 1960 | Chile | 9.5 | 2,000 | Tsunami | 8.0 | Convergent with subduction |
| 2. | 1964 | Alaska | 9.2 | 131 | Tsunami | 2.2 | Convergent with subduction |
| 3. | 2004 | Sumatra, Indonesia | 9.1 | 227,900 | Tsunami | 12.6 | Convergent with subduction |
| 4. | 2011 | Honshu, Japan | 9.0 | 20,900 | Tsunami | 232.6 | Convergent with subduction |
| 5. | 1952 | Kamchatka, Russia | 9.0 | 2,340 | Tsunami | unknown | Convergent with subduction |

## **2** The five deadliest earthquakes since 1950

The number of deaths caused by an earthquake is a part of its intensity (see 10.9). The deadliest earthquakes occur in areas with high population densities and buildings that are not built following earthquake-resistant buildings codes. As a result, most of the deadliest earthquakes occur in developing countries.

| Rank | Year | Location | Magnitude | Estimated Number of Deaths | Cause of Many of the Deaths | Recovery Cost (2015 billion US dollars) | Plate Boundary |
|------|------|----------|-----------|---------------------------|----------------------------|-----------------------------------------|----------------|
| 1. | 2010 | Haiti | 7.0 | 316,000 | Buildings collapsing | 8.0 | Transform |
| 2. | 1976 | Tangshan, China | 7.5 | 242,800 | Buildings collapsing | 5.6 | None |
| 3. | 2004 | Sumatra, Indonesia | 9.1 | 227,900 | Tsunami | 12.6 | Convergent with subduction |
| 4. | 2008 | Sichuan, China | 7.9 | 87,600 | Buildings collapsing | 95.0 | Convergent with no subduction |
| 5. | 2005 | Pakistan | 7.6 | 86,000 | Buildings collapsing | 5.2 | Convergent with no subduction |

## ❸ The five costliest earthquakes since 1950

The cost of recovery from earthquakes is also a part of earthquake intensity (see 10.9), since it is a measure of how much damage is done. The costliest earthquakes occur in areas with high populations and expensive property and building values. Strict building codes often result in building not fully collapsing, but the buildings themselves and the many expensive items inside may be damaged. Costly earthquakes tend to occur in developed countries.

| Rank | Year | Location | Magnitude | Estimated Number of Deaths | Cause of Many of the Deaths | Recovery Cost (2015 billion US dollars) | Plate Boundary |
|---|---|---|---|---|---|---|---|
| 1. | 2011 | Honshu, Japan | 9.0 | 20,900 | Tsunami | 232.6 | Convergent with subduction |
| 2. | 1995 | Kobe, Japan | 6.9 | 5,500 | Buildings collapsing | 156.0 | Convergent with subduction |
| 3. | 2008 | Sichuan, China | 7.9 | 87,600 | Buildings collapsing | 95.0 | Convergent with no subduction |
| 4. | 1994 | Northridge, California | 6.7 | 72 | Heart attacks | 65.2 | Transform |
| 5. | 1980 | Naples, Italy | 6.5 | 2,740 | Buildings collapsing | 57.7 | Convergent with subduction |

## ❹ Map of earthquakes

Here is a map showing the locations of the earthquakes on the three lists above.

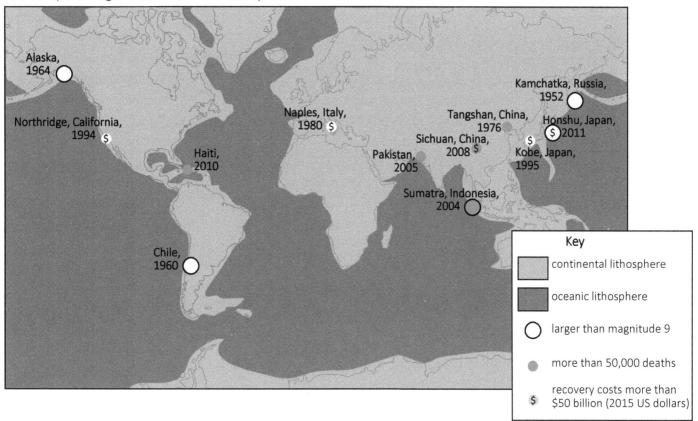

## Check

☐ Summarize patterns that explain why an earthquake may have large magnitude, be deadly, or be costly.
☐ Explain why it is unlikely for a single earthquake to be ranked as one of the largest, deadliest, and costliest of earthquakes.

## Chapter 10

### End of Chapter Questions: Student Debates

For each of the following questions, determine which student you agree with and explain why.

1. **Three students are discussing where earthquakes tend to occur.**

   **Student 1:** Earthquakes tend to happen in tropical areas near the equator where rocks are hot and able to bend elastically before rebounding.

   **Student 2:** Earthquakes tend to happen along the coast of all oceans and islands where rocks are wet and have low friction.

   **Student 3:** Earthquakes tend to happen near plate boundaries where rocks are stressed and have friction.

2. **Two students are discussing how many small earthquakes would need to occur to prevent a large magnitude earthquake from happening.**

   **Student 1:** Two magnitude 3 earthquakes add up to one magnitude 6 earthquake, so a few small magnitude 3 earthquakes could prevent a magnitude 6 from happening.

   **Student 2:** No, one large magnitude earthquake releases a thousand times more energy than a small earthquake, so thousands of magnitude 3 earthquakes would need to happen to prevent one magnitude 6 earthquake.

3. **Three students are discussing how an epicenter of an earthquake is found.**

   **Student 1:** It is identified as the area where shaking by surface waves was first felt by people.

   **Student 2:** It is the location where the highest amount of damage was done at the surface.

   **Student 3:** It is located by using information from body wave arrivals from three seismometers.

4. **Two students are discussing earthquake prediction.**

   **Student 1:** Geologists cannot predict earthquakes, but the very short-term warnings and long-term forecasts are improving.

   **Student 2:** Actually, geologists are getting better at accurately predicting exact earthquake occurrences, just like they are getting better at hurricane and volcanic eruption prediction.

5. **Three students are discussing the cause of most tsunami.**

   **Student 1:** Most tsunami are caused by large storms, such as hurricanes that create waves through powerful winds and low air pressure.

   **Student 2:** Most tsunami are caused by large, underwater earthquakes that create waves by moving the seafloor.

   **Student 3:** You are both right, since tsunami can be caused by earthquakes and hurricanes, and the largest tsunami occur when both happen at the same time.

### End of Chapter Questions: Short Answer

Using your own words or sketching and labeling a diagram, answer the following questions.

6. Your college president asks you to determine whether a large magnitude earthquake is likely to hit your campus in the next 10 years. List three types of data you would use during your investigation. Explain what each source of data would tell you about the likelihood of earthquake.

7. Your campus has a seismometer that recently recorded an earthquake. Give step-by-step directions to fellow students explaining how to determine where that earthquake occurred.

8. A friend says "Earthquakes tend to happen in locations with certain weather." Do you agree or disagree with your friend? Justify your response with at least three lines of supporting evidence.

9. Two towns are built near two different faults. Town A is more frequently and severely damaged by earthquakes than Town B. Hypothesize at least five distinct explanations why there is a difference.

10. Create a table to compare and contrast at least three separate aspects of earthquakes along the transform plate boundary in California and earthquakes along the convergent plate boundary in Washington state. Things to consider include earthquake size, earthquake depth, and potential hazards.

11. Your friends want to buy a house in an area that tends to have earthquakes. Your friends are relieved to learn that the house is not on a fault, so they do not want to get earthquake insurance. Create an argument for why your friends should still get earthquake insurance.

12. Explain why the largest magnitude earthquakes are not always the worst.

**Hints:** For each question, see the sections listed here for information relevant to answering it.

**1.** (10.3) **2.** (10.4) **3.** (10.1, 10.6) **4.** (10.7) **5.** (10.10) **6.** (10.1, 10.2, 10.3, 10.4, 10.5) **7.** (10.2, 10.6) **8.** (10.2, 10.3, 10.12) **9.** (10.3, 10.4, 10.7, 10.8, 10.9, 10.10, 10.11, 10.12) **10.** (10.3, 10.7, 10.8, 10.9, 10.10, 10.11, 10.12) **11.** (10.1, 10.4, 10.8, 10.9, 10.10, 10.11) **12.** (10.3, 10.4, 10.7, 10.8, 10.9, 10.10, 10.11, 10.12)

# Chapter 11:
# Earth's History

## Chapter Objectives

When you are finished reading this chapter, you should be able to …

• explain how to determine the relative ages of a sequence of events preserved in the rock record (11.1–11.5).

• summarize how to determine the numerical age of bedrock (11.6–11.7).

• explain how to integrate information obtained from bedrock to determine the geologic history of an area (11.1–11.10).

• summarize important events in Earth's history (11.9–11.14).

• explain how geologists determine Earth's history and give examples (11.9–11.14).

# 11.1 – 11.8 Age of Bedrock

In this section you will learn how geologists determine the order of the events that form rocks, giving their relative age. You will also learn the processes geologists use to determine the numerical age of rocks.

## Frequently Used Terms

The terms listed here are used repeatedly throughout this section, so by learning them before you read this section, you can focus your mental energy on the concepts presented.

**bedrock** The rock that makes up the solid component of Earth's crust; every place on Earth has bedrock underneath it, sometimes exposed at the surface where you can see it and sometimes deep beneath soil, sediments, and buildings.

**fossil** The preserved remains or evidence of a prehistoric living organism that died in the geologic past.

**half-life** The number of years it takes for half of the unstable atoms to radioactively decay into stable atoms.

**numerical age** The age of a rock or event as a number (e.g., this igneous rock is 65 million years old); commonly determined by using radiometric dating.

**radioactive decay** To change or convert from an unstable atom to a stable atom through the process of releasing energy and/or particles.

**radiometric dating** Determining the numerical age of a rock by using unstable atoms and their half-lives.

**relative age** The age of a rock or event compared to something else (e.g., this igneous rock is older than that sedimentary rock). It is determined by using relative dating.

**relative dating** Determining the relative ages of bedrock and the sequence of events by using guiding principles of relationships between rocks and knowledge of how they form.

**rock record** History of geologic events recorded in rock.

**unconformity** An erosion surface that is preserved in the rock record indicating there is time missing from the rock record.

**unstable atom** An atom that does not last forever because its nucleus is not stable, so it converts, or radioactively decays, into a stable atom; for example the unstable atom uranium-235 radioactively decays into the stable atom lead-207.

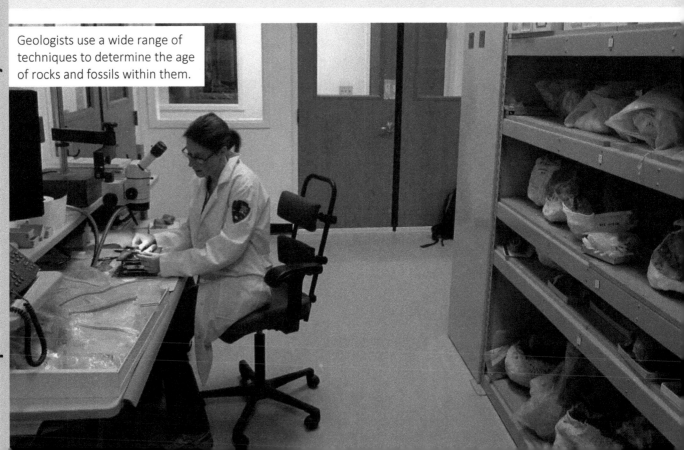

Geologists use a wide range of techniques to determine the age of rocks and fossils within them.

# 11.1 Relative Dating: Which Rock Layer Is Older?

**Key Concept:** Geologists use guiding principles to determine the relative ages of sedimentary bedrock layers. Relative dating determines which rock is older or younger than other rock, putting the events of rock formation in sequence. It does not determine the numerical age of rock, such as 100 million years old, which is described later in this chapter. The first guiding principle for relative dating is that a sedimentary rock layer beneath another rock layer has been there longer, so it is older **1**. The second guiding principle is that sedimentary layers start off as flat and horizontal **2**. A final guiding principle is that geologists can use fossils in rocks to determine the relative ages of rock because life changes over time **3**.

## **1** Guiding principle: Principle of superposition

As long as sedimentary rock layers have not been disturbed, such as the horizontal layers shown in the photo, the layer at the bottom formed first, and is therefore the oldest layer. Similarly, the layer at the top formed last and is therefore the youngest layer.

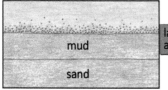
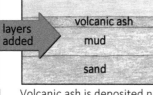
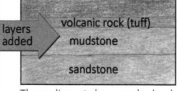

Mud is deposited on top of sand. It is younger than the sand.

Volcanic ash is deposited next and is younger.

The sediments become bedrock. The sandstone is the oldest layer.

## **2** Guiding principle: Principle of original horizontality

As sediments are deposited, the vast layers start off horizontal and flat. If geologists observe sedimentary rock layers that are not horizontal, such as the ones shown in the photo, they can interpret that the layers have been tilted or folded after they were deposited. Therefore, the tilting or folding is younger. This deformation is often caused by directional stress at a convergent plate boundary (see 9.11 and 9.13).

Sediments are deposited in flat layers and form sedimentary rock.

The folding occurred more recently than the formation of the rock, so it is younger.

## **3** Guiding principle: Fossils change over time

Fossils are the evidence of ancient organisms preserved in rock. The diversity of living organisms has changed over time, with new plants and animals emerging and others going extinct. Geologists can use fossils to determine relative ages of sedimentary rock layers. For example, rock that contains dinosaur bones is older than rock that contains horse bones.

Some species are buried by sediments and become fossils in sedimentary rock, providing a snapshot of life at the time the rock formed.

As species adapt to their changing environment, their descendants have a slightly different appearance. Some species go extinct.

The descendants continue to change. The youngest layer of rock can be identified because it has the most recent set of fossils.

**Check**  Before you continue, you should be able to answer each check without looking at the page.

☐ Describe three guiding principles that geologists use to determine the relative age of rock layers.
☐ Draw three labeled sketches of sedimentary rock layers that demonstrate the sequence of events using the three guiding principles.

# 11.2 Relative Dating: Which Feature Is Older?

**Key Concept:** Geologists use many guiding principles to figure out the relative order of events that affect bedrock.

Bedrock is older than features that affect it. For example, if a fault or an igneous dike cuts through bedrock, the original bedrock is older than the fault or intruding magma that formed the dike **1**. In addition, magma or lava can affect and interact with bedrock in ways that indicate that the resulting igneous rock is younger than the original bedrock **2**.

## **1** Guiding principle: Principle of cross-cutting relationships

When geologists find a feature, such as fault or dike, that cuts across, or cross-cuts, bedrock, it indicates that the original bedrock is older than the features that cut across it.

fault (younger)

dike (younger)

**Fault**

Bedrock moves on either side of a fault during an earthquake (see 9.10), so the fault cuts across older existing bedrock layers. The fault is younger than the bedrock.

**Dike**

A dike is an igneous intrusion that forms when magma creates, flows along, and fills a crack (see 7.1). The resulting igneous rock that makes up the dike cuts across older existing bedrock layers. The igneous dike is younger than the original bedrock.

## **2** Guiding principle: Contact metamorphism and inclusions

When geologists find igneous rock in contact with other bedrock, close examination of clues in the rocks can help determine whether the magma that became the igneous rock intruded into the preexisting rock or whether the other bedrock formed after the igneous rock was present.

contact metamorphism        igneous rock (younger)

inclusion            igneous rock (younger)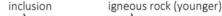

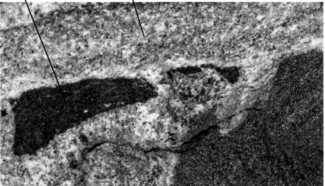

**Contact metamorphism**

The heat from magma raises the temperature of the bedrock it comes in contact with and contact metamorphoses that bedrock. After the magma cools to become part of the bedrock, the contact metamorphism remains.

**Inclusions**

Inclusions form when pieces of existing bedrock break off and become included in younger bedrock. For example bedrock can break off and become trapped in younger magma or become part of younger sedimentary rock.

## Check

☐ Describe two guiding principles used to help determine the age of rock features relative to each other.
☐ Draw two labeled sketches that demonstrate two principles that can be used to determine the relative order of events.

# 11.3 DATA AND DIAGRAMS: Ages of Bedrock in Cross-Section

**Key Concept:** A cross-section shows interpretations of bedrock and structures beneath Earth's surface. This diagram shows an example of an interpretation of the relationship of the orientations of igneous and sedimentary rocks and structures beneath the surface at a particular location **1**. To create a diagram like this, geologists make maps of the bedrock at Earth's surface. They then use the mapped relationships and knowledge of how rocks form to make an interpretation of their orientations and resulting relationships beneath the surface. In some cases, geologists are able to drill down to see bedrock beneath the surface to verify their interpretations. Tips on how to read this cross-section are below **2**. Use the questions to practice interpreting cross-sections **3**.

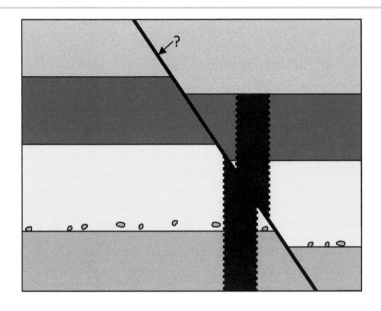
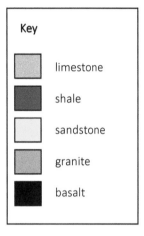

## **1** How to read the diagram

First make sure you understand that the diagram shows a vertical cross-section from the side showing what is underground. It is not a map looking down from the top showing the surface. Each of the colored areas is labeled as a different rock type in the key.

## **2** An example of what you might interpret

Sandstone is older than the shale because the sandstone layer is below the shale layer.

## **3** Questions

**1. What does this diagram show?**
a. An aerial photo of the surface
b. A sketch showing rocks as they would look if you viewed from a plane.
c. A photo of an outcrop of rocks in a steep cliff.
d. A sketch showing rocks as they would look if you cut into the ground.

**2. Based on observations you can make of the diagram, what is the diagonal line labeled "?"?**
a. Sedimentary layer
b. Fault
c. Unconformity

**3. The many short lines next to the basalt indicate contact metamorphism. Why didn't the basalt metamorphose the limestone?**
a. The basalt eroded after it contact metamorphosed rocks and cooled before the limestone formed.
b. The basalt was too cool to metamorphose the limestone.
c. The basalt is younger than the limestone, so contact metamorphism could not happen.

**4. Is the granite older or younger than the sandstone and why?**
a. The granite is younger because pieces of it are inclusions in the sandstone.
b. The granite is younger because it contact metamorphosed the sandstone.
c. The granite is older because pieces of it are inclusions in the sandstone.
d. The granite is older because it contact metamorphosed the sandstone.

**5. What is the correct sequence of events, from oldest to youngest?**
a. limestone, shale, sandstone, granite, basalt, fault
b. granite, sandstone, shale, limestone, fault, basalt
c. granite, sandstone, shale, basalt, limestone, fault
d. sandstone, shale, limestone, fault, basalt, granite

# 11.4 Erosion and Unconformities

**Key Concept:** Surfaces that indicate when erosion occurred in the past can be preserved in the rock record as unconformities. The rock record is the geologic history recorded in the bedrock, and it preserves information about the initial formation of and changes to bedrock. Erosion occurs when bedrock is exposed at Earth's surface, weathered, and transported away, removing information about the geologic history preserved in those rocks **1**. If the conditions in that area change, sediments may be deposited instead of eroded **2**. As a result of the erosion, there may be gaps in time that the rock does not record, called unconformities.

## **1** Bedrock erodes at the surface

When bedrock is exposed to physical and chemical weathering at Earth's surface (see 8.1 and 8.2), it can erode. Over tens of millions of years, the bedrock that forms entire mountain ranges can erode flat, resulting in a large area with a significant amount of bedrock removed. This process removes information about past environments that had been preserved in the rock, creating a gap in the geologic record.

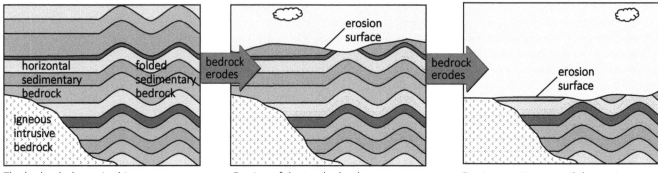

The bedrock shown in this cross section is intrusive igneous and sedimentary bedrock.

Erosion of the top bedrock exposes the deep bedrock. The sediments resulting from erosion are transported and deposited elsewhere.

Erosion continues until the environment changes. For example, a rising sea level would cause this area to be underwater and sediments to be deposited.

## **2** Sediments may be deposited on erosion surfaces

If an environment changes from one where erosion dominates to one where deposition dominates (see 8.14 and 8.15), then sediments are deposited on a surface where erosion previously occurred. The erosion surface separating the original bedrock from the younger sedimentary layers is called an unconformity. Unconformities indicate there is time missing from the rock record. They can be divided into three types based on the type or orientation of the original, eroded bedrock.

### Types of unconformities

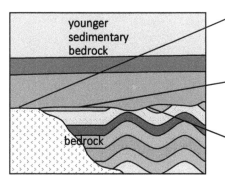

**Nonconformity** – An unconformity where the eroded bedrock is igneous or metamorphic. These rock types originally form deep beneath the surface. Deep bedrock requires a significant amount of erosion to expose it, so geologists interpret nonconformities to indicate an extensive amount of erosion.

**Disconformity** – An unconformity where the eroded bedrock is horizontal sedimentary rock layers. Disconformities are often difficult to identify because horizontal sedimentary layers are deposited on top of horizontal layers, so the record may appear continuous.

**Angular unconformity** – An unconformity where the eroded bedrock is sedimentary rock layers at an angle to the new sedimentary layers. The angle occurs because the original sedimentary layers tilt or fold deep beneath the surface. Similar to nonconformities, geologists interpret angular unconformities to indicate an extensive amount of erosion.

## Check

☐ Explain why the rock record is not continuous but may have gaps.
☐ Give two examples of scenarios that form unconformities that are easy to identify and one that forms an unconformity that is difficult.

# 11.5 Correlating Rock from Different Areas

**Key Concept:** Bedrock can be matched with, or correlated to, bedrock in other areas to determine the geologic history of **a larger area.** A single location at Earth's surface where bedrock is exposed at the surface is called an outcrop, and it contains a record of a limited geologic time recorded in that location **1**. The relative dating guiding principles described previously are useful for determining the history of that individual outcrop. To find out the history of a longer period of time, geologists must match, or correlate, the rock records of multiple individual areas to one another **2**. Correlation is particularly important in areas where there are unconformities, and parts of the geologic history were not preserved.

## **1** Outcrops represent a limited time

No place on Earth has had sediments continuously deposited since Earth began. Therefore, each location contains bedrock from only a small part of Earth's history.

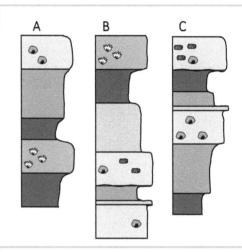

Geologists study different locations and determine the relative ages of the rocks in each outcrop to create a geologic history of each individual area, such as at Outcrops A, B, and C on the map. However, the relative ages between the individual locations are initially unknown.

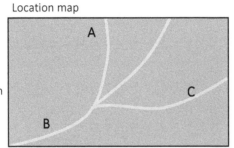

Location map

## **2** Correlation

To correlate and combine the geologic histories recorded in individual outcrops, geologists look for the same rock layer in different outcrops, based on distinct characteristics and fossils within them.

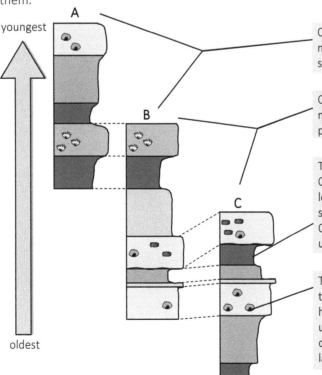

youngest

Particularly useful for correlation are fossils of species of organisms that lived in widespread locations and existed for a short period of time. These fossils are called index fossils. Also useful are volcanic ash layers because they formed during geologically short events. Notice on the diagram that correlation fills in gaps in individual rock records left by unconformities.

oldest

Outcrops A and B are correlated by matching an index fossil (🌸) and sedimentary rock layers.

Outcrops B and C are correlated by matching an index fossil (🐚) and a pink volcanic ash layer.

There is no record of this layer in Outcrop B. It was eroded in this area, leaving behind the unconformity seen in Outcrop B. Correlation with Outcrop C helps geologists better understand the history of the area.

This fossil is of a species that existed throughout the entire geologic history recorded in the area. It is not useful for correlation because it cannot be pinpointed to any one layer or moment in history.

## Check

☐ Explain how multiple geologic histories interpreted from multiple areas are combined to give one complete history.
☐ Describe two reasons why it is helpful to combine geologic histories of individual locations.

# 11.6 Half-Life

**Key Concept:** Geologists use unstable atoms to figure out the numerical ages of minerals formed in rock. A numerical age of rock is expressed by a number, such as 100 million years old, so it is different from the relative age. There are several techniques to determine the numerical age of a rock, and a common one is to use unstable atoms in rock **1**. Unstable atoms convert, or radioactively decay, to become stable atoms **2**. The rate of radioactive decay is measured using half-lives, which is the length of time it takes half of the unstable atoms to convert to stable atoms **3**.

## **1** Geologists determine numerical ages of minerals

Geologists may learn the relative ages of rocks while examining outcrops and maps. However, to figure out the geological history of an area, it is also often useful to determine numerical ages. Numerical ages are determined by collecting minerals from rocks and analyzing those minerals in a lab for unstable atoms and the stable atoms that they have radioactively decayed into.

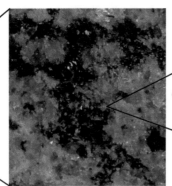

A geologist collects a piece of an igneous rock that has certain minerals that can be used to determine the numerical age.

These minerals are composed, in part, of unstable atoms that bonded with other atoms as the minerals formed. Some of the unstable atoms radioactively decay to become stable atoms, and the resulting stable atoms remain bonded as part of the mineral.

A geologist measures the relative number of stable and unstable atoms in minerals to calculate the numerical age of this igneous rock.

## **2** Unstable and stable atoms pairs

The nucleus of an atom contains protons and neutrons. Some atoms are unstable because of the particular number of neutrons contained. Unstable atoms radioactively decay by releasing energy and particles to become an atom with a nucleus that is stable.

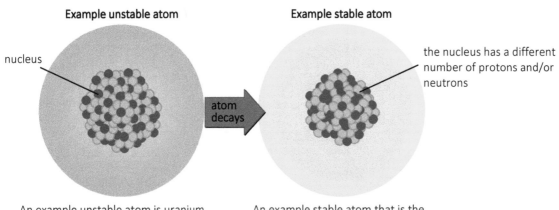

**Example unstable atom**

nucleus

atom decays

**Example stable atom**

the nucleus has a different number of protons and/or neutrons

An example unstable atom is uranium with 238 protons plus neutrons in its nucleus ($^{238}$U). It radioactively decays by emitting protons, neutrons, and energy.

An example stable atom that is the product of radioactive decay is lead with 206 protons and neutrons in the nucleus ($^{206}$Pb).

# 3 Determining the number of half-lives

In the time period of one half-life, half of the unstable atoms radioactively decay into the corresponding stable atom so that the number of unstable atoms is reduced by half. The length of time for each half-life, such as 1.3 billion years, remains the same, even as there are fewer and fewer unstable atoms left. To determine the number of half-lives that have elapsed, which is essential for calculating the numerical age, geologists examine the percentage of unstable atoms that remain, as shown in the table below.

| Number of half-lives | 0 half-lives | 1 half-life | 2 half-lives | 3 half-lives |
|---|---|---|---|---|
| | 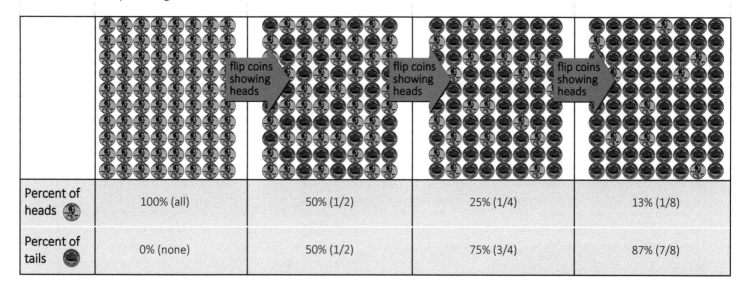 half of unstable atoms decay → | half of unstable atoms decay → | half of unstable atoms decay → | |
| Percent of unstable atoms ○ | 100% (all) | 50% (1/2) | 25% (1/4) | 13% (1/8) |
| Percent of stable atoms ● | 0% (none) | 50% (1/2) | 75% (3/4) | 87% (7/8) |

### Half-life of coin flips analogy

In this analogy, each coin is an atom. If the coin is showing heads, it is unstable, but if it is showing tales, then it is has radioactively decayed to a stable atom. Every "unstable" coin showing heads is flipped during one half-life with a set length of time. It has an equal chance of remaining heads or decaying to tales, representing the equal chance of radioactive decay for unstable atoms. Notice how the relative percentage of coins that are head and tails can determine the number of half-lives.

| | | flip coins showing heads → | flip coins showing heads → | flip coins showing heads → | |
|---|---|---|---|---|---|
| Percent of heads | 100% (all) | 50% (1/2) | 25% (1/4) | 13% (1/8) |
| Percent of tails | 0% (none) | 50% (1/2) | 75% (3/4) | 87% (7/8) |

# Check

□ Review the steps a geologist needs to go through to determine the numerical age of a rock.
□ Explain the relationship between unstable atoms, half-lives, and numerical age.
□ Summarize how the fraction or percent of unstable and stable atoms changes over several half-lives.

# 11.7 Using Half-Life in Radiometric Dating

**Key Concept:** To determine numerical age, geologists multiply the number of half-lives by the length of the half-life.
The most useful unstable atoms in geology have half-lives that are long enough to determine ages in millions or billions of years ❶ and are commonly found in rocks, such as igneous rocks ❷. The number of half-lives is measured in a lab by comparing the amount of unstable and stable atoms in a mineral. Once determined, the number of half-lives is then multiplied by the known length of time of the half-life for that unstable atom to determine the numerical age of when the mineral formed ❸. This relationship between the percentage of radioactive atoms and the age of the mineral can be represented by a graph ❹. This process of determining the numerical age of a rock by using unstable atoms and their half-lives is called radiometric dating.

## ❶ Unstable atoms that are useful for radiometric dating

To be useful in geology, an unstable atom needs to meet two criteria. First, it needs to be relatively common. Second, it needs to radioactively decay very slowly with a long half-life. This criteria is necessary because atoms with very short half-lives would radioactively decay completely before a mineral could be analyzed, leaving no unstable atoms for calculating the age. For this reason, unstable atoms with short half-lives, such as carbon-14, are only useful for dating recent geologic events.

| Unstable atom → Stable Atom | Half-life | Useful range of rock ages |
|---|---|---|
| Uranium ($^{238}U$) → Lead ($^{206}Pb$) | 4.5 billion years | 10 million years to Earth's beginning |
| Uranium ($^{235}U$) → Lead ($^{207}Pb$) | 0.7 billion years | 10 million years to Earth's beginning |
| Potassium ($^{40}K$) → Argon ($^{40}Ar$) | 1.3 billion years | 50,000 years to Earth's beginning |
| Carbon ($^{14}C$) → Nitrogen ($^{14}N$) | 5,730 years | 100 to 70,000 years |

## ❷ Rocks that are useful for radiometric dating

Rocks must fit the following criteria to be radiometrically dated: they contain minerals with unstable atoms, those minerals form when the rock forms, and none of the unstable or stable atoms escape out of the mineral after it forms. Only some types of rock, particularly igneous rock, form in such a way that ensures all three criteria are met.

### Igneous rock

Most magma contains unstable atoms, such as uranium-238 and potassium-40, that bond with other atoms to form minerals as the magma cools and rock forms. The stable atoms, such as lead-206 or argon-40, do not initially bond in these mineral structures. Later, after the unstable atoms decay, the resulting stable atoms remain bonded within the mineral and do not escape. Therefore, geologists can date when these minerals form. The numerical age of granite indicates when the magma cooled into minerals that form the rock.

### Sedimentary rock

Sediments come from a variety of places to form sedimentary rocks. If a geologist tries dating a sedimentary rock, the resulting dates measure when the minerals in the individual sediments initially formed in their original location, not the date the sediments were deposited and formed rock. Sedimentary rock, therefore, cannot be directly dated using unstable atoms. The numerical age of sandstone does not indicate when the sediments were deposited.

### Metamorphic rock

The parent rocks of some metamorphic rocks contain unstable atoms, such as uranium-238 and potassium-40. When bonds break and reform while minerals recrystallize during metamorphism, unstable and stable atoms may escape out of the mineral. As the metamorphic rock cools below a certain temperature, the unstable and stable atoms remain trapped in the minerals, and geologists may be able to date when this happens. The numerical age of gneiss may indicate an age late in the long process of metamorphism.

# ❸ Determining numerical age

Once geologists have found an appropriate rock, measured the percentage of an unstable atom that is still left in a mineral, and calculated the number of half-lives that have elapsed, they can calculate the age of the rock. The age of the rock is the number of half-lives an unstable atom in the rock has undergone multiplied by how long one half-life of that unstable atom lasts. As we saw earlier, the half-lives of common unstable atoms are known, making the calculation possible.

## Formula

number of half-lives  x  half-life length  =  age of rock

**Example:** A mineral with 25% $^{235}$U atoms and 75% $^{207}$Pb atoms has gone through 2 half-lives (see 11.6). The half-life of $^{235}$U is 0.7 billion years, so the mineral is 1.4 billion years old.

2 half-lives  x  0.7 billion years  =  1.4 billion years

### Determining numerical age of pizza analogy

In this analogy each piece of pizza represents one unstable atom. Half of the pieces of pizza are eaten during one pizza half-life. For example, if the pizza's half-life is 1 hour, and there are 25% of the pizza slices remaining, then the pizza was delivered 2 half-lives ago, or 2 hours ago, which is the pizza's numerical age.

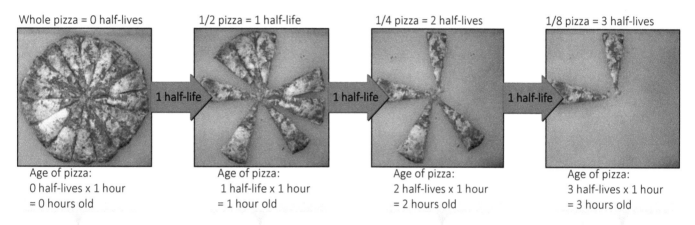

Whole pizza = 0 half-lives        1/2 pizza = 1 half-life        1/4 pizza = 2 half-lives        1/8 pizza = 3 half-lives

1 half-life          1 half-life          1 half-life

Age of pizza:
0 half-lives x 1 hour
= 0 hours old

Age of pizza:
1 half-life x 1 hour
= 1 hour old

Age of pizza:
2 half-lives x 1 hour
= 2 hours old

Age of pizza:
3 half-lives x 1 hour
= 3 hours old

# ❹ Determining numerical age using a graph

A graph of the percentage of unstable atoms remaining compared to the number of half-lives helps visualize how the numerical age is determined. For example, if there are 25% of unstable atoms remaining, then the mineral has gone through 2 half-lives, as shown by the gray arrows. The number of half-lives can be translated to the time elapsed for a particular unstable atom. In the example of $^{40}$K, 2-half-lives would mean the mineral is 2.6 billion years old.

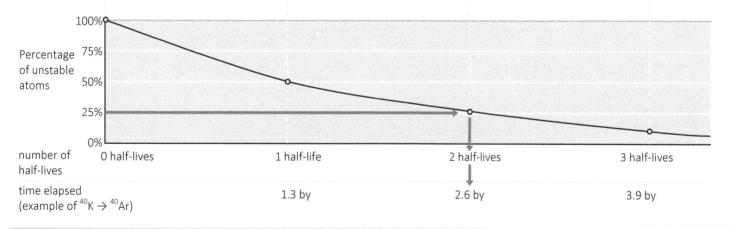

Percentage of unstable atoms

100%
75%
50%
25%
0%

number of half-lives: 0 half-lives        1 half-life        2 half-lives        3 half-lives

time elapsed (example of $^{40}$K $\rightarrow$ $^{40}$Ar): 1.3 by        2.6 by        3.9 by

# Check

☐ Compare the formation of minerals in the three rock types and explain what events can be radiometrically dated.
☐ Explain how the numerical age of rock is calculated and what two pieces of information are needed.
☐ Walk through a specific example of how to determine the numerical age of a rock using an common unstable atom.

# 11.8 Combining Relative and Radiometric Dating

**Key Concept:** Dating sedimentary rock and fossils requires combining relative and radiometric dating. Although sedimentary rock and fossils cannot be directly radiometrically dated, as discussed in 11.7, geologists can determine a range for their age. First, geologists determine the relative order of events in an outcrop. Then, the numerical ages of igneous rocks are determined, giving ages older and younger than the sedimentary rock **1**. The determined age range of the sedimentary rock layers and fossils can then be used to date fossils and sedimentary rock layers in other locations **2**.

## **1** How geologists determine the age of fossils

Most fossils cannot be radiometrically dated directly. The carbon that was in the living organism is often replaced during fossilization. Even when the original carbon remains, the half-life of carbon-14 is too short to date fossils older than 70,000 years because almost all carbon-14 has decayed by that time. Therefore, geologists determine the age range of fossils in an outcrop by combining relative and numerical ages, as shown.

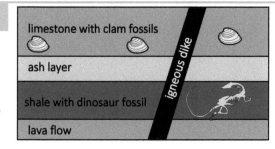

**Step 1: Determine the relative ages**
Geologists use the guiding principles of relative dating to determine the relative ages of rocks in the outcrop.

Youngest
5. igneous dike
4. limestone with clam fossils
3. ash layer
2. shale with dinosaur fossil
1. lava flow

**Step 2: Determine the numerical ages**
Geologists determine the numerical age of the igneous rocks in the outcrop by using radiometric dating.

igneous dike = 65 million years
ash layer = 70 million years old
lava flow = 80 million years old

**Step 3: Combine relative and numerical ages**
Geologists narrow down the age of the fossils within sedimentary rock using the ages of igneous rocks that are older and younger than the sedimentary rock.

limestone with clams = 70-65 million years old
shale with dinosaur = 80-70 million years old

## **2** Using fossils to date rocks and other fossils

Once the age range of fossils has been determined in one area, these fossils can then be used, through correlation, to determine the ages of rocks and fossils in other locations. Correlation is matching rocks in different locations (see 11.5). Index fossils are fossils that are particularly useful for correlation because these species only existed for a geologically short time and are widespread. The clam in this example is a good index fossil.

In the above outcrop, the clam fossil is determined to be between 65 and 70 million years old. In the nearby location shown to the right, a 67 million year old lava flow is younger than the clam fossil, helping to further narrow the age range of the clam fossils.

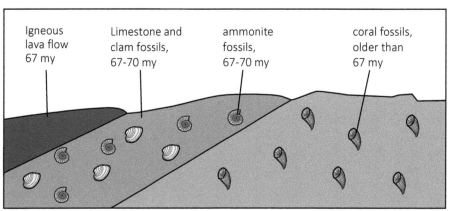

Igneous lava flow 67 my

Limestone and clam fossils, 67-70 my

ammonite fossils, 67-70 my

coral fossils, older than 67 my

The ammonite fossils are found exclusively in the same layer as the clam fossils, so they have the same age range as determined through correlation. The coral fossils are entirely below the clam fossils and must be older.

## Check

☐ Explain how the ages of sedimentary rocks and fossils are determined.
☐ Describe how the ages of fossils can be used to determine the ages of other fossils.

# 11.9 – 11.14 Earth's Timeline

In this section, you will learn how geologists divide Earth's history into different periods of time, some geological and biological events that happened during each time, and how we know.

## Frequently Used Terms

The terms listed here are used repeatedly throughout this section, so by learning them before you read this section, you can focus your mental energy on the concepts presented.

**era**  A division of Earth's history, such as the Paleozoic Era, Mesozoic Era, and Cenozoic Era.

**mass extinction**  The extinction of a large percentage of living organisms within a relatively short length of geologic time; most mass extinctions took fewer than 100,000 years to occur.

**Pangaea**  The most recent of many "super" continents made up of all Earth's continents together as one; it formed when continents came together at convergent plate boundaries, and it broke apart due to divergent plate boundaries.

**vertebrate**  Animal with a backbone, spinal cord, and head, such as fish, amphibians, reptiles, birds, and mammals.

This skull of a meat-eating dinosaur is an example of a fossil used by geologists to learn more about Earth's past.

# 11.9 Geologic Time Scale

**Key Concept:** Geologists divide Earth's history into different time periods to create the geologic time scale. Just as you divide your life into different time periods, such as teen-age and middle-age, geologists divide Earth's long history into different time periods, each with its own name ❶. The resulting geologic time scale is used by geologists to speak the same language about the age of different fossils or rocks. The divisions between time periods are based on changes in living organisms in the past, with extinctions often forming the boundaries ❷.

## ❶ Simplified geologic time scale

Geologists divide Earth's history into time periods of different lengths, similar to how historians divide history into time periods, such as the Medieval Age or the Ming Dynasty. Defining divisions of geologic time allows geologists to easily and consistently communicate the age of the fossils and rocks. Notice in the figure below that Precambrian time covers most of Earth's history, and it is followed by the Paleozoic Era, Mesozoic Era, and Cenozoic Era.

### Notation for dates
Ages are given as millions of years (My) old or billions of years (By) old. One billion years is 1,000 million years, so Earth is 4,500 million years or 4.5 billion years old. To help put it in perspective, 1 million days is 2,788 years.

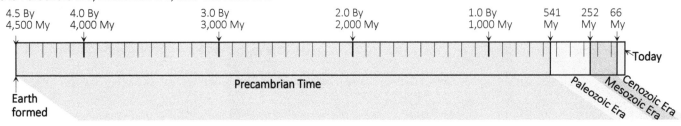

## ❷ Determining the divisions

Geologic eras are divided into periods. These periods are distinguished by geologically significant changes in living organisms that mark the beginnings and endings over the past 600 million years. One change that commonly marks a division is a mass extinction, which is a rapid decrease in the number and variety of living organisms. Precambrian times in Earth's history are longer and less finely divided because very little information has been preserved.

### Vertebrates through geologic time
Animals with a backbone, spinal cord, and head are called vertebrates. They evolved and diversified during the past 600 million years, as shown in the diagram beneath the timeline. These animals are discussed in more detail on the Paleozoic, Mesozoic, and Cenozoic Era pages.

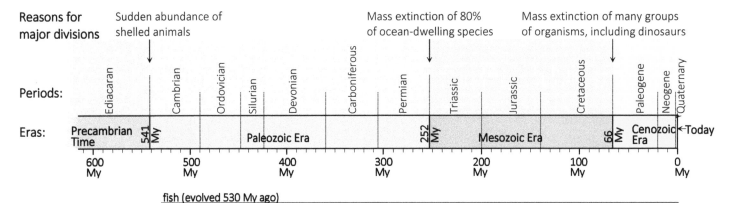

## Check

☐ Name the four major time periods in Earth's history, and put them in order.
☐ Summarize how divisions of geologic time are made.

# 11.10 Determining Events in Geologic Time

**Key Concept:** Geologists interpret how bedrock forms and the features and fossils within it to determine Earth's history.

To determine Earth's past environments of the continents—their climate and locations of plate boundaries, mountains, and shallow seas—geologists examine clues within rocks that were formed in those environments **1**. In addition to clues from the rock itself, fossils in rock tell us about past living organisms and how the types of organisms changed over Earth's history **2**. The two themes of changes to the continents and changes to living organisms are shown in the next four pages about each of Earth's major eras.

## 1 Changes in the environment of the continents

The continents have rearranged, combined, split, and been affected by different climates as plates and plate boundaries move. Geologists learn this history by studying rocks today. The following pages give examples of geologists' observations and their interpretations of the environment and plate tectonic setting, as illustrated in this map of North America showing rocks of different ages.

### Example: Convergent plate boundary

Examples of evidence that allow geologists to identify a location as having been a convergent plate boundary in the past:

- Igneous rock, such as granite, because it forms where oceanic lithosphere subducts and causes the mantle to melt (see 6.11).

- Metamorphic rock, because it forms where there are high pressures and temperatures under mountain ranges (see 9.7).

- Folded and faulted bedrock, because it forms where pressure is greater in one direction than another as the plates come together (see 9.13).

### Example: Land and water

Examples of sedimentary bedrock and features that allow geologists to identify whether locations were land or water in the past:

- Limestone, because it forms underwater in shallow seas and often contains marine fossils (see 8.14).

- Coal, because it forms in swamps and wetlands and often contains fossils of plants (see 8.15).

- Unconformities, because they form where bedrock is exposed as land to weathering and erosion (see 11.4).

## 2 Changes in living organisms

Geologists learn about extinct organisms by studying fossils in the bedrock. The diversity of living organisms changes as the environment changes. If a new characteristic helps a species reproduce more, that characteristic accumulates in a population of organisms. If this trend continues, that population may become different enough from their ancestors to be considered a new species.

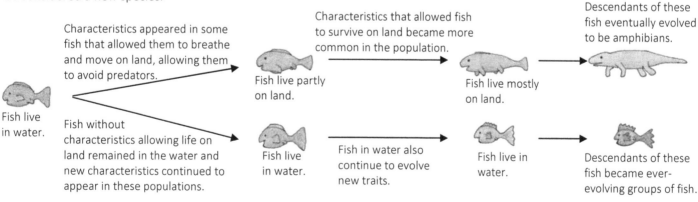

Fish live in water.

Characteristics appeared in some fish that allowed them to breathe and move on land, allowing them to avoid predators.

Fish without characteristics allowing life on land remained in the water and new characteristics continued to appear in these populations.

Fish live partly on land.

Characteristics that allowed fish to survive on land became more common in the population.

Fish live mostly on land.

Descendants of these fish eventually evolved to be amphibians.

Fish live in water.

Fish in water also continue to evolve new traits.

Fish live in water.

Descendants of these fish became ever-evolving groups of fish.

## Check

☐ Describe how geologists have figured out what continents were like in the past.
☐ Discuss how geologists know that living organisms changed over time and why they have changed.

# 11.11 Precambrian Time

**Key Concept:** Precambrian time makes up most of Earth's history and includes the formation of the continents and the appearance of living organisms. Precambrian time stretches from Earth's formation 4.5 billion years ago to the beginning of the Paleozoic Era, 541 million years ago. During this time, the beginnings of the continents formed, and they combined at convergent plate boundaries to form the cores of the continents today **1**. No life existed when Earth first formed, and most living organisms throughout the Precambrian were single-celled **2**. Animals first appeared at the very end of the Precambrian, although they were simpler than the animals we see today.

## **1** Changes in continents

The Earth, rocks, continents, and supercontinents formed.

### Protocontinents form
Partial melting of basalt crust, as described in 6.5, created more felsic crust that could not subduct because of its low density. These locations with thicker, low density crust collided together to form protocontinents. Geologists determined that these collisions occurred because most very old Precambrian rocks are igneous granite and metamorphic gneiss, both of which form at convergent plate boundaries.

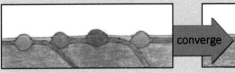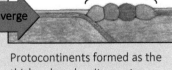

protocontinent

converge

Areas of low density, thicker crust formed because of partial melting of rock at hotspots and convergent plate boundaries with subduction.

Protocontinents formed as the thicker, low density crust collided together at convergent plate boundaries and combined instead of subducted.

### Oldest rocks
The oldest rock found by geologists is the Acasta gneiss in Canada at 4.0 billion years old. Rocks older than this have been changed by processes that are part of the rock cycle.

### Earth forms
The solar system formed from a nebula (see 2.2).

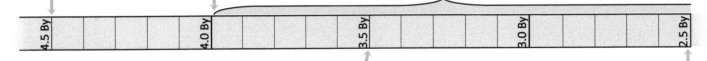

4.5 By | 4.0 By | 3.5 By | 3.0 By | 2.5 By

## **2** Changes in life

Living organisms appeared, and they remained ocean-dwelling and single-celled for most of the billions of years in the Precambrian.

### First living organisms
Simple, single-celled organisms similar to modern bacteria lived in the Precambrian seas. Geologists find evidence of their existence in sedimentary structures called stromatolites, as fossils of single cells, and in particles of carbon that result from photosynthesis. The atmosphere had low levels of oxygen, as evidenced by minerals in sedimentary rocks, such as pyrite, that cannot exist for long in the presence of oxygen.

### Stromatolites become abundant
Stromatolites form from mats of seafloor bacteria that trap layer upon layer of sediments. Stromatolites, and therefore the bacteria that form them, became more abundant as the shallow seas environment on stable continental margins became more extensive as protocontinents become continents. Geologists have found stromatolite fossils in widespread rocks of this age.

Reference timeline: Precambrian Time

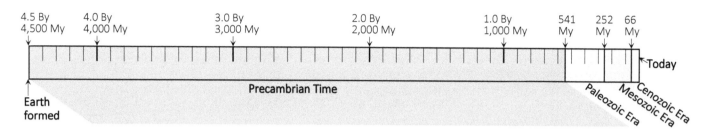

## Continents form

Protocontinents collided to form the cores of modern-day continents, creating stable continental margins ideal for living organisms. This process was similar to the processes forming protocontinents, but at a larger scale. Geologists have found similar evidence, including metamorphic rocks, folds, and faults. For example, each rock on the map of North America below represents bedrock that formed during collisions of separate protocontinents.

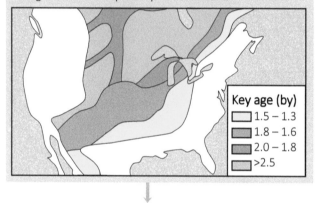

## Supercontinent Rodinia

Continents collided together to form a single continent, called the supercontinent Rodinia. Rock that formed at convergent plate boundaries, such as igneous granite and metamorphic gneiss, is found in a pattern around the edges of the continents where they collided and is dated to the same time period. Rodinia then separated again several hundred million years later, before the end of the Precambrian.

## Snowball Earth

Earth was mostly covered in ice during two pulses of an extreme ice age. Geologists have found evidence of vast glaciers during this time, including sediments deposited by glaciers on continents around the world (see 16.11). This image of Saturn's moon Enceledus may look similar to how Earth looked at this time.

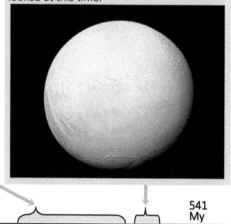

## First complex organisms

Living organisms remained single-celled and ocean-dwelling, but some groups became more complex with a cell nucleus, similar to amoeba and algae today. Many of them created oxygen through photosynthesis. Geologists find evidence in fossils of individual cells. The rising abundance of oxygen in the atmosphere is indicated by sedimentary rocks, called banded iron formations, made up of minerals that contain iron bonded with oxygen. Banded iron formations are evidence that living organisms were producing oxygen. They are an important source of iron mined today.

## Abundant animal fossils

After the Snowball Earth ice age ended, the first complex organisms eventually produced enough oxygen that oxygen levels in the atmosphere rose to be high enough for animals to become abundant. Animals are made up of many complex cells and require oxygen to breathe. They likely initially evolved at least a hundred million years before this, but they were not yet abundant and widespread. Geologists have identified fossils of animals that lived together in shallow sea environments. Similar to other animals at this time, the animal fossilized in this rock was soft-bodied and lived on the seafloor.

## Check

☐ Describe how the continents changed throughout the Precambrian time period.
☐ Describe how living organisms changed throughout the Precambrian time period.

# 11.12 Paleozoic Era

**Key Concept:** **The Paleozoic Era was characterized by the formation of Pangaea and the movement of living organisms onto land.** The Paleozoic Era occurred after the Precambrian time period and extended from 541 to 252 million years ago. During this era, the continents converged to form a new supercontinent, called Pangaea **1**. Animals first appeared at the end of Precambrian time, and the beginning of the Paleozoic Era is marked by the appearance of animals with shells, which continued to thrive throughout the era **2**. A group of early fish evolved into more complex fish, lobe-finned fish, amphibians, and finally reptiles. Despite the variety and abundance of living organisms, the end of the Paleozoic Era is marked by a major mass extinction.

## **1** Changes in continents

The supercontinent Pangaea formed and North America was often covered by shallow seas.

### Shallow seas cover North America

Much of the North American continent was, at times, underwater. Geologists determined this because they found sedimentary rock, such as limestone, throughout the center of what is now North America, indicating the extent of the area under water. The presence of unconformities in the outcrops suggests that at other times, sea level was lower and erosion occurred on the exposed land. Paleozoic-aged sedimentary rock layers that formed in shallow seas are found in what is now the Grand Canyon.

### Pangaea begins forming

The oceanic lithosphere between continents subducted until the continents began to converge to form the supercontinent Pangaea. Geologists found igneous and metamorphic rocks that formed in this way at convergent plate boundaries around the edges of the Paleozoic continents. Geologists radiometrically dated the igneous rocks to learn they were formed in the Paleozoic Era.

541
My

550 My     500 My     450 My     400 My

## **2** Changes in life

Shelled animals and vertebrates evolved and changed, and plants and animals moved to the land.

### Animals with shells appeared

The beginning of the Paleozoic Era, 541 My ago is marked by the geologically sudden appearance of many groups of animals that had shells that protected them from predators. These animals include the ancestors of modern-day snails, clams, and corals. Shelled animals are important to geologists because hard parts like shells increase the chance that an animal is preserved as a fossil, so geologists can use these fossils for learning about past life, relative dating, and correlation. Many of the abundant animals are not common anymore in modern oceans, such as the trilobites shown here.

trilobites

### Fish evolve sturdy fins

Early vertebrates in the Paleozoic Era were fish, and a group of fish, called lobe-finned fish, evolved sturdy bones and muscles in their fins. These allowed them to move on land if necessary. The significance to scientists is that all vertebrates with four legs (or two legs and two arms or wings) descended from a group of lobe-finned fish whose sturdy fins evolved into legs.

sturdy fin with bones and muscle

**Reference timeline: Paleozoic Era**

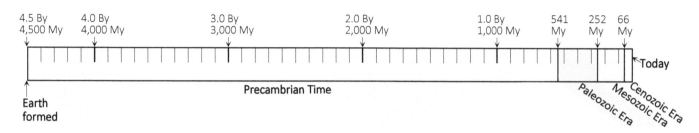

Earth formed — Precambrian Time — Paleozoic Era — Mesozoic Era — Cenozoic Era — Today

## Many swamps exist

Wide, flat areas along ancient coasts resulted in large coastal swamps like the modern-day one shown here in Tasmania. Geologists have determined that when plants growing in swampy areas die, burial in the low-oxygen environment turns those plants into coal deposits. When they identified many layers of coal, geologists used relative and absolute dating techniques to determine the coal was formed during this time period. Land plants and animals, amphibians in particular, lived in Paleozoic Era swamps.

## Supercontinent Pangaea

Continents collided together to form the supercontinent Pangaea which lasted for approximately one hundred million years before splitting apart. One line of evidence for these collisions is that the folded, faulted, and metamorphosed bedrock in the present-day Appalachian Mountains indicates that area was a large mountain range formed at a continent-continent convergent plate boundary between North America and Africa, as shown on the map.

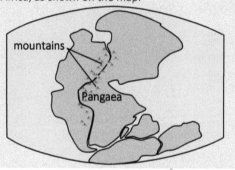

mountains

Pangaea

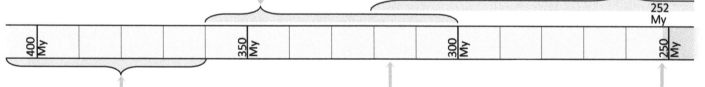

400 My — 350 My — 300 My — 250 My — 252 My

## Plants adapt to land

Plants were initially small and moss-like, but during this time they evolved roots and stems that could transport water, allowing them to grow large and form extensive forests. Plant roots help to stabilize sediments, so plants helped to slow down the erosion of land. Plants created previously non-existent swampy and forested habitats, which allowed for amphibians to evolve.

## Reptiles appear

A group of lobe-finned fish evolved into amphibians, and a group of amphibians evolved into reptiles. Both amphibians and reptiles have a head, tail, and four legs. However, a key difference is that reptile eggs have a protective covering, so reptiles can lay their eggs on land, unlike amphibians. This characteristic allowed reptiles to live in a wider range of habitats on land. For example, they could live in the interior of the supercontinent Pangaea, which developed a very dry climate because it was far from the rain-producing ocean.

## Mass extinction

Most species, including about 80% of ocean-dwelling species, went extinct at the end of the Paleozoic Era 252 My ago. The cause was complex. Geologists have found massive lava flows that caused greenhouse gasses to be released into the atmosphere, which lead to warming temperatures. The warmer oceans circulated poorly, causing parts to lose oxygen, resulting in conditions too harsh for most marine life.

## Check

☐ Describe how the continents changed throughout the Paleozoic Era.
☐ Describe how living organisms changed throughout the Paleozoic Era.
☐ Describe how vertebrates changed throughout the Paleozoic Era.

# 11.13 Mesozoic Era

**Key Concept:** The Mesozoic Era was characterized by the breakup of Pangaea and the continued diversification of vertebrates on land, in the oceans, and in the sky. The Mesozoic Era extended from 252 to 66 million years ago. During this time, the supercontinent Pangaea broke up into the continents we see today. As North America moved westward away from the other continents, subduction began on the West Coast, and the Atlantic Ocean formed off the East Coast **1**. Reptiles first evolved in the Paleozoic Era, but they diversified during the Mesozoic Era with some of them evolving into swimming and flying reptiles, dinosaurs, birds, and mammals **2**. A mass extinction marks the end of the Mesozoic Era.

## **1** Changes in continents

The Supercontinent Pangaea broke up, forming the modern-day continents, and islands collided with the west coast.

### Subduction begins under western North America

Along the western coast of North America, oceanic lithosphere subducted under the North American plate, causing the processes associated with convergent boundaries with subduction, such as folding and faulting of bedrock. The volcanoes resulting from subduction have since eroded away, but large areas of granite are now exposed at the surface as evidence of past magma chambers. This granite in Yosemite National Park in California is evidence of Mesozoic subduction.

### Pangaea begins breaking up

Divergent plate boundaries split the supercontinent apart, forming oceans between the modern-day continents. For example, the Atlantic Ocean formed between North America and Africa. Geologists interpret sedimentary rocks to have formed from sediments deposited in the rift valley between the continents, and the age of the newly-formed seafloor indicates when Pangaea pulled apart.

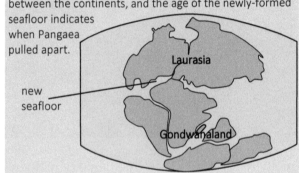

252 My

250 My    200 My    150 My

## **2** Changes in life

Reptiles dominated the Earth, with small mammals, dinosaurs, and birds appearing.

### Dinosaurs evolve

Dinosaurs, a group of reptiles that lived on land, evolved from other reptiles, and they diversified throughout the Mesozoic Era to become the dominant land vertebrates. One group of dinosaurs had feathers and evolved into modern birds. Other groups of non-dinosaur reptiles swam in the oceans and flew through the skies. Dinosaurs began small, but diversified to be larger and more exotic-looking.

### Mammals evolve

Mammals evolved from a group of reptiles and began as small rat-like animals. Most mammals differ from other animal groups in that they give birth to live young, produce milk for their young, and have hair or fur. Mammals remained small and relatively insignificant until the dinosaurs went extinct at the end of the Mesozoic Era.

**Reference timeline: Mesozoic Era**

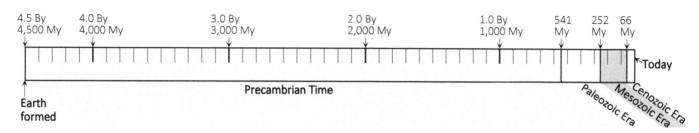

**Land adds to western North America**

Subduction of oceanic lithosphere under the North American plate continued. Islands did not subduct and instead joined onto the western part of the continent. This did this because they were made of rock that was not dense enough to subduct. Geologists know this because they have identified areas of bedrock along the west coast that formed elsewhere.

West coast of the North American continent.

The island was added to the continent.

North America grew as islands were added.

**Shallow seas cover the continent**

The sea level was high enough to cover part of North America with a shallow sea teaming with life. Geologists find extensive limestone layers in central North America containing marine fossils, indicating that that area was once underwater.

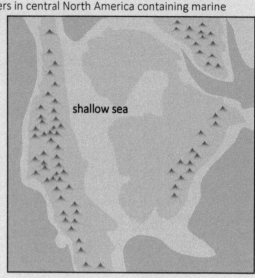

shallow sea

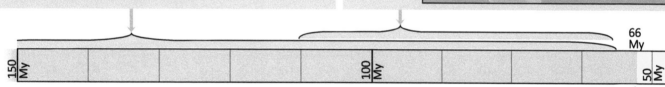

**Life in shallow seas**

Shelled animals that swam or floated in the water became more abundant, and their shells were key components of sediments, forming the rock limestone. Ammonites (squid-like animals with shells, see right) were predators in the ocean, but the top predators were swimming reptiles. Many of the changes to marine life were a result of developing defenses due to the expansion of predators. A swimming reptile is shown eating a fish in this scene from Mesozoic seas.

**Mass extinction**

Many groups of organisms, including dinosaurs, went extinct, most likely because a meteor hit Earth, sending dust and ash into the atmosphere that blocked the Sun, causing ecosystems to collapse. Geologists have identified many pieces of evidence for an impact of this size, including an impact crater of the correct size and age in Mexico.

## Check

☐ Describe how the continents changed throughout the Mesozoic Era.
☐ Describe how living organisms changed throughout the Mesozoic Era.
☐ Describe how vertebrates changed throughout the Mesozoic Era.

# 11.14 Cenozoic Era

**Key Concept:** **The Cenozoic Era, which includes today, features the current arrangement of continents, cooler climate, and the dominance of mammals.** The Cenozoic Era extends from 66 million years ago through today, so it is the time period during which we live. During this time, the continents continue their motion from the breakup of Pangaea through their current positions **1**. The climate cooled during the Cenozoic Era, eventually resulting in Earth's most recent ice age. Mammals replaced reptiles as the dominant animal and diversified into the large variety we see today, adapting to the changing climate and the appearance of grassland environments **2**. Modern humans lived during the Ice Age. Living organisms will continue to change and evolve in the future.

## **1** Changes in continents

The continents continue to move after the break-up of Pangaea, and the Ice Age began.

### Continents continue to move apart

The separating continents caused some oceans to grow and others to shrink. Geologists use seafloor ages to reconstruct the size of the past ocean based on the ages of the ocean lithosphere. For example, the Atlantic Ocean is growing as oceanic lithosphere is created at the divergent plate boundary. The shrinking Pacific Ocean has convergent plate boundaries with subduction around its margins. The ocean between India and Asia completely subducted, resulting in a continent-continent convergent plate boundary forming the Himalayan Mountains.

### The climate cools

Earth's temperature cooled, causing glaciers to form on Antarctica on the South Pole. As more water was tied up in glaciers, the sea level dropped. The cooling temperature was caused by the changing distribution of Earth's heat as continents blocked ocean circulation and the decrease in carbon dioxide in the atmosphere as the Himalayan Mountains weathered. Geologists interpret the temperatures based on evidence such as temperatures recorded in atomic differences in oxygen in shells in seafloor sediments.

## **2** Changes in life

Mammals dominated the Earth.

### Early mammals diversify

The extinction at the end of the Mesozoic Era opened many opportunities for surviving species to reproduce and diversify. Fossil evidence indicates that, although mammals initially remained small, they diversified after the extinction of Mesozoic reptiles. They continued to diversify throughout the Cenozoic Era. Many of the modern groups of mammals, such as rodents, primates, hoofed mammals, elephants, carnivores, and whales, first appeared in the early Cenozoic Era.

### Ocean predators change

The top predators of the Mesozoic oceans, reptiles, went extinct at the end of the Mesozoic Era. During the early Cenozoic Era, a group of carnivorous land mammals evolved into whales, as evidenced by a series of fossils with features that characterized a change from land animals to water-dwelling animals. Whales, along with the groups of sharks that survived the Mesozoic extinction, became the new top predators in the ocean. This early whale would not have walked well on its four legs on land, but its webbed feet helped it swim in the water.

Reference timeline: Cenozoic Era

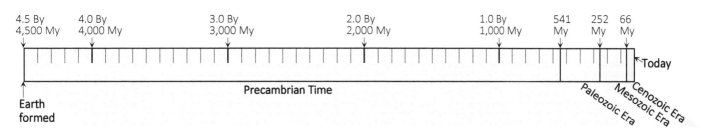

The Ice Age occurs

Geologists determined that Earth cooled to the point where glaciers covered much of North America based on the sediments they deposited. The map shows the maximum extent of glaciers covering North America during the Ice Age. Earth is currently in an interglacial period within the Ice Age, and glaciers are smaller now.

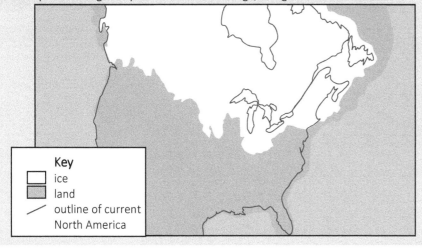

Key
☐ ice
▨ land
╱ outline of current North America

Future locations of continents

This map shows the current locations of the continents on Earth. This configuration will continue to change as divergent plate boundaries create now ocean crust and convergent plate boundaries subduct it or combine continents. Geologists can use modern plate motions to interpret where continents may be in the future.

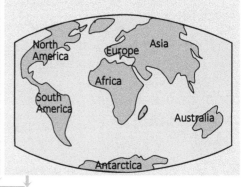

Grasslands evolve

Grasses evolved in the cooler Cenozoic climate, forming new environments of grasslands in which a variety of animals diversified into new species. One line of evidence for the grasslands is that geologists have found fossilized pollen dated to the Cenozoic Era. Animals with characteristics that allowed them to thrive in the grasslands diversified. Grasslands have only existed in the Cenozoic Era, and the long, thin legs of early horses, as shown here, helped them survive in this environment.

Life in the Ice Age

Many large mammals, such as mammoths, survived during the Ice Age because a large size conserves heat better than a small size. Early humans evolved from a group of primates during this time of Ice Age climate and extensive grasslands, with modern humans (Homo sapiens) appearing 0.2 million years (200,000 years) ago. Early humans built shelters, took care of their sick, and created art as shown in this cave drawing.

## Check

☐ Describe how the continents changed throughout the Cenozoic Era.
☐ Describe how living organisms changed throughout the Cenozoic Era.

## End of Chapter Questions: Student Debates

For each of the following questions, determine which student you agree with and explain why.

1. Two students are discussing if the rock layer at the top of an outcrop is always the youngest.

   **Student 1:** Since layers pile up over time, the rock layer at the top of a sequence is always the youngest rock.

   **Student 2:** That's true for sedimentary rocks, but if the layers are cut by an igneous rock, that igneous rock will be the youngest.

2. Two students are discussing whether the numerical age of an igneous rock can be estimated by looking at it.

   **Student 1:** No, you need sophisticated lab equipment to precisely measure the abundance of certain atoms in minerals in the rock.

   **Student 2:** Yes, some rocks look older than others, so you can use how the minerals look to estimate the numerical age.

3. Two students are discussing whether dinosaurs lived during the Ice Age.

   **Student 1:** Dinosaurs went extinct millions of years before the Ice Age began.

   **Student 2:** Both dinosaurs and the Ice Age happened so long ago that they were likely at the same time.

4. Three students are discussing how to determine the age of dinosaur bones.

   **Student 1:** You can use carbon-14 to radiometrically date the bones.

   **Student 2:** Actually, you can't date the bones themselves, but you can use unstable atoms to date the sedimentary rocks the bones are in.

   **Student 3:** You need to radiometrically date igneous rocks, and then use relative dating to determine the age of the dinosaur bones.

5. Three students are discussing when life first appeared on Earth.

   **Student 1:** Life appeared when Earth formed, 4.5 billion years ago at the beginning of the Precambrian.

   **Student 2:** Life appeared about a half billion years after Earth formed during the Precambrian.

   **Student 3:** Life appeared about 500 million years ago at the end of the Precambrian.

## End of Chapter Questions: Short Answer

Using your own words or sketching and labeling a diagram, answer the following questions.

6. Imagine and draw a cross section or an outcrop, and list the relative ages for each of the rocks or events. Your drawing must demonstrate at least four relative dating guiding principles.

7. Two outcrops are located in two different locations. The rocks in Outcrop A are easier to date than the rocks in Outcrop B. Hypothesize at least three distinct explanations why there is a difference.

8. A geologist identifies an igneous rock and a sedimentary rock as Mesozoic in age. Explain, using specific examples, how the geologist could make this interpretation for each of the rocks.

9. There are two similar outcrops of sedimentary rocks 10 miles apart, but the second outcrop does not have one of the layers present in the first outcrop. Write two hypotheses explaining why the layer is missing. To test your hypotheses, describe two observations you could make or data you could collect by visiting the outcrops. Explain what the observations or data would tell you about your two hypotheses.

10. Explain why it is more difficult to correlate Precambrian age rocks than rocks that are younger in age.

11. Draw a table to compare the continents and the environments in the Precambrian, Paleozoic, Mesozoic, and Cenozoic Eras.

12. You have a time machine and are designing a trip for vacationers who want to experience a variety of environments with different types of life. Make a list of four stops you would visit, including the time period and location. Write a short description of each stop, identifying the environment and life at each stop and how you know they would be there

13. A friend says "The continent of North America has not changed much in the past billion years." Do you agree or disagree with your friend? Justify your response with at least three lines of supporting evidence.

**Hints:** For each question, see the sections listed here for information relevant to answering it.

**1.** (11.1, 11.2) **2.** (11.6, 11.7) **3.** (11.13, 11.14) **4.** (11.8) **5.** (11.11) **6.** (11.1, 11.2, 11.3, 11.4) **7.** (11.1, 11.2, 11.3, 11.7, 11.8, 11.9) **8.** (11.1, 11.5, 11.6, 11.7, 11.13) **9.** (11.4, 11.5) **10.** (11.1, 11.5, 11.8, 11.9, 11.11, 11.12, 11.13, 11.14) **11.** (11.9, 11.11, 11.12, 11.13, 11.14) **12.** (11.10, 11.11, 11.12, 11.13, 11.14) **13.** (11.10, 11.11, 11.12, 11.13, 11.14)

# Chapter 12:
# Climate

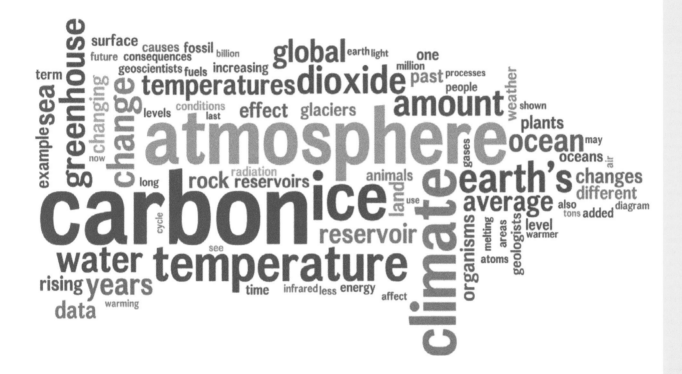

## Chapter Objectives

When you are finished reading this chapter, you should be able to …

• explain the relationship between climate, weather, global climate change, the carbon cycle, and the intensity of the greenhouse effect (12.1–12.5).

• explain how and why climate is currently changing, has changed in the past, and will change in the future (12.6–12.12).

• summarize the evidence for and consequences of global climate change (12.6, 12.11–12.17).

# 12.1 – 12.5 Climate and the Carbon Cycle

In this section, you will learn how the amount of carbon dioxide in the atmosphere changes and how it affects Earth's climate through the greenhouse effect.

## Frequently Used Terms

The terms listed here are used repeatedly throughout this section, so by learning them before you read this section, you can focus your mental energy on the concepts presented.

**carbon cycle**  The geologic model describing how carbon moves between reservoirs, through processes such as volcanic eruptions and breathing.

**carbon dioxide**  A gas, comprised of two oxygen atoms bonded to one carbon atom ($CO_2$), that makes up a very small proportion (0.04%) of Earth's atmosphere.

**carbon reservoir**  Locations on Earth where there is a significant amount of carbon, such as in the ocean, in the air, in organisms, and in rock.

**climate**  The long-term average of daily weather conditions of an area.

**fossil fuel**  Fuel—such as coal, natural gas, and oil—that formed from the remains of ancient organisms, such as plants and single-celled organisms.

**greenhouse effect**  The absorption of infrared radiation by greenhouse gases in a planet's atmosphere; the absorption causes the planet's average surface temperature to be higher than it would be without greenhouse gases in the atmosphere.

**greenhouse gas**  A gas that traps infrared radiation (felt as heat) in the atmosphere, such as carbon dioxide and methane.

**infrared radiation**  Wavelengths of light energy that people cannot see but which we can feel the effects of as heat energy.

**light energy**  Energy that may be radiated in a broad spectrum with different wavelengths.

**visible radiation**  Wavelengths of light energy that our eyes detect and we see as light.

The Deepwater Horizon oil rig in the Gulf of Mexico caught fire in 2010. Burning oil is a key way that carbon is added to the atmosphere.

# 12.1 Weather, Climate, and Atmospheric Carbon

**Key Concept:** Climate is the long-term average of daily weather conditions. Climate and weather are both related to the atmosphere, so people often confuse one for the other. Weather is the condition of the atmosphere at a particular place and specific time, such as whether it is sunny and windy in the afternoon **1**. Climate, in comparison, is general weather characteristics of a particular place over decades, such as whether the area is arid or tropical **2**. As a planet, Earth's global climate is primarily affected by its average temperature, which is influenced by the composition of the atmosphere, including the amount of the greenhouse gas carbon dioxide in it **3**.

## **1** Weather

Weather is the day-to-day state of the atmosphere, and it includes extreme events such as hurricanes. Meteorologists use data to forecast hourly or daily weather. Weather refers to a smaller region and not to the whole Earth.

## **2** Climate

Climate is the long-term average of weather conditions over decades. Geoscientists use data to study how climate was different in the past and how it might change in the future. Climate can refer to either a small region or the whole Earth.

The weather for the day shown in this California desert is sunny, cold, and snowy. A single weather event, such as a snowstorm, does not change the climate of this region.

The climate of this California desert is arid, which means there is a low amount of precipitation such as rain or snow. Sunny, hot days are more likely than snowy days, but day-to-day weather will vary.

The weather for the day shown in this East Coast forest is sunny, hot, and dry. A single weather event does not change the climate of this region.

The climate for this East Coast forest is temperate, which means the average temperatures are not extremely hot or cold throughout the year. Sunny, rainy, and snowy days are all common as the day-to-day weather varies.

## **3** Global climate and carbon in the atmosphere

Global climate, which is the average climate of the whole planet, depends significantly on the planet's average temperature. The planet's average temperature is related to the amount of carbon dioxide in the atmosphere. Therefore, to understand Earth's global climate, it is important to study carbon dioxide in the atmosphere.

### Earth's average temperature and carbon dioxide

Earth's average temperature is determined by its distance from the Sun and the composition of the atmosphere (see 2.10). In particular, greenhouse gases in the atmosphere, such as carbon dioxide, affect temperature because they trap light energy and warm the atmosphere through a process called the greenhouse effect (see 12.2).

### Changing carbon dioxide

Changing the composition of the atmosphere, particularly greenhouse gases such as carbon dioxide, changes the global temperature and therefore the global climate. Geoscientists study how carbon cycles into and out of the atmosphere to better understand this relationship.

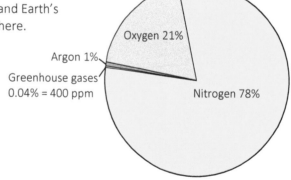

Carbon dioxide ($CO_2$), makes up much less than 1% of Earth's atmosphere. This small amount of carbon dioxide has a big impact on average surface temperature. Without it, Earth would be a frigid -18°C (0°F), but with the carbon dioxide, Earth is a comfortable 15°C (59°F).

---

**Check**    Before you continue, you should be able to answer each check without looking at the page.

☐ Compare and contrast weather and climate.
☐ Explain why a single extreme weather event does not change the climate or reflect a changing climate.
☐ Explain the relationship between global temperature, global climate, and greenhouse gases in the atmosphere.

# 12.2 Carbon Dioxide and the Greenhouse Effect

**Key Concept:**  Gases like carbon dioxide cause the greenhouse effect, which increases Earth's average temperature.
Energy from the Sun warms Earth's surface, which then emits energy into the atmosphere in the form of infrared radiation. Certain gases in the atmosphere, called greenhouse gases, absorb and re-emit this infrared radiation, keeping it in the atmosphere for longer. The resulting warming of the atmosphere is called the greenhouse effect **❶**. The greenhouse effect is more intense with more greenhouse gases, such as carbon dioxide, in the atmosphere **❷**.

## ❶ How the greenhouse effect works

Light energy from the Sun is made up of light with a spectrum of wavelengths. For example, visible radiation is the range of wavelengths that our eyes detect. In contrast, infrared radiation has longer wavelengths than visible radiation. Instead of detecting it with our eyes, people feel its effects as heat. Visible light from the Sun warms Earth's surface, and the surface emits that energy into the atmosphere as infrared radiation. Greenhouse gases in the atmosphere temporarily trap this infrared radiation, increasing Earth's average temperature, called the greenhouse effect.

Key

↓ Sun's visible light

• greenhouse gas

• other molecules in the atmosphere

⤴ infrared light from Earth's surface

1. Visible radiation from the Sun has minimal interactions with molecules in the atmosphere. It therefore passes through the atmosphere to the surface, just as visible radiation passes from the Moon and stars, though the atmosphere, to our eyes.

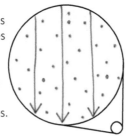

2. Visible radiation is absorbed by Earth's surface, transferring energy to the surface. As the ground heats up, it emits infrared radiation.

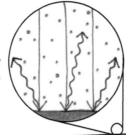

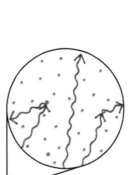

3. Greenhouse gases in the atmosphere include carbon dioxide, methane, and water. They absorb the infrared radiation emitted from Earth's surface. They re-radiate the infrared radiation in random directions, keeping the energy in the atmosphere as heat and causing temperatures to rise.

## ❷ Results of the greenhouse effect

A large amount of greenhouse gases will cause the infrared radiation to stay in the atmosphere for a long time, resulting in a more intense greenhouse effect and a higher temperature. Carbon dioxide is the most common greenhouse gas. Therefore, atmospheres with abundant carbon dioxide have an intense greenhouse effect. Geoscientists who study other planets have observed this relationship.

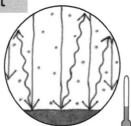

If there is no carbon dioxide in the atmosphere, as on the Moon, there is no greenhouse effect, so the average temperature is relatively cold.

If there is a small amount of carbon dioxide in the atmosphere, as on Earth, there is a minimal greenhouse effect and a moderate temperature.

If there is a large amount of carbon dioxide in the atmosphere, as on Venus, there is an intense greenhouse effect and a relatively hot temperature.

## Check

☐ Describe how the greenhouse effect works.
☐ Explain why the intensity of greenhouse effect varies.

# 12.3 Reservoirs of Carbon

**Key Concept:** Carbon exists in four major reservoirs: the atmosphere, rock, organisms, and water. As previously discussed, carbon bonded to oxygen in the form of carbon dioxide ($CO_2$) plays a key role in the greenhouse effect because it is an important greenhouse gas in the atmosphere. The element carbon also exists in other forms, such as bonded to other atoms to form minerals in rock. The general locations on Earth in which carbon is found, such as the atmosphere, rock, organisms, and water, are called carbon reservoirs **1**. Geoscientists model how the carbon behaves in each reservoir, as well as how carbon transfers from one reservoir to another, which helps them understand how changing the balance of carbon in one reservoir will affect other reservoirs.

## **1** Major reservoirs of carbon

Carbon atoms throughout Earth bond to other atoms, such as those that form carbon dioxide molecules in the atmosphere. In order to model the behavior of carbon atoms, geoscientists categorize where carbon is found into four major reservoirs: rock, atmosphere, organisms, and water. If carbon leaves one reservoir, it enters one of the others.

### Atmosphere

Carbon atoms in this reservoir are primarily bonded with oxygen atoms in the form of carbon dioxide ($CO_2$). Although carbon dioxide makes up a small fraction of a percent (0.04%) of the atmosphere, as a greenhouse gas it plays a significant role in controlling Earth's global climate because of the greenhouse effect (see 12.2). In addition, the atmosphere is an important link between reservoirs because carbon can easily move into and out of the atmosphere, as we will see in 12.4. As shown in the photo, Earth's atmosphere can be seen from space.

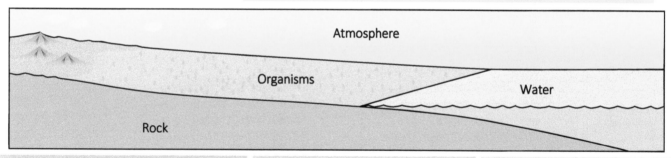

### Rock
Carbon in this reservoir bonds to other atoms to form stable carbonate minerals, such as calcite ($CaCO_3$). Carbon atoms are also in fossil fuels, such as natural gas and coal. Rock changes through slow geologic processes, so carbon tends to remain stored in this reservoir for long periods of time (millions of years). The sedimentary rock limestone shown in the photo contains abundant carbon.

### Organisms
Carbon is an important atom in this reservoir, bonding primarily to oxygen and hydrogen atoms to form molecules that compose organisms. Organisms include plants and animals on land and in the ocean, as well as their dead remains. For example, forests are made up of carbon-based trees, other plants, and animals.

### Water
Carbon in this reservoir is primarily dissolved in water (mostly in oceans). Some of it chemically reacts with the water molecules to form carbonic acid, making the ocean water slightly acidic. Although you cannot see it in the photo, the ocean has abundant dissolved carbon.

## Check
☐ Describe the carbon in each of the four reservoirs of carbon.
☐ Give examples of carbon in each reservoir.

# 12.4 The Carbon Cycle

**Key Concept:** The carbon cycle is a model showing how carbon moves between reservoirs. There are many processes, both natural and man-made, that affect the amount of carbon that moves from one reservoir to another **1**. Geoscientists model the cycling of carbon to investigate what causes the amount of carbon in each reservoir to change **2**. As carbon moves between reservoirs, it spends more time in some reservoirs than others **3**. The amount of carbon in a reservoir changes if the amount coming in and leaving are not equal, and these changes, particularly the amount of carbon in the atmosphere, affect Earth's life. Measurements show that people are currently increasing the amount of carbon in the atmosphere reservoir, which in turn is affecting the intensity of the greenhouse effect and changing Earth's global climate.

## **1** Carbon cycle processes

The carbon cycle is the movement of carbon atoms between carbon reservoirs, mostly through chemical reactions that change the bonding of carbon atoms to other atoms. When carbon leaves one reservoir, it enters another reservoir. Therefore, all the processes are both outputs from one reservoir and inputs into another, so they are in both columns.

| Carbon reservoir | Inputs: How carbon enters reservoirs | Outputs: How carbon leaves reservoirs | How people affect the carbon cycle (see 12.5) |
|---|---|---|---|
| **Rock** Includes bedrock, minerals, and fossil fuels | **Carbonate minerals precipitate out as rock:** Carbonate minerals form when carbon atoms bond with dissolved ions in water from chemical weathering of previous rock and precipitate out. **Dead organisms transform into fossils fuels:** Fossil fuels containing carbon form in rock when organisms are buried and transform over millions of years. | **Volcanoes erupt:** Volcanic eruptions release carbon dioxide that was dissolved in magma into the atmosphere. | Driving cars, flying planes, and producing electricity burn fossil fuels that contain carbon. Removing fossil fuels from rock decreases the carbon in the rock reservoir (long-term storage). |
| **Organisms** Includes land and ocean plants and animals and decaying organic matter | **Plants photosynthesize:** Plants on land and single-cell plant-like plankton in the ocean grow through photosynthesis by removing carbon from the atmosphere. | **Animals breathe and dead organisms decompose:** Animals breathe, exhaling carbon dioxide gas; dead organisms decompose, releasing carbon dioxide gas into the atmosphere. **Dead organisms transform into fossils fuels:** Organisms are buried and transformed over millions of years into fossil fuel in rock. | The burning of plants, mainly trees, increases the input of carbon into the atmosphere. |
| **Water** Includes oceans, rivers, and groundwater | **Oceans absorb:** Oceans, rain, and other bodies of water dissolve carbon from the atmosphere. | **Oceans release:** Oceans and other bodies of water release dissolved carbon to the atmosphere. **Carbonate minerals precipitate out as rock:** Carbon and dissolved ions bond to precipitate carbonate minerals, forming rock. | Increased carbon in the atmosphere means increased carbon dissolved in the ocean. The carbon dioxide chemically reacts with water to form carbonic acid, making the ocean more acidic. |
| **Atmosphere** Includes the air above Earth's surface | **Volcanoes erupt:** Volcanic eruptions release carbon as carbon dioxide dissolved in magma. **Animals breathe and dead organisms decompose:** Carbon is exhaled as animals breathe, and it is released as dead life decomposes. **Oceans release:** Oceans and other water release dissolved carbon. | **Plants photosynthesize:** Carbon is used by land plants and single-celled plant-like plankton as they grow. **Oceans absorb:** Carbon is dissolved in oceans, rain, and other bodies of water. | Burning fossil fuels releases carbon into the atmosphere. This additional carbon increases the intensity of the greenhouse effect. |

# 2 Carbon cycle model

The carbon cycle model involves input and output processes that move carbon between reservoirs as described in detail in the table to the left. This model was created and used by geoscientists to better understand the impact of different processes and activities on the amount of carbon in the different reservoirs. The processes shown here are all natural processes. The impacts people have on the carbon cycle are shown in 12.5.

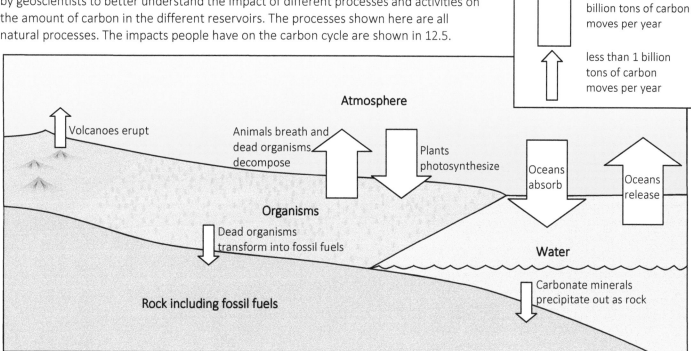

# 3 Sizes of reservoirs and rates of carbon movement

The amount of carbon that moves into and out of reservoirs and the rate at which it moves is not related to the actual size of the reservoir.

**Rock** in Earth's crust is the largest carbon reservoir, but carbon enters and leaves slowly through geologic processes over hundreds of millions of years. Therefore, the rock reservoir is important for long-term storage of carbon.

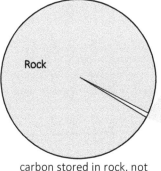
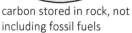

carbon stored in rock, not including fossil fuels

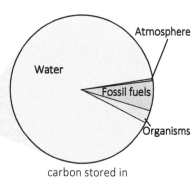

carbon stored in other reservoirs

The **atmosphere** is the smallest reservoir, but carbon enters and leaves relatively quickly over decades. Therefore, small changes to the amount of carbon moved into and out of it can have a dramatic effect on the amount of carbon in the atmosphere reservoir. These changes affect Earth's global climate causing a sustained change in the world's long-term weather conditions.

**Organisms** are a small carbon reservoir, and carbon enters and leaves quickly over seasons, years, and decades.

**Fossil fuels** are a small carbon reservoir, but they trapped carbon for millions of years. However, people are extracting and burning them, considerably speeding up the rate at which carbon leaves to tens to hundreds of years.

**Water** is a large reservoir compared to most other reservoirs. Water in contact with the atmosphere absorbs and releases carbon quickly over years and decades. In comparison, water in the deep ocean stores carbon for hundreds to thousands of years.

# Check

☐ Summarize how carbon naturally moves between the four reservoirs.
☐ Discuss how people are affecting the amount of carbon entering and leaving the atmosphere.
☐ Give two examples showing how the size of a carbon reservoir relates to the rate of inputs and outputs for that reservoir.

# 12.5 DATA AND DIAGRAMS: People and Atmospheric Carbon

**Key Concept:** Diagrams with arrows and equations can show the balance of inputs and outputs to a reservoir over time. The arrows in this diagram and the equation above it focus on how people affect the movement of carbon through the reservoirs as part of the carbon cycle. These arrows do not match the arrows in 12.4 because the arrows in the previous diagram include only natural processes, and these are additional changes due to the activities of people **1**. To create a diagram like this, geoscientists compile vast amounts of information from scientific studies and governments' reports. Tips on how to read this diagram are below **2**. Use the questions to practice interpreting arrow diagrams **3**.

| extra carbon people add to the atmosphere | minus | extra carbon removed naturally from the atmosphere | = | total extra carbon added to the atmosphere |
|---|---|---|---|---|
| 6.4 + 1.6 billion tons | − | 2.6 + 2.2 billion tons | = | 3.2 billion tons |

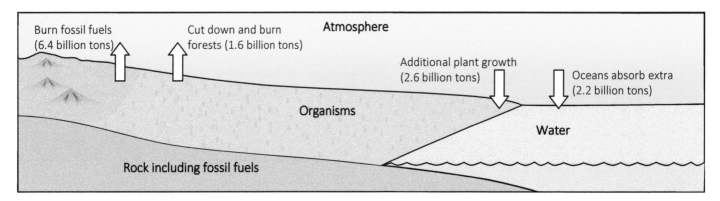

## 1 How to read the diagram

Find the four reservoirs of carbon and examine the arrows that link them, indicating the movement of carbon from reservoir to reservoir. Compare the arrows with the equation and relate them to each other.

## 2 An example of what you might interpret

Burning fossil fuels and removing plants causes 8 billion more tons of carbon to be added to the atmosphere each year than what would be added through natural processes.

## 3 Questions

**1. What does this diagram show?**
a. all carbon added to and removed from the atmosphere reservoir
b. carbon added to and removed from the atmosphere reservoir due to people's activity
c. how people can reduce the amount of carbon added to the atmosphere reservoir

**2. Based on this diagram, what human activities add carbon to the atmosphere reservoir?**
a. additional plant growth
b. additional plant growth and absorbing by oceans
c. burn fossil fuel
d. burn fossil fuel and cut forests
e. burn fossil fuel, cut forests, additional plant growth, and absorbing by oceans

**3. Is the carbon added by people to the atmosphere reservoir all removed naturally? How can you tell from this diagram?**
a. Yes, there are arrows showing removal from the atmosphere
b. Yes, two arrows show additions and two show removals
c. No, there are no arrows showing it returns to the rock reservoir
d. No, the amount removed is less than the amount added

**4. What equation would you use to calculate how the amount of carbon in the organism reservoir is changing as a result of human activity?**
a. 2.6 − 1.6 = 1.0 billion tons of carbon added
b. 4.8 − 1.6 = 3.2 billion tons of carbon added
c. 4.8 + 1.6 − 2.6 = 3.8 billion tons of carbon added
d. 8.0 − 4.8 = 3.2 billion tons of carbon added

**5. How is the amount of carbon in different reservoirs changing as a result of human activity?**
a. Carbon in the atmosphere is increasing, carbon in rock is increasing, carbon in living organisms is staying the same, and carbon in the ocean is decreasing.
b. Carbon in the atmosphere is increasing, carbon in rock is decreasing, carbon in living organisms is increasing, and carbon in the ocean is increasing.
c. Carbon in the atmosphere is increasing, carbon in rock is decreasing, carbon in living organisms is decreasing, and carbon in the ocean is increasing.
d. Carbon in the atmosphere is staying the same, carbon in rock is increasing, carbon in living organisms is staying the same, and carbon in the ocean is decreasing.

# 12.6 – 12.10 Climate and Climate Change

In this section, you will learn about how and why the climate has changed in the past, and what that might mean for the future.

## Frequently Used Terms

The terms listed here are used repeatedly throughout this section, so by learning them before you read this section, you can focus your mental energy on the concepts presented.

**global climate change**  A sustained change in the world's long-term weather conditions.

**global warming**  The current global climate change that is caused by a global increase in temperature due to a more intense greenhouse effect.

**ice age**  A period in Earth's history when the average temperature is a few degrees cooler than normal, resulting in extensive glaciers covering large parts of Earth's surface; the most recent Ice Age began about 2 million years ago and continues through today, although we are in a warm period within it.

Geoscientists store cores of ice from glaciers that have trapped bubbles of air from Earth's past. Studying these helps them learn about Earth's past and possible future.

# 12.6 Climate Data for the Last 150 Years

**Key Concept:** Recent climate change is due to rapidly increasing greenhouse gases, particularly carbon dioxide, in the atmosphere. As described earlier, changes in the amount of greenhouse gases in the atmosphere affect the intensity of the greenhouse effect, which changes average global temperatures. Geoscientists use numerous techniques to measure carbon dioxide levels and temperature over the past 150 years **1**. It is clear that based on the data, both carbon dioxide levels and temperature are increasing **2**. This relationship is in agreement with predictions made based on our understanding of how the greenhouse effect works. Geoscientists who study climate and the carbon cycle have determined that the additional carbon dioxide added to the atmosphere by people is causing the recent changes in Earth's global climate.

## **1** Collecting data for the last 150 years

In the past 150 years or so, geoscientists have been able to directly measure temperature using thermometers. Thermometers can measure surface air temperature, air temperature high in the atmosphere, and deep and shallow ocean water temperature. More recently, satellites have measured air, land surface, and ocean surface temperatures. Carbon dioxide measurements are done by collecting air samples, often using balloons to sample higher in the atmosphere, like the one shown in the photo. One of the best records of carbon dioxide levels has been taken continually at Mauna Loa, Hawaii since 1958 (see below).

## **2** Data for Earth's past 150 years

As shown in the graph, over the past 150 years, both Earth's temperature and the level of carbon dioxide in Earth's atmosphere have increased dramatically. This change is significant because it is happening at a rate faster than what has been previously recorded in Earth's history. The amount of carbon dioxide in the atmosphere is higher than it has been in the past 800 thousand years (see 12.7). This dramatic rise in carbon dioxide levels is caused by people putting carbon dioxide into the atmosphere faster than it is removed naturally through the processes in the carbon cycle, mostly by burning fossil fuels (see 12.5).

### Climate Change
The resulting increase in temperature due to the enhanced greenhouse effect is resulting in global climate change. As Earth's average temperature rises, the term "global climate change" is a more descriptive and appropriate term than "global warming" because the changing temperature affects the amount of precipitation and other aspects of climate (see 12.1).

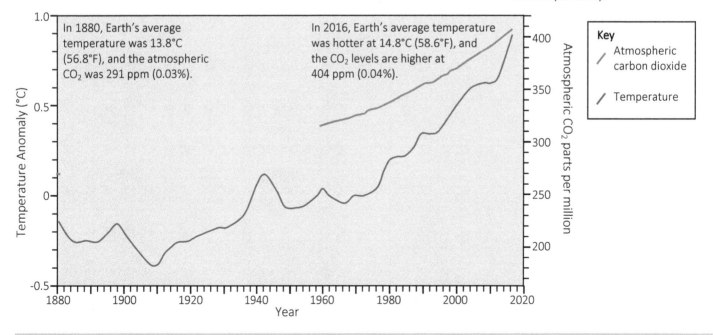

## Check

☐ Summarize how geoscientists determine past temperatures and carbon dioxide levels over the last 150 years.
☐ Explain how the levels of carbon dioxide in the atmosphere and temperature in Earth's past relate to each other.

# 12.7 Climate Data for the Last 800,000 Years

**Key Concept:** Geoscientists collect climate data from glacial ice to study Earth's temperature and carbon dioxide levels during the past 800,000 years. To better understand the significance of recent changes in temperature and carbon dioxide levels over the last 150 years, it is helpful to examine Earth's past to put them in context. To do this, geoscientists study air bubbles in glacial ice that preserved the atmosphere from when the ice formed **1**. When compared to the range of temperatures in the last 800,000 years, Earth is currently in a warmer period, and the levels of carbon dioxide are higher **2**.

## **1** Collecting data for the last 800,000 years

We cannot go back in time and measure past air temperature with a thermometer. Therefore, geoscientists must measure temperatures and carbon dioxide levels of the past million years through indirect measurements. As described below, an important source of data comes from glacial ice. In addition, there are other pieces of evidence, such as the varying thickness of tree rings, growth bands in coral, and layers deposited in lakes, that geoscientists can use to interpret changing temperature and climate conditions in the past.

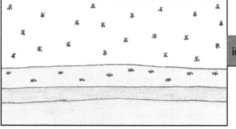

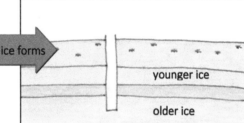

Snow falls on land. New snow is added on top of older snow, compacting it to become layers of glacial ice with bubbles of trapped air.

Geoscientists drill into the glacial ice and remove ice cores with layers with trapped air bubbles. They bring the ice cores to a lab for analysis.

At the lab, geoscientists analyze air bubbles in each layer. Geoscientists can directly measure the amount of carbon dioxide. To determine temperature, they measure atomic differences in oxygen atoms that were caused by differing temperatures.

## **2** Data for Earth's past 800,000 years

Earth's current temperature is near the highest levels during the past 800,000 years. In comparison, the carbon dioxide levels in the atmosphere are much higher than any point during this time. The graph below shows a repeating pattern of increasing and decreasing temperatures and carbon dioxide levels. The time graphed is the second half of the Ice Age that began about 2 million years ago.

### Ice Age

Ice ages are times when glaciers cover continents, such as the glaciers on Antarctica and Greenland today. Geoscientists interpret this graph to determine that Earth is currently in a warm period of the Ice Age.

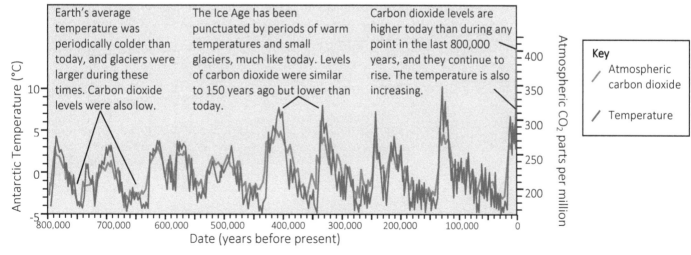

## Check

☐ Summarize how geoscientists determine past temperatures and carbon dioxide levels over the last 800,000 years.
☐ Explain how the levels of carbon dioxide in the atmosphere and temperature in Earth's past relate to each other.

# 12.8 Climate Data for the Last 600 million Years

**Key Concept:** Geoscientists collect climate data from sediment cores to study Earth's temperature and carbon dioxide levels during the last 600 million years. Analyzing ice cores is only useful for studying past times when there were glaciers. There were no glaciers before the Ice Age began about 2 million years ago, so geoscientists use other strategies to determine ancient temperatures. For example, geoscientists study ocean sediment to learn about climates over the last 600 million years **1**. The results of sediment analysis show that Earth is currently in one of the several ice ages that have occurred in Earth's past **2**.

## **1** Collecting data for the last 600 million years

Geoscientists collect evidence of Earth's temperatures prior to one million years ago in sediments and sedimentary rocks, which are the only source of data from that long ago. Fossils of plants and plant pollen tell researchers what plants were present at different points in ancient history, revealing what the climate must have been like. In addition, similar to how geoscientists use atomic difference in oxygen atoms in ice, geoscientists can learn the temperature of ancient oceans by using those atomic differences in oxygen in shells of plankton that form layers of sediment on the seafloor after they die.

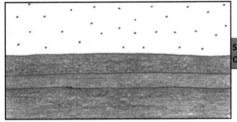

Sediment with plankton shells fall on the seafloor. More sediment continues to fall on the older sediments, forming into layers.

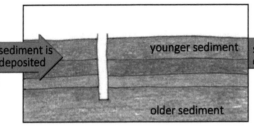

Geoscientists drill into sediment and remove sediment cores with shells in layers. They bring the sediment cores to a lab for analysis.

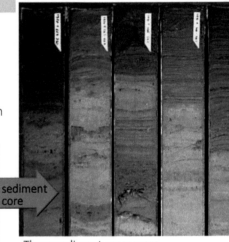

These sediment cores were removed from the seafloor by geoscientists in a scientific research vessel and are being analyzed layer by layer.

## **2** Data for Earth's past 600 million years

Earth's average temperature has varied over the last 600 million years. We are currently in a warm period during an overall cooler ice age. Plants and animals today, including people, are adapted to live in these cooler temperatures. Most things living in North America today could not have survived the different climate of the past. When the global climate changes considerably, living organisms need to adapt, or they will go extinct.

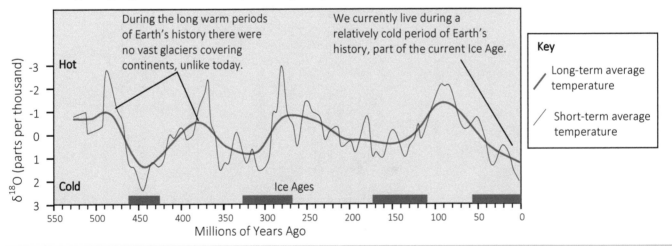

## Check

☐ Summarize how geoscientists determine past temperatures over the last 600 million years.
☐ Compare Earth's current temperature to those during the past 600 million years.

# 12.9 Causes of Climate Change

**Key Concept:** Climate change can occur on short and long term time scales, and may be caused both by human activity and by natural processes. Although human activity often dominates current discussions of climate change, short term causes of climate change also include natural processes like volcanic eruptions and meteor impacts **1**. Cycles relating to Earth's orbit cause medium term variations in climate of tens to hundreds of thousands of years **2**. Long term influences, which affect whether or not Earth is in an ice age, are determined by plate tectonics and ocean circulation **3**.

## **1** Short term causes of climate change

Carbon dioxide and temperature began to dramatically increase around 150 years ago, which corresponds to when people started burning large quantities of fossil fuels. As described in 12.5, this process transferred carbon into the atmospheric carbon reservoir and intensified the greenhouse effect, causing climate change. Other causes of short term climate change include volcanic eruptions and meteor impacts. In both cases, ash thrown into the atmosphere blocks the light energy from the Sun from hitting Earth's surface, initially cooling the climate, and any carbon dioxide that was released stays in the atmosphere tens to hundreds of years longer, warming the climate.

**Example past 150 years:** At a few points in Earth's history, such as at the end of the Paleozoic Era, massive volcanic eruptions released tremendous amounts of carbon dioxide. The resulting global warming possibly contributed to major mass extinctions. Current eruptions, like this one in Iceland, are much smaller than ones that dramatically changed climate in the past.

## **2** Medium term causes of climate

Variations in temperature lasting tens of thousands to hundreds of thousands of years are influenced by variations in Earth's orbit, which can become more circular or more elliptical over time, and by the change in the tilt of Earth's axis, both in terms of the amount of tilt and the direction of tilt as Earth orbits the Sun. These variations affect the distribution of light energy from the Sun hitting Earth each season.

**Example past 800,000 years:** During the current Ice Age, glaciers repeatedly grew as global temperature cooled and shrunk as global temperatures warmed as a result of a combination of these medium term variations in climate. This map shows the size of the glacial ice at Earth's North Pole 18,000 years ago during the Pleistocene Ice Age.

**Pleistocene** (18,000 years ago)

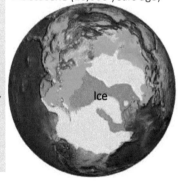

Ice

## **3** Long term causes of climate change

The variations lasting tens to hundreds of millions of years are influenced by the movement of continents by plate tectonic processes. The position of the continents influences ocean circulation. The circulation of the oceans helps to distribute heat around the globe, so continental position affects global climate. Continents at the poles can also affect climate if glaciers grow over them, cooling the globe due to amplification by positive feedback (see 12.14). Finally, the weathering process removes carbon dioxide from the atmosphere, so a large amount of rock newly exposed to weathering, such as during mountain building, may cool the climate.

**Example past 600 million years:** As the Himalayan Mountains grew at a continent-continent convergent plate boundary beginning 50 million years ago, a large amount of rock began to weather. Atmospheric and oceanic circulation changed, and Earth's average temperature cooled. Glaciers formed on Antarctica, located at the South Pole. This map shows the different arrangement of Earth's continents 50 million years ago, when it was much warmer.

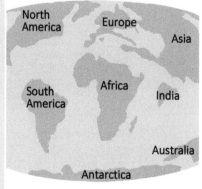

North America    Europe    Asia

South America    Africa    India

Australia

Antarctica

## Check

☐ Explain why Earth's temperature might change on the short term, medium term, and long term time frame.
☐ Give an example of Earth's temperature change in the short term, medium term, and long term.

# 12.10 Earth's Future Climate

**Key Concept:** Geoscientists use their understanding of geologic processes and the way climate has behaved in the past to model what is likely to happen in the future. By learning how the greenhouse effect works and how carbon cycles between different reservoirs, geoscientists can better understand the potential impact of the carbon dioxide in the atmosphere on future global climate. Geoscientists study the past to create and test computer models of climate **1**. They can then use that understanding of how climate works to project how changes in carbon dioxide levels in the atmosphere will impact the future climate under different scenarios of greenhouse emissions **2**. For example, if people around the world continue to release carbon dioxide to the atmosphere at the current rate for the next 100 years, the average global temperature in 2100 will be about 4°C (8°F) warmer than today.

## **1** Learning about past climate...

As previously described, geoscientists use a variety of methods to determine Earth's past temperature. Each method has its own strengths and weaknesses, which is why geoscientists try to use more than one. The black line below indicates the most likely global temperature in the past. The surrounding gray area shows the range of variations in temperatures through different measurement techniques, such as measuring air temperature over land or ocean water temperature.

## **2** ...Helps geoscientists figure out future climate

Geoscientists use the past climate to create sophisticated climate models that use computers to model how different conditions influence the climate. Once they understand what happened in the past and what is happening now, they can apply that understanding to model potential future climates. The three color lines on the graph show potential future global temperatures depending on different greenhouse gas emission scenarios. These scenarios depend on scientific and socioeconomic data, like population growth, economic growth, air pollution, land use, and energy sources. The bar at the end of each line shows the possible range of potential temperatures through slightly different modeled conditions.

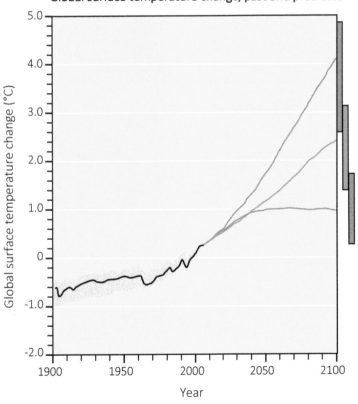

Global surface temperature change, past and predicted

The scenario that results in the highest future global temperatures (purple) assumes that global greenhouse gas emissions by people continue to rise through 2100.

The scenario that results in an approximately 2°C (4°F) rise in temperature by 2100 assumes that greenhouse gas emissions peak this century and decline after that.

The scenario that results in the lowest future temperature (green) assumes that global greenhouse gas emissions by people peak by 2020 and quickly declines soon after. This scenario is unlikely, given the current consumption of fossil fuels and lack of policy in many countries, including the Unites States, to dramatically decrease emissions.

## Check

☐ Explain how geoscientists create models of future global temperatures.
☐ Summarize projects of Earth's future temperature using different scenarios of greenhouse gas emissions.

# 12.11 – 12.17 Consequences of Global Climate Change

In this section, you will learn about the effects of climate change and the evidence that geoscientists collect to learn what happened in the past, what is happening now, and what will happen in the future.

## Frequently Used Terms

The terms listed here are used repeatedly throughout this section, so by learning them before you read this section, you can focus your mental energy on the concepts presented.

**ecosystem** The living organisms in a given area and their physical environment, which is influenced by the climate.

**glacier** Ice on land that flows downhill due to gravity; it forms from snow.

**positive feedback** A change in one thing that causes a change in something else, which increases the original change, resulting in continually amplifying the initial change; positive refers to the amplification, not that it is good or beneficial.

**sea ice** Ice floating in the ocean formed from freezing ocean water.

Hurricanes Irma, Jose, and Katia existed together in the Atlantic Ocean and Caribbean Sea in 2017. Hurricanes are more likely to form over warmer water.

# 12.11 Consequences: Rising Temperature

**Key Concept:** Geoscientists use many different techniques to measure average global temperatures and have observed many consequences of rising global temperatures. As we saw previously, data collected from glaciers, ocean sediments, and long-term direct measurements of air and ocean temperature all indicate that recent temperatures are rising more quickly than recorded in Earth's history **1**. The rising average temperature causes more wide-reaching consequences that may be less obvious, such as changing amounts of rainfall, decreasing amounts of ice, rising sea levels, and changing ecosystems **2**.

## **1** Evidence for rising temperature

Examples of ways that geoscientists use to decipher Earth's past temperatures were previously discussed in this chapter. Each method of gathering temperature data has its own strengths and weaknesses and gives a picture from an individual location. However, when the measurements gathered by different techniques at a large variety of locations are combined, they all tell the same story: that Earth's average temperature has increased at a dramatic rate in the last 150 years. It is this overlap from multiple sources of data that is particularly convincing to scientists that the overall interpretation of rising temperatures is accurate.

### Evidence: Data sets agree Earth's temperature is rising

Each line in this graph represents data gathered by different groups of scientists using different methods of measuring Earth's past temperature. Although they are not in perfect agreement, you can see that they all agree that the average temperature was fairly constant for most of the last thousand years and started increasing approximately 150 years ago. The most accurate interpretation of global temperature is made by comparing and combining temperature records measured using different methods and locations.

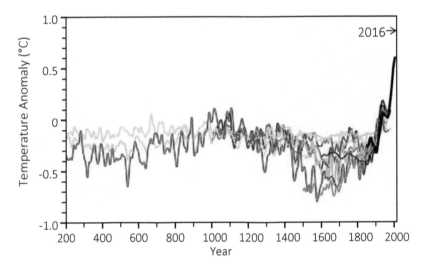

### Evidence: Rising temperatures vary by location

The current increase in temperature is not exactly the same everywhere in the world. Using the United States as an example, the average temperature from midcentury (1951 to 1980) was compared to recent average temperatures (1991 to 2012). The red shades indicate an increase in temperature, with the deep red color showing the largest increase. The blue colors indicate locations that are experiencing cooler average temperatures. The temperature change depends on the influence of factors such as ocean temperatures and large-scale circulation in the atmosphere. Heat waves are becoming more common everywhere.

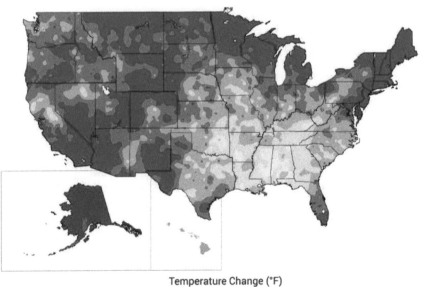

Temperature Change (°F)

# 2 Consequences and effects of rising temperature

Average global temperatures will continue to increase, since carbon dioxide levels in the atmosphere are continuing to rise. The five warmest years recorded have all occurred since 2010. Average global temperatures are expected to warm 1 to 5°C (2 to 9°F) degrees by 2100, depending on the amount of carbon dioxide released into the atmosphere. However, not every year will be warmer and not every location will increase in temperature equally. Areas that undergo less warming will be affected by the many secondary consequences of rising temperatures, described below.

### Example: Changing precipitation (details in 12.12)

Rising temperatures cause entire climates to change, with some areas becoming wetter and others becoming drier. Warmer air can hold more moisture than colder air, so the amount of rain or snow that can fall on a location at one time increases, often causing worse flooding or snowstorms. Individual storms or droughts may not be a sign of climate change, but many are becoming more frequent as climate changes. For example, droughts are happening in California more often causing the amount of water in lakes and reservoirs, like Folsom Lake, to decrease significantly.

2016

2015

### Example: Melting ice (details in 12.13)

Rising temperatures cause ice to melt, such as ice in glaciers on land, ice frozen in the ground, and sea ice on the ocean. The melting ice directly affects the plants and animals that live on or near the ice, but it also transfers water to the ocean, which can cause sea level to rise and ocean circulation to change. Melting ice frozen in the ground causes the land to settle and move, damaging houses and roads built on it. An example of a melting glacier is the Lillian Glacier in Olympic National Park, Washington. It became much smaller and thinner over the 105 years between when these two photographs were taken.

1905

2010

### Example: Rising sea level (details in 12.15)

Rising temperatures melt ice on land, and the resulting water transfers to the ocean, raising the sea level. In addition, the ocean water itself is warming as global temperatures rise, and warming water expands. Therefore the oceans themselves are expanding, causing a further rise in sea level. The rising water levels are flooding what was once dry land and allowing storm waves to reach further inland. For example, the gray areas are land on the image of southern Louisiana in 1932. By 2011, land loss is shown where the grey is now blue, and new land is shown as green. Along with global sea level rise, southern Louisiana is impacted by several other factors that increase land loss.

1932

2011

### Example: Changing ecosystems (details in 12.16)

Rising temperatures cause the areas in which plants and animals live to change. An ecosystem is the community of plants and animals and their physical environment, so if the environment changes, the ecosystem also changes. Plants and animals must migrate to new areas or adapt to these changing conditions, or they may become extinct. For example, polar bears may go extinct because the sea ice which they use as a hunting platform is melting faster than their populations can adapt to the changes in their ability to access food.

## Check

☐ Summarize evidence for rising global temperature.
☐ Describe consequences of rising global temperature.

# 12.12 Consequences: Changing Precipitation

**Key Concept:** The amount of precipitation is changing in different locations, resulting in changes to these areas' climate. In addition to temperature, one of the key descriptors of a region's climate is precipitation. Geoscientists measure the amount of snowfall and rainfall in different locations and compare those values to past records and future projections based on increasing global average temperatures **1**. Based on these comparisons, geoscientists have determined that the amount of precipitation in different locations is changing as Earth warms, with some areas becoming wetter and others drier. Extreme weather events, such as droughts, are also becoming more frequent as Earth warms **2**.

## **1** Evidence of changing precipitation

Geoscientists measure different aspects of rain and snowfall: how much falls, where it falls, and when it falls. They compare these measurements to past measurements, such as those described in historical records, and then use that data to generate computer models to explain the past behavior and project future behavior. The data indicate that the amount, distribution, and timing of rain and snowfall across the planet are changing because higher average temperatures affect how the atmosphere and ocean are heated, which changes their large-scale circulation patterns.

**Evidence: Heavy rainfall events**
The annual total precipitation change in the United States is changing compared to the 1901-1960 average, as shown. Computer climate models project this trend will continue because warmer air holds more moisture, so it has the potential to rain or snow more.

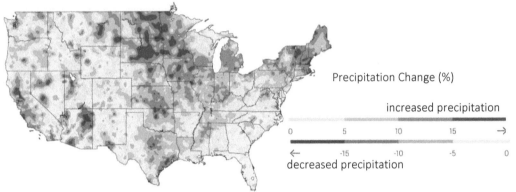

Precipitation Change (%)

increased precipitation

| 0 | 5 | 10 | 15 | → |

← -15 -10 -5 0
decreased precipitation

## **2** Consequences and effects of changing precipitation

Global climate change is a sustained change in the world's long-term weather conditions. Different atmospheric circulation patterns result in changing climates, with some areas becoming wetter and other areas becoming drier. Below drought and increased rainfall are discussed as specific examples of consequences. In other locations other extreme weather events, such as blizzards and thunderstorms, are becoming more common and more severe.

**Example: Drought**
As global climate change continues, some areas are experiencing less rainfall and more evaporation, resulting in a drier climate with more frequent droughts, affecting crop production.

**Example: Increased rainfall**
Some areas are flooding more frequently due to increased rainfall, and the floods are more severe. In this photo, a flood near the Souris River, North Dakota damaged homes in 2011.

## Check

☐ Summarize evidence for changing precipitation.
☐ Describe three consequences and effects of changing precipitation.

# 12.13 Consequences: Melting Ice

**Key Concept:** Glaciers and sea ice are melting, with consequences extending far beyond the areas immediately surrounding the ice. As global temperatures rise, ice around the world is melting. Glaciers on land, both in mountains and covering Antarctica and Greenland, are getting smaller, as is the sea ice in the polar oceans. Measurements of glaciers and sea ice show that not only is ice covering a smaller area, it is also getting thinner **1**. In addition to adding water to the ocean, this decrease in the amount of ice is affecting people's water supply, reducing animals' habitats, and increasing the heat absorbed by Earth's surface as less sunlight is reflected back to space **2**.

## **1** Evidence of melting ice

Most glaciers and sea ice are shrinking, measured by both the area covered as well as ice thickness. Geoscientists use satellite data, photographs of glaciers over time, GPS, and maps made at different points in time to determine the extent of ice coverage and its thickness in the past and today.

### Evidence: Glaciers
Glaciers are large masses of ice on land that slowly flow due to gravity. The amount of ice in a glacier is a balance between the amount of snow that is added in the winter and the amount of ice that melts in the summer. Around the world, the vast majority of glaciers are getting smaller as melting increases.

### Evidence: Sea ice
Sea ice forms from freezing sea water and floats in the ocean. As with glaciers, the amount of sea ice is a balance between the ice that forms in the winter and the ice that melts in the summer. As can be seen in the graph showing the sea ice extent in September in the Arctic and in the images to the right, the amount of sea ice in the Arctic is decreasing.

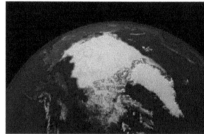
Sea ice at the North Pole in 1979

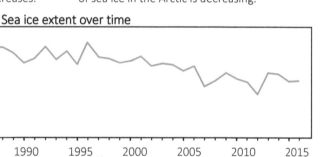
Sea ice extent over time

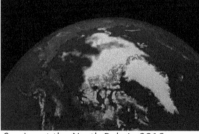
Sea ice at the North Pole in 2016

## **2** Consequences and effects of melting ice

Glaciers and sea ice affect more than just the areas in which they are found because of the impact of glacial meltwater and the reflective properties of ice.

### Example: Rising sea level
Melting glaciers contribute to sea level rise because their melt water eventually enters the ocean (see 12.15).

### Example: Changing river flow
Water from melting glaciers contributes to rivers, so if there is too much melting, flooding along rivers can be worsened. Also, some cities and towns are dependent primarily on glacier melt water for their water supply during the dry seasons. If there are no longer glaciers to melt, they will not have a reliable source of water.

### Example: Amplified warming
Compared to land and water, ice and snow reflect more of the Sun's light energy back to space. Melting ice and snow exposes more land and water, increasing the amount of the Sun's energy that is absorbed and emitted as infrared radiation, adding to Earth's warming. This warming, in turn, melts even more ice, which amplifies warming, resulting in a positive feedback loop (see 12.14). Another example of amplified warming through a positive feedback loop is when the ice frozen in the ground melts and allows organic matter to start decomposing, releasing methane, a greenhouse gas.

### Example: Circulation changes
The formation and melting of sea ice affect the density of nearby ocean water, which changes the circulation of the oceans. Ocean circulation affects circulation of air in the atmosphere. As less sea ice forms and more melts, parts of the ocean circulation pattern are slowing down. This has an impact on a wide variety of factors including plankton and animals living in the ocean and the conditions of the nearby atmosphere and land.

## Check

☐ Summarize evidence for decreasing ice, both glaciers and sea ice.
☐ Describe the consequences and effects of decreasing ice, both glaciers and sea ice.

# 12.14 DATA AND DIAGRAMS: Positive Feedback Cycles

**Key Concept:** The results of a positive feedback loop can be illustrated as a time-sequence diagram. The two diagrams below are related, as the loop diagram shows a positive feedback loop, and the time-sequence diagram shows its results over time. A positive feedback loop means that changes are amplified from panel to panel (negative feedback means that the changes are reduced, and these terms do not describe whether the changes are good or bad) **1**. To create a diagram that illustrates this concept using the example of melting ice, geoscientists measure the amount of light energy that is reflected off of different surfaces and use models to analyze how changing the surface changes the surface temperature. Tips on how to read this diagram are below **2**. Use the questions to practice interpreting feedback loop diagrams **3**.

The loop diagram and the time-sequence diagram show different ways to convey the same relationship between the amount of ice, the light energy that is absorbed, and the global temperature.

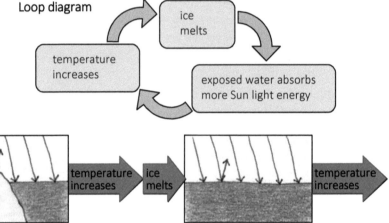

Loop diagram

**Time-sequence diagram**

Ice reflects most light energy and absorbs very little, resulting in a low temperature.

Land and water absorb more light energy than ice does.

More land and water are exposed, absorbing more light energy, increasing the temperature.

## **1** How to read the diagram

After examining what is changing in each diagram individually, compare the two diagrams to see how a process represented as a loop can have results that can be shown as changing over time.

## **2** An example of what you might interpret

In both diagrams, when there is less ice, Earth's surface absorbs more Sun light energy, resulting in warmer temperatures which cause more ice to melt.

## **3** Questions

**1. What do the diagrams above show?**
a. how decreasing ice leads to warmer temperatures
b. how ice becomes greenhouse gases that warm temperature
c. how melting ice cools the ocean water temperature
d. how ice has a minimal effect on Earth's temperature

**2. The relationship between temperature and ice shown in the time-sequence diagram can be graphed, as shown by the black line in the diagram below. Which location on the graph shows the relationship between the surface temperature and the amount of ice at the beginning of the time-sequence diagram?**
a) Location A
b) Location B
c) Location C
d) Location D

**3. If ice grew larger without an initial change in the temperature, how would that affect the future temperature?**
a. It would increase the future temperature, so more ice would form.
b. It would increase the future temperature, so more ice would melt.
c. It would decrease the future temperature, so more ice would form.
d. It would decrease the future temperature, so more ice would melt.

**4. Why is this relationship between the amount of ice present on Earth and global temperature an example of positive feedback?**
a. less ice results in a positive, or good, increase in global temperatures
b. less ice causes warmer temperatures which decreases the amount of ice
c. less ice and warm temperatures work together, producing an end result

**5. Negative feedback, unlike positive feedback, causes the initial change to be reduced instead of increased. Which of the following examples is an example of a negative feedback loop?**
a. Warmer arctic grasslands cause trapped carbon to be released into the atmosphere as greenhouse gases.
b. Warmer air holds more water vapor, which is a greenhouse gas.
c. A warmer and wetter climate causes more chemical weathering of rocks, which removes carbon dioxide from the atmosphere.

# 12.15 Consequences: Rising Sea Level

**Key Concept:** **Sea level is rising, submerging some coastal land.** As rising global temperatures cause glaciers on land to melt, the resulting water flows into the ocean, increasing the amount of water in the ocean. In addition, the whole ocean is warming as the atmosphere warms, and warmer water expands and takes up more space than cooler water. Together, these factors are causing a rise in sea level. Measurements of sea level show that it is rising on average around the world about 0.3 cm (0.1 inches) per year **1**. Low-lying land close to sea level will be under water in the future, and storm waves will reach further inland, causing more damage **2**. If you have visited the coast, you have likely visited an area that is being affected by rising sea level.

## **1** Evidence of rising sea level

Measurements of sea level around the world are averaged together to determine how the global sea level has changed. Geoscientists collect these data by measuring the height of water at different locations on the coast, by observing water levels using satellites, and by comparing to historical records.

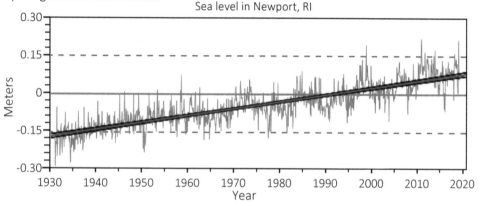

**Evidence: Rising sea level**
As can be seen in this graph from Newport, Rhode Island, sea level has risen over the past 90 years of measurements.

**Key**

/ Linear Sea Level Trend

/ Monthly mean sea level

## **2** Consequences of rising sea level

Areas that have not typically been directly affected by the ocean are now being directly affected by rising sea levels, particularly during high tides and storms. The majority of people around the world lives near the coast and are potentially affected by rising sea levels.

### Example: Land is submerged
Sea level is now high enough that some areas that were previously dry land are now covered by ocean water. This is most apparent during high tide. For example, the flat coastal region of Hains Point, Washington, D.C. now regularly floods during high tide.

### Example: Land is eroded
A higher sea level means that storm waves are reaching further inland, flooding and eroding more land. For example, these photographs taken before and after a storm near San Francisco, CA, show the extent to which the storm eroded the coast and a road along it.

## Check
☐ Summarize evidence for rising sea level.
☐ Describe the consequences and effects of rising sea level.

# 12.16 Consequences: Changing Ecosystems

**Key Concept:** Changing conditions caused by the changing climate affect plants and animals that are adapted to existing conditions. As local climates change, populations of plants and animals that cannot tolerate the new conditions must migrate or adapt, or they may go extinct. This change can be seen in the altered timing of seasonal activities, expanded or reduced ranges of habitats, and increased number of extinctions **1**. Farms producing food are also affected by changing climate. In addition, the ocean environment is becoming warmer and more acidic, affecting many animals **2**.

## **1** Evidence of changing ecosystems

An ecosystem is all of the living organisms in an area and their environment. Changes in the environment due to climate change can mean that some populations of plants and animals thrive. However many plants and animals are not well-adapted to the new conditions and must migrate, or they will decline in number. For example, the date that some flowers bloom and some animals mate is getting earlier as spring conditions start earlier. Ocean ecosystems are changing due to warmer average global temperatures and greater acidity of the water.

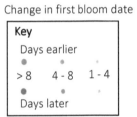
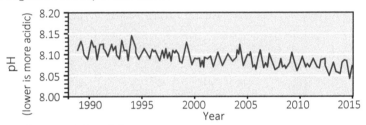

**Evidence: First bloom dates**
The date of first blooming in many species has changed dramatically between 1951-1960 and 2006-2015.

**Evidence: Acidity of the ocean**
Carbonic acid forms when carbon dioxide dissolves in water. As more carbon dioxide dissolves in the oceans, they have become more acidic.

## **2** Consequences and effects of changing ecosystems

Ecosystems involve the interaction of plants and animals with the environment. Therefore, if the environment changes through changing temperatures or levels of rainfall, then the relationships among organisms in the ecosystem must also change.

**Example: Agriculture**
Agricultural crops grow under certain climate conditions. As conditions change, the crop productivity may increase in some areas and decrease in others. In areas where the amount of rainfall is decreasing, such as parts of the Midwest and Southwest, farmers must generally irrigate their crops, as shown in the photo. However, crop failures will become more common because of droughts and heat waves. In addition, the ranges and effects of pests, weeds, and plant diseases are increasing. As a result, food prices may be unstable and rise. Long term, farmers need to be flexible with their crops.

**Example: Aquaculture**
Aquaculture is farming food in water, such as fish, shellfish, and seaweed. As with farming on land, different types of aquaculture require certain climate conditions. Rising temperature and sea level affect the range of the location in which certain animals and plants can be grown. Also, extreme weather can cause a decrease in productivity. In addition, increasingly acidic ocean water is negatively impacting shellfish, such as oysters, because shells are made of carbonate minerals that dissolve in acid. The stressed coral shown in the photo is an example of how these factors can potentially cause a decrease in organisms.

## Check

☐ Summarize evidence for changing ecosystems.
☐ Describe consequences and effects of changing ecosystems.

# 12.17 DATA AND DIAGRAMS: Reduce Your Carbon Footprint

**Key Concept:** Tables organize characteristics to show similarities and differences. This table organizes information about how people can reduce their carbon footprint. A carbon footprint is the amount of carbon dioxide an individual person adds to the atmosphere **1**. To create a table like this, geoscientists compile vast amounts of information from scientific studies and government reports on energy usage. Tips on how to read this table are below **2**. Use the questions to practice interpreting simple tables **3**.

Actions that each reduce a carbon footprint by 100 pounds of carbon dioxide per year

| Home | Temperature | Laundry | Recycling | Food | Driving |
|---|---|---|---|---|---|
| • Replace three incandescent light bulbs with energy star light bulbs | • Turn up air conditioning temperature in the summer by 3°C | • Wash clothes in cold water for 2 loads per week | • Recycle aluminum and steel cans | • Eat no meat for 2 days per month | • Reduce the number of miles you drive by 2 per week |
| • Enable power management features on your computer | • Turn down heat on winter nights by 2°F | • Use clothes line instead of dryer for 10% of laundry | • Recycle glass and plastic | • Replace eating 5 pounds of beef per year with 5 pounds of chicken | • Carpool once every few months for your commute |

## 1 How to read the diagram

Read the title, and then identify what is being shown in the columns. Then, you can read through the boxes to determine how the information in each column relates to the title.

## 2 An example of what you might interpret

If you wanted to reduce your carbon footprint, you could make changes to your food choices by eating no meat for a couple days a month or by replacing some of the beef you eat with chicken.

## 3 Questions

1. What does the table show?
a. ways to reduce one person's contribution to the atmosphere carbon reservoir by 100 pounds of carbon dioxide
b. how 100 pounds of carbon dioxide are put into the atmosphere reservoir
c. advantages and disadvantages of different techniques to remove carbon from the atmosphere reservoir

2. How much would you save if you reduced the amount you drive by 10 miles per week?
a. 100 pounds of carbon dioxide per year
b. 200 pounds of carbon dioxide per year
c. 500 pounds of carbon dioxide per year

3. How much would you save if you did five of the choices?
a. 5 pounds of carbon dioxide per year
b. 250 pounds of carbon dioxide per year
c. 500 pounds of carbon dioxide per year

4. If everyone in the United States (330 million people) did one of these things, how much less carbon dioxide would be emitted each year?
a. 0.3 million pounds
b. 33 million pounds
c. 33,000 million pounds

5. How might this table be useful to you and your friends?
a. It shows how carbon is put into the atmosphere from other reservoirs
b. It shows that it is easy to reduce carbon from being added to the atmosphere without large lifestyle changes
c. It shows the expenses required to prevent carbon from being added to the atmosphere
d. It shows how to directly remove carbon from the atmosphere

## End of Chapter Questions: Student Debates

For each of the following questions, determine which student you agree with and explain why.

**1. Two students are discussing climate change and cooling.**

**Student 1:** I heard that a few places around the word are cooling, which means that climate change cannot be happening.

**Student 2:** Climate change describes the average conditions around Earth, and a few cooling locations are more than balanced by many places getting warmer.

**4. Two students are discussing positive feedback.**

**Student 1:** Positive feedback means that a cycle causes a small change to get bigger and bigger.

**Student 2:** Positive feedback means that a cycle causes changes that have a positive effect.

**3. Three students are discussing Earth's past and current temperatures.**

**Student 1:** Earth's temperature and carbon dioxide levels are hotter now than they have ever been in the past, so we should be very concerned.

**Student 2:** Earth's temperature has gone up and down naturally in the past, so we don't need to be concerned about the changing temperature now.

**Student 3:** Although Earth's temperature has varied in the past, it is now changing faster than we've seen, so we should be concerned.

**2. Four students are discussing how the greenhouse effect works.**

**Student 1:** The carbon dioxide acts like a glass barrier or a blanket that holds heat in the atmosphere, heating up the atmosphere.

**Student 2:** The carbon dioxide is heated up by visible light energy directly from the sun, heating it up and therefore heating up the atmosphere.

**Student 3:** The carbon dioxide absorbs light energy in the atmosphere and slows it from escaping the atmosphere, heating up the atmosphere.

**Student 4:** The carbon dioxide produced by burning fuels is hotter than the surrounding air, heating up the atmosphere.

**5. Three students are discussing what they can do about climate change.**

**Student 1:** The problem is so big that, that I can't do anything meaningful to make a difference.

**Student 2:** I can make a difference, but I would have to make big and difficult changes to my lifestyle.

**Student 3:** There are big changes I could make, but my small changes can make a difference.

## End of Chapter Questions: Short Answer

Using your own words or sketching and labeling a diagram, answer the following questions.

6. Two planets are found around two different stars. Planet A is hotter than Planet B. Hypothesize at least three distinct explanations why there is a difference.

7. Draw a table to compare and contrast at least four separate aspects of the greenhouse effect and climate change. Things to consider include what they are, processes involved, relationship to each other, and influence of people.

8. Explain using a labeled sketch how the carbon cycle would be different if there was no limestone or plants.

9. Based on what you know about global climate, write a hypothesis explaining the average temperature 55 million years ago (see 12.7) and why you think so. To test your hypothesis, describe one piece of data you would collect and what it would tell you about your hypothesis.

10. A friend says "Current climate change is a result of Earth's natural cycles, not people." Do you agree or disagree with your friend? Justify your response with at least 3 lines of supporting evidence.

11. Identify and explain at least three ways in which climate change has affected you or will affect you.

12. Imagine you discover a new planet. Identify and justify your choice of 5 pieces of data you could collect to determine whether that planet currently has a changing climate.

13. Imagine you need to create a presentation to convince people that climate change is happening and caused by people. Select what you think are the four most convincing pieces of data to include in your presentation. Explain your choice.

14. Explain to your friend at least five reasons why they should do something to slow down climate change.

**Hints:** For each question, see the sections listed here for information relevant to answering it.

**1.** (12.1, 12.7) **2.** (12.2) **3.** (12.7) **4.** (12.11, 12.12) **5.** (12.15) **6.** (12.1, 12.2, 12.3, 12.4, 12.12) **7.** (12.1, 12.2, 12.4, 12.5, 12.6, 12.7) **8.** (12.2, 12.3, 12.4) **9.** (12.2, 12.4, 12.6, 12.7, 12.8) **10.** (12.4, 12.5, 12.6, 12.7, 12.8) **11.** (12.9, 12.10, 12.11, 12.13. 12.14) **12.** (12.6, 12.7, 12.8, 12.9, 12.10, 12.11, 12.13. 12.14) **13.** (12.6, 12.7, 12.9 to 12.14) **14.** (12.7, 12.9 to 12.15)

# Chapter 13: Streams

## Chapter Objectives

When you are finished reading this chapter, you should be able to …

• summarize the water cycle and streams' roles in it (13.1–13.3).

• compare and contrast the appearance of mountain, braided, and meandering streams and their roles in the rock cycle (13.4–13.5).

• explain how people affect floods and try to control them (13.6–13.10).

Focus on Geology

# 13.1 – 13.6 Streams and Cycles

In this section, you will learn that in geology, the water cycle is a fundamental concept. Streams transport water and sediments, and different streams have a variety of characteristics.

## Frequently Used Terms

The terms listed here are used repeatedly throughout this section, so by learning them before you read this section, you can focus your mental energy on the concepts presented.

**deposit** When sediments that were being transported are no longer moving and are left in place; deposition tends to happen when there is not enough transportation energy when the water slows down to continue moving the sediment.

**discharge** The amount of water that flows past a particular point in a stream per second; it is often measured in cubic feet per second.

**erosion** The initial movement of sediments away from the soil or bedrock from which they weathered; in this case, after rock is eroded, streams begin to transport them.

**evaporation** When a liquid becomes a gas, such as liquid water becoming water vapor.

**floodplain** The flat land made up of deposited sediments that stream water covers when there is too much to contain in the stream channel.

**high-energy and low-energy stream** The ability of a stream to transport sediments, with high-energy streams often being quicker, more turbulent, and more able to transport sediments.

**infiltration** Water soaking into the ground from the surface.

**precipitation** Rain and snow.

**river** Another word for a large stream.

**sediments** Pieces resulting from weathering of preexisting rock, either pieces of broken rock or pieces that form when dissolved ions bonds together.

**stream channel** A long, narrow low area where water flows downhill due to gravity.

**stream** Surface water flowing through a stream channel; the entire stream system includes the stream channel and the floodplain.

**transport** The movement of sediments.

**water reservoir** Locations on Earth where there is a significant amount of water, such as in the ocean, in the air, and in the ground.

Many cities, such as Boston, Massachusetts shown here, are located on the edges of large rivers and may be impacted by floods.

# 13.1 Reservoirs of Water

**Key Concept:** Water is found in natural reservoirs on Earth. Similar to carbon discussed in 12.3, water is also found in different locations, called reservoirs. Although you may be familiar with water on Earth's surface, in Earth's atmosphere, and in Earth's oceans, water is also found within the ground as groundwater and frozen as ice in glaciers **1**. Most of Earth's water is saltwater in the ocean **2**.

## **1** Water reservoirs

There are five general locations where a significant amount of water temporarily remains, called reservoirs. Within these reservoirs, water on Earth exists in different phases as liquid (water), solid (ice), and gas (vapor).

**Glaciers**
The glacier reservoir includes frozen water (ice) slowly moving downhill on land (see 16.9 for details).

**Surface water**
The surface water reservoir consists of streams, rivers, lakes, and swamps (see 13.3 for details).

**Atmosphere**
The atmosphere reservoir holds evaporated water vapor in the air that may condense into clouds.

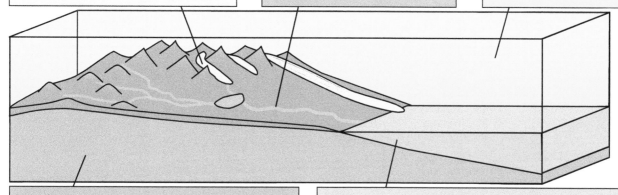

**Groundwater**
The groundwater reservoir is water that has infiltrated, or soaked, into the ground and filled spaces within rock and between sediments (see 14.3 for details).

**Ocean**
The ocean reservoir encompasses large bodies of salt water. Ocean water is salty because streams carry dissolved ions into the ocean. When the water evaporates, the dissolved salt ions are left behind.

## **2** Relative size of reservoirs

The oceans contain most of Earth's water, but it is salty and is not useful for many of our purposes. Most freshwater is frozen in glaciers or is underground. Although surface water is the most visible, the water in the streams, rivers, lakes, and swamps makes up only a tiny portion of Earth's water. The atmosphere and surface water reservoirs combined are only 0.3% of all fresh water, but they are important because they affect people, plants, and animals and move water between other reservoirs.

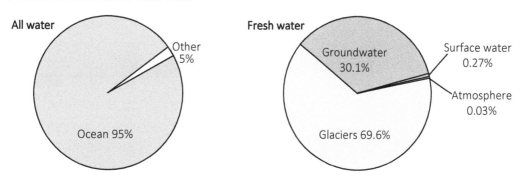

**Check** Before you continue, you should be able to answer each check without looking at the page.
☐ Describe the five reservoirs of water.
☐ Compare the relative sizes of water reservoirs.

# 13.2 The Water Cycle

**Key Concept:** **Water continually moves between reservoirs in, on, and above Earth's surface.** You have seen examples of processes that move water if you have ever watched rain falling or a river flowing **1**. This constant movement of water between reservoirs can be shown as a model called the water cycle **2**. Using a model to depict how water moves through reservoirs is useful because many of the processes happen on timescales too long or over areas too large for people to watch, and geoscientists can investigate activities that cause the amount of water in each reservoir to change. The water cycle is an important theme that relates directly to streams (Chapter 13), groundwater (Chapter 14), oceans (Chapter 15), and glaciers (Chapter 16).

## **1** Water cycle processes

There are many processes that cause water to move between reservoirs, as shown below. Water also moves within reservoirs. Water in glaciers, streams, groundwater, and raindrops moves downward due to gravity, and water within ocean and atmospheric currents moves because of density differences.

| **Precipitation** | **Evaporation** | **Infiltration** | **Seep** | **Melt** | **Sublimation** | **Flow** |
|---|---|---|---|---|---|---|
| Water vapor in the atmosphere becomes rain or snow that falls. | Liquid water becomes gaseous water vapor in the atmosphere. | Liquid water soaks into the ground and remains liquid. | Liquid water flows out of the ground and remains liquid. | Solid water ice becomes liquid water. | Solid water ice becomes gaseous water vapor in the atmosphere. | Water moves and remains liquid. |

## **2** The water cycle model

The continual movement of water between reservoirs is called the water cycle. The total amount of water on Earth does not change, but water enters and leaves the reservoirs as inputs and outputs. The water cycle does not follow a single path, making a circle from one reservoir to the next as the word "cycle" may imply. Instead, water is constantly moving, within reservoirs and from one reservoir to another.

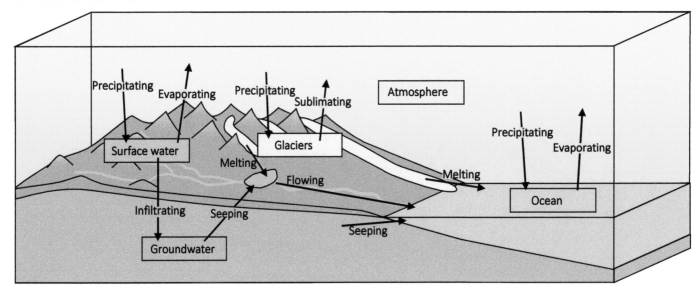

## Check

☐ Describe the processes that cause water to move between the different reservoirs.
☐ Determine at least four steps involved along two possible paths through the water cycle.

# 13.3 Streams' Role in the Water Cycle

**Key Concept:** Streams and rivers are part of the surface water reservoir and transport water across Earth's surface between other reservoirs. Both the words "stream" and "river" describe water flowing at Earth's surface along a specific path. Stream is the general term, and river is used to describe a large stream. Although streams and rivers hold a tiny percentage of all the water on Earth, they play a major role in transporting water across Earth's surface. Water that is added to a stream from another reservoir is called an input **1**. Water that leaves the stream to go to another reservoir is called an output **2**. Given enough time, the outputs may once again become inputs, which is why we say the water "cycles."

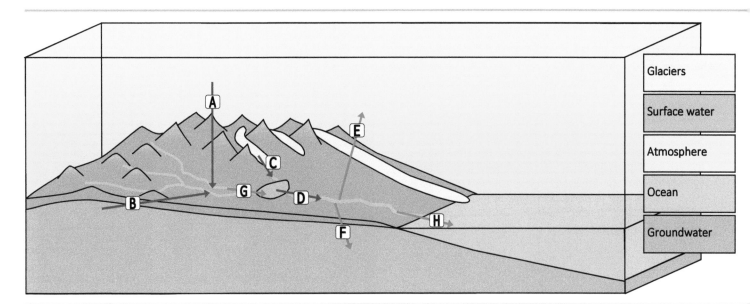

## 1 Stream reservoir inputs

As water moves through the water cycle, it enters streams as inputs in a variety of ways, as shown by the green arrows. Streams play an important role by continuously moving water from rain and melted snow and ice downhill across Earth's surface.

**A** From the Atmosphere reservoir
Rain or snow falls directly into streams.

**B** From the Groundwater reservoir
Water that has previously infiltrated into the ground slowly seeps out to the surface, so streams are gaining water.

**C** From the Glacier reservoir
Ice forming the glaciers melts and water flows across the surface forming streams.

**D** From the Surface water reservoir
Water flows along the surface into streams. Surface water, such as lakes or swamps, may feed streams.

## 2 Stream reservoir outputs

As water moves through the water cycle, it leaves streams as outputs and enters other reservoirs as shown by the red arrows. Streams are an essential link for moving surface water from land back to the ocean, which is the lowest location for water to flow.

**E** To the Atmosphere reservoir
Stream water evaporates.

**F** To the Groundwater reservoir
Stream water may infiltrate into the ground, so the stream is losing water. In dry climates, infiltration is a common way that water leaves streams, unlike areas with abundant rainfall.

**G** To the Surface water reservoir
Streams flow into other surface water, such as lakes and swamps. These can be thought of as temporary resting places for water in streams.

**H** To the Ocean reservoir
Stream water flows into the ocean. This is the main way that water leaves streams. The ocean is the lowest level that streams reach.

## Check

☐ Describe four ways that water enters the stream reservoir and where it comes from.
☐ Describe four ways that water leaves the stream reservoir and where it goes.
☐ Summarize why streams are an important component of the water cycle.

# 13.4 Types of Streams

**Key Concept:** There are many types of streams with a variety of appearances. Although the word "stream" may trigger a particular image in your mind, geologists define and classify streams based on their appearances due to the steepness of the land surface and amount of sediment transported by the stream **1**. A stream has a stream channel through which it flows, and it may have a surrounding floodplain where water naturally overflows when there is too much to fit within the stream channel **2**. Stream channels do not necessarily remain in the same place but may change paths within the floodplain, especially for meandering streams **3**.

## **1** Stream appearances

Streams have different appearances depending on their steepness and how much clastic sediment, such as gravel, sand, and mud, they are transporting.

### Mountain stream

Mountain streams form where water flows over bedrock through relatively steep-sided mountain valleys. This type of valley has a pointy bottom like the letter "V". Mountain streams may carve canyons and have rapids and waterfalls. The steep slopes result in water that is turbulent and has a high enough energy to erode, or wear away, bedrock and to transport large sediments, such as boulders and gravel as well as smaller sediments. For example, this mountain stream in Vermont formed and flows through a valley with steep sides and a pointy bottom.

### Braided stream

Braided streams are not as steep as mountain streams, and they tend to look like a braid, as there are multiple channels that divide and recombine. The stream transports abundant loose sediments of all sizes. However, it cannot continuously transport all of the sediments, so the water deposits a large amount of them in the channel, creating islands that divide the stream channels. The water flows through a several channels that may change locations. This braided stream in Katmai National Park in Alaska has temporary islands made of sand and gravel.

### Meandering stream

Meandering streams form where the land is generally flat. The flat slope results in curving, looping streams that look like a winding ribbon. Meandering streams transport sand- and mud-sized sediments, and they are often fairly large because many streams have added water to them. Over time, the stream channel does not remain in the same location but meanders over the floodplain. Most cities built next to streams are built next to meandering streams. This meandering stream is brown because of the mud being transported by the water.

# 2 Stream parts

A stream has a channel and may have a surrounding floodplain. The name of a stream is typically given to only the stream channel, even though the floodplain is also part of the stream system. The photo of the stream in Missouri shows a meandering river flowing through a channel within a clearly defined floodplain used for farming.

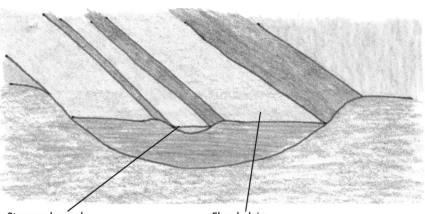

stream channel          flood plain

**Stream channel**
The stream channel is the current location of the long, narrow low area in the ground where water flows.

**Flood plain**
The floodplain is the land that the stream water covers when there is too much to contain in the stream channel.

# 3 Meandering streams

The stream channel of meandering streams changes location in the floodplain over years to decades as the stream erodes the outside of a curve and deposits sediment on the inside. As the location of the stream channel changes, meanders may be cut off and form a curved lake on the floodplain called an oxbow lake.

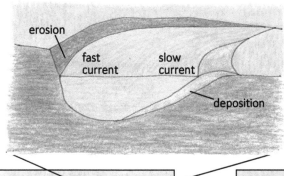

erosion

fast
current          slow
current

deposition

The water on the outside of a curve flows faster, causing the floodplain to erode, and the stream channel location shifts in this direction. The water on the inside of the curve flows more slowly, allowing sediments to settle and be deposited, and the stream channel shifts away from this location.

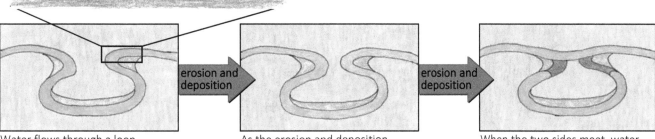

erosion and deposition

erosion and deposition

Water flows through a loop, eroding the outside of the curve and depositing sediment on the inside.

As the erosion and deposition continue, the stream channel shifts location and the two ends of the loop move closer together.

When the two sides meet, water flows along the new, direct path. The old loop is cut off and is called an oxbow.

# Check

□ Compare and contrast three different types of stream.
□ Describe the two parts of a stream system.
□ Explain why a stream channel shifts location and describe the feature that results.

# 13.5 Streams' Role in the Rock Cycle

**Key Concept:**  **Streams play an important role in transporting sediments in the rock cycle.** If you have ever seen a muddy river or sand in a stream, you have seen streams moving sediments as part of the rock cycle. Streams erode bedrock, transport sediments, and deposit sediments **1**. However, different types of streams have differing relationships between these processes **2**. Mountain streams flow down steep slopes, so they erode the bedrock and transport large-sized sediments. Braided streams transport a wider range of sediments, often depositing them within the multiple stream channels that make up this kind of stream. Meandering streams will generally transport and deposit large amounts of small-sized sediments.

## **1** Rock cycle processes related to streams

A stream can erode bedrock to create sediments or erode previously-deposited sediments. Streams transport the sediments and deposit them when the speed of the water slows down.

| Weathering and erosion | Transportation | Deposition |
|---|---|---|
| Streams can erode bedrock of any rock type, often after physical and chemical weathering or a landslide loosens it. This erosion primarily occurs in mountains and other steep areas, although sediments deposited on the floodplain can also be eroded and transported. | Streams move clastic sediments by carrying them in the water or by bouncing and rolling them along the bottom. Low-energy streams only transport small clastic sediments, such as mud, while high-energy, fast and turbulent streams transport small and large clastic sediments, such as gravel. Angular sediments broken from bedrock become more rounded as they rub together while being transported by streams. All streams transport dissolved ions (see 8.9). | After transportation, sediments are deposited where water slows down, and the sediments settle and stop moving. The resulting deposited sediments are layered and are different depending on the type of stream. If these sediments become sedimentary bedrock, they will typically form layers of conglomerate, sandstone, and shale. |

## **2** Stream types and the rock cycle

Different types of streams have a different balance between weathering and erosion, transportation, and deposition. Erosion tends to play a larger role where the streams are steep and high-energy, such as in the mountains, and deposition plays a larger role in flatter, low-energy areas, such as in meandering streams. During a flood when the amount of water is higher than normal, the erosion and transportation processes in all streams are increased.

|  | Weathering and erosion | Transportation | Deposition |
|---|---|---|---|
| Mountain streams | There is a lot of erosion of both bedrock and deposited sediments because streams are steep so the water is turbulent with high energy. | A variety of sizes of sediments are transported, from boulders and gravel to sand and mud. | There is little to no deposition. |
| Braided streams | There is some erosion, but it generally only affects the deposited sediments on top of the bedrock and not the bedrock itself. | Small to large sediments, such as sand and gravel, are typically transported, and even larger sediments may be transported when there is a flood. | Sand and gravel are deposited throughout the stream channel, often forming temporary islands. Mud is generally not deposited because it is continuously transported. |
| Meandering streams | There is erosion of previously deposited sediments that occurs particularly on the outside of the stream curve. | Smaller sediments, such as mud and sand, are typically transported. Larger sediments, such as gravel, are transported during floods. | Sand is frequently deposited on the inside of the stream curve. Mud and sand are deposited on the floodplain during flooding. |

## Check

☐ Explain how streams fit into the rock cycle, in terms of erosion, transportation, and deposition.
☐ Compare and contrast erosion, transportation, and deposition for mountain streams, braided streams, and meandering streams.

# 13.6 Stream Discharge

**Key Concept:** The amount of water flowing through a stream varies for different streams, along the length of a stream, and over time. The amount of water flowing through a stream is called the discharge **1**. The discharge is higher for larger streams and for streams where the water is flowing faster. Discharge varies depending on the size of the area that drains into the stream, the location along the length of the stream, and the temporary changes associated with the amount of water entering or exiting the stream **2**.

## **1** Discharge

The amount of water flowing past a specific point in a stream is the stream's discharge, which geologists commonly measure in cubic feet per second (or cubic meters per second). One cubic foot is about the size of a large watermelon, so if a small stream has a discharge of 100 cubic feet per second, imagine 100 watermelons moving past you each second.

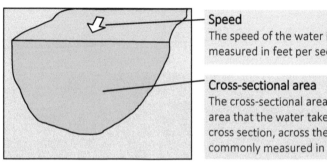

**Speed**
The speed of the water is commonly measured in feet per second.

**Cross-sectional area**
The cross-sectional area of a stream is the area that the water takes up in a slice, or cross section, across the stream, and it is commonly measured in square feet.

**Discharge**
The discharge is calculated by multiplying the cross-sectional area by the speed of the water through that cross section.

cross-sectional area x speed = discharge

## **2** Discharge varies

The discharge of a stream depends on the size of the area that adds water to the stream, and the discharge changes downstream with distance. It can also change temporarily as a result of abundant rain, snow melt, and other events.

**Size of drainage basin**
The area of land that drains into a stream is called the drainage basin. Streams that drain larger areas tend to have higher discharges than streams that drain smaller areas.

A large drainage basin forms a stream with a larger discharge.

A small drainage basin forms a stream with a smaller discharge.

**Discharge over distance**
As streams flow downhill, they join with other streams. Therefore, the discharge of a stream tends to increase downstream.

Streams join together forming a stream with a larger discharge.

**Temporary changes**
Inputs to a stream can change over time, such as an increase in precipitation or a decrease in glacial melt. Therefore, the discharge of a stream can temporarily increase or decrease from its normal level. A large increase can cause a flood.

The stream with a normal discharge flows through the stream channel.

The larger discharge causes the stream to overflow onto the floodplain.

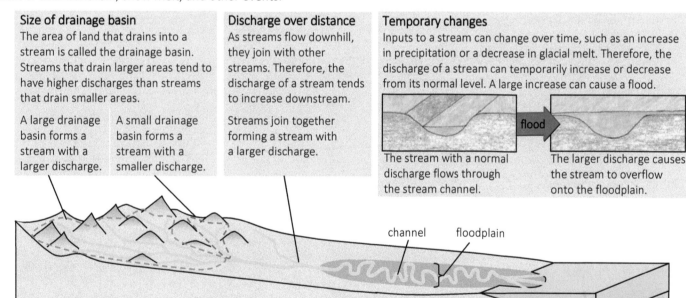

channel          floodplain

## Check

☐ Define the discharge of a stream.
☐ Give examples of how a stream's discharge might be increased or decreased.

Focus on Geology

# 13.7 – 13.10 Floods and Flood Control

In this section, you will learn that geologists view floods as a natural process of streams. Smaller floods are more common than larger floods, and people use various strategies to prevent them.

## Frequently Used Terms

The terms listed here are used repeatedly throughout this section, so by learning them before you read this section, you can focus your mental energy on the concepts presented.

**downstream** The direction in which the water is flowing in a stream.

**flood** When there is too much water for the stream channel and the water spreads onto the floodplain.

**flood control** Attempts to reduce or limit the negative impacts of floods.

The month-long flood in Cedar Rapids, Iowa in 2008 was due to wave after wave of rainstorms that caused the river to flow out of its channel.

# 13.7 Types of Floods

**Key Concept:** Floods occur when water in a stream overflows the stream channel. Although a flood might seem like a rare, newsworthy disaster, flooding is actually a common behavior of streams. Floods occur when the stream discharge is larger than what the stream channel can hold, and water flows onto the floodplain. Floods are commonly grouped into two categories based on their duration and extent of the area affected: regional floods and flash floods. Regional floods are widespread, long-lasting floods that tend to occur on meandering streams in flat areas **1**. Flash floods happen quickly and tend to be local, often happening after sudden rainfall in dry climates **2**.

## **1** Regional floods

Regional floods affect a large area and usually last for days to weeks. They often occur when extended rainfall and snowmelt add water through surface flow to streams. Water that infiltrates into the ground also seeps slowly into the streams. The stream inputs result in a discharge that is more than the stream channel can hold, so the water overflows onto the floodplain as a flood. Regional floods tend to occur on medium-to-large discharge meandering streams with broad floodplains. The regional flood shown in the photo occurred in Nashville, Tennessee in 2010 and lasted for over two weeks.

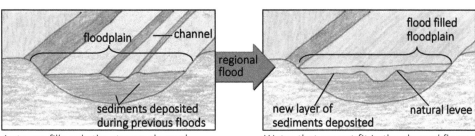

A stream fills only the stream channel during normal flow, and the floodplain is dry. The flat floodplain is made from sediments deposited as water slowed down on the floodplain during previous floods.

Water that cannot fit in the channel flows onto the floodplain. Sand is deposited near the channel, creating a higher area called a natural levee. Smaller sediments are deposited on the floodplain.

## **2** Flash floods

Flash floods are local floods that occur within hours of a severe rainstorm. They often occur when a sudden additional input of water into the stream causes the water level to quickly rise in height and overflow the channel. Flash floods last for hours and occur on all types of small-to-large discharge streams. However, they particularly occur in mountain streams or braided streams where there is little infiltration. This lack of infiltration results in quicker flooding because infiltrated water flows into the stream more slowly than surface flow.

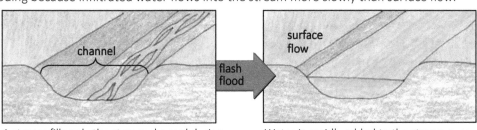

A stream fills only the stream channel during normal flow. When a large amount of rain suddenly falls on the surrounding area, it quickly flows across the surface into the stream.

Water is rapidly added to the stream over hours. The water stays concentrated in a smaller area without a broad floodplain to fill, and it causes short-term flooding.

## Check
☐ Describe what happens to cause a flood.
☐ Compare and contrast the area affected, duration, and effects of infiltration for regional floods and flash floods.

# 13.8 Flood Frequency and Size

**Key Concept:** Large floods are less common than small floods, but people make floods larger by reducing infiltration through paving and building. Geologists describe the difference in the size of floods in several ways. The discharge, or amount of water flowing through a stream, is one way to describe a flood. Another way to describe a flood's size is to use how often floods of that size occur on a stream **1**. As infiltration decreases, the maximum size of floods increases because rain water rushes across the surface into the stream more quickly and over a shorter period of time **2**. People decrease infiltration of water into the ground by building roads and buildings. This human impact is causing geologists' calculations that are based on past records of how often a flood occurs to often underestimate the chance of a large flood.

## **1** Large floods are rarer than small floods

Large floods require a tremendous amount of water, so they do not happen as frequently as small floods. The amount of water to cause a large flood varies by stream. For example, the discharge during a large flood on a small stream may be the same as the discharge during a small flood on a large stream. For perspective, large floods on the Mississippi River have discharges near 28,000 cubic meters per second (1,000,000 cubic feet per second), which is equivalent to approximately 1000 buses of water driving by each second. As a result of the differences between streams, the size of a flood on a particular stream is often defined, not by the amount of water, but by how often it occurs.

| Description of how often a flood occurs | Small Flood | Medium-Sized Flood | Large Flood |
|---|---|---|---|
| **Recurrence interval**<br>The recurrence interval is how many years on average there are between floods. This number is an average, so there could be two floods of a particular size in one year, followed by many years of no floods. The recurrence interval is calculated by dividing the number of years floods have been recorded by the number of floods that size. For example, if in 100 years there have been 5 floods, the recurrence interval is 20 years (100/5=20). | 2 years | 20 years | 100 years |
| **X-year flood**<br>How often a flood occurs can also be expressed by the concept of an X-year flood, with the X being the recurrence interval. Although they are the same thing, geologists prefer to talk about a recurrence interval for a flood because it is less likely to cause the misconception that past behaviors of streams can be used to predict the year of the next flood. However, terms like 20-year flood or 100-year flood are often used in the media. Again, remember that a 20-year flood does not happen once every twenty years like clockwork, but it happens, on average, every twenty years. | 2-year flood | 20-year flood | 100-year flood |
| **Chance of occurring each year**<br>The chance a flood of a particular size occurs each year is calculated by dividing 1 by the recurrence interval and converting to a percent (e.g. a flood that has a recurrence interval of 20 years has a 1/20 or 5% chance of happening in any given year). Small floods with a shorter recurrence interval have a greater chance of happening each year compared to large floods.<br><br>$$\frac{1}{\text{Recurrence interval}} \times 100 = \text{percent chance a flood occurs each year}$$ | 50% | 5% | 1% |

# 2 People affect flood frequency and size

Even without touching a stream, people increase the size and frequency of floods by reducing the infiltration of water into the ground. Paving and building in an area decreases the infiltration rate. Water that infiltrates flows slowly through the ground, eventually reaching the stream. Less infiltration results in rainwater rushing across the surface and into the stream quickly, causing higher floods. As a result, when geologists use records of past floods to calculate how often floods of different sizes occur, these predictions may underestimate the likelihood of future big floods unless the effect of development is taken into account.

### Abundant infiltration of rain
Sediments (including soil) tend to have a lot of spaces within them, making them permeable to water to allow infiltration.

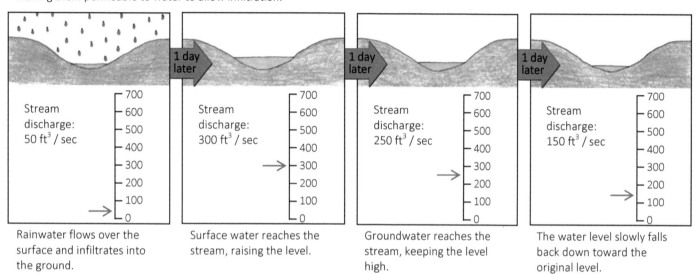

Rainwater flows over the surface and infiltrates into the ground.

Surface water reaches the stream, raising the level.

Groundwater reaches the stream, keeping the level high.

The water level slowly falls back down toward the original level.

### Little infiltration of rain
Roads, parking lots, buildings, and other impermeable surfaces decrease the amount of rainwater that can infiltrate into the ground. Storm drains are built to transport water directly to streams as quickly as possible.

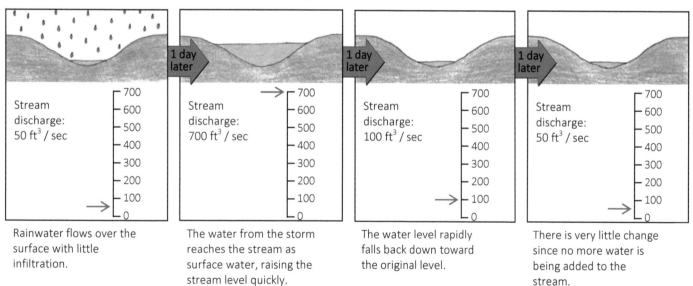

Rainwater flows over the surface with little infiltration.

The water from the storm reaches the stream as surface water, raising the stream level quickly.

The water level rapidly falls back down toward the original level.

There is very little change since no more water is being added to the stream.

## Check

☐ Compare three ways geologists describe how often floods of a particular size occur.
☐ Explain how people affect flood frequency and size.

# 13.9 DATA AND DIAGRAMS: Stream Discharge and People

**Key Concept:** Line graphs can show how a variable changes over time for different locations. This graph shows stream discharge after a single rainstorm for two similar-sized streams flowing through nearby areas in western Washington state ❶. To create a graph like this, geologists in the United States Geological Survey (USGS) install instruments that monitor the stream discharge on many streams. Tips on how to read this graph are below ❷. Use the questions to practice interpreting graphs ❸.

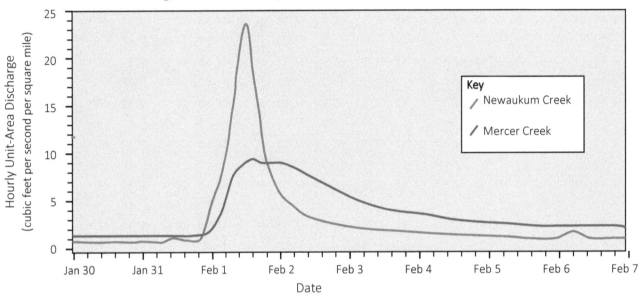

Stream discharge over time for a single rainstorm in similar-sized streams

## ❶ How to read the diagram

Determine what variables are shown on the two axes of the graph and the key. In this case, notice that the vertical axis takes the area of the drainage basin into consideration, so streams with slightly different areas can be directly compared. The horizontal axis identifies the length of time.

## ❷ An example of what you might interpret

If you compare the two lines on the graph, you will notice that the discharge for both show an increase followed by a decrease, although the pattern is different for two streams.

## ❸ Questions

**1. What does the graph show?**
a. the discharge for two streams over time, highlighting how stream size affects the discharge
b. the discharge for a single stream over time, for two rainstorms of different size
c. the discharge for two streams over time, accounting for differences in the drainage basin size

**2. Which stream has the largest peak discharge (per square mile)?**
a. Mercer Creek
b. Newaukum Creek
c. They are the same

**3. Which stream has water reach it more slowly and over a longer period of time?**
a. Mercer Creek
b. Newaukum Creek
c. They are the same

**4. Recall how buildings and roads affect the amount of infiltration and how quickly water reaches streams. Which stream is most likely to drain an area with a lot of buildings and roads?**
a. Mercer Creek
b. Newaukum Creek
c. They are the same
d. It is impossible to tell

**5. What would happen to Newaukum Creek if a large city was built along it?**
a. It would flood less because the maximum discharge would decrease but cover a longer period of time, unlike either stream on the graph.
b. It would flood the same amount because the maximum discharge would remain unchanged, similar to how it is now.
c. It would flood more because the maximum discharge would increase but cover a shorter amount of time, similar to Mercer Creek.

# 13.10 Controlling Floods

## Key Concept:
People try to control floods using various techniques that often change the natural stream. As you have likely seen in the news, floods can be devastating, so people try to decrease their destructive power. Two general strategies that prevent water from flowing onto the floodplain are: increasing the amount of water that can flow through a stream before it floods and reducing the stream's discharge **1**. Levees, which raise the height along stream channels **2**, and widening and straightening stream channels **3** both increase the amount of water that can flow through a stream. To reduce flood discharge, water can be prevented from quickly reaching the stream, such as through the use of retention ponds **4** and flood-control dams built across the stream **5**. Finally, restricting development in the floodplain helps people avoid some of the devastating consequences of floods **6**. All these techniques have advantages and disadvantages.

## 1 Strategies to control floods

Floods occur when there is too much water to fit within the stream channel. Therefore, methods in flood prevention tend to follow the general strategies below. As you read through the five common ways to reduce the impact of floods on people, keep these principles in mind.

| Increase amount of water that can flow through a stream | Reduce the maximum flood discharge | Restrict building |
|---|---|---|
| Increasing the amount of water that can flow through a stream allows more water to be added without it spilling onto the floodplain. This strategy includes building levees and changing the channel. | Reducing the maximum flood discharge by extending the length of time over which water arrives prevents streams from reaching levels high enough to spill onto the floodplain. This strategy includes retention ponds and flood-control dams. | In addition to attempting to control floods, another way to reduce the damage caused by floods is for people to avoid building in areas that frequently flood. |

## 2 Levees

Levees are barriers on the sides of a stream channel that are built to reduce the likelihood that the stream will flow onto the floodplain. They artificially increase the amount of water a stream channel can hold by increasing the stream channel's cross sectional area. Levees may be as simple as dirt or sandbags piled up (as shown in the photo), but some are made of stronger, more permanent materials, such as concrete.

**Advantages:** Small levees are often cost-effective and are generally straightforward in their construction.

**Disadvantages:** Over time, levees trap sediments within the channel. This reduces the depth of the stream channel, which reduces the cross sectional area and causes a greater likelihood of flooding. Floodwater higher than the levee will do as much or more damage than if the levee was not there. Levees need regular maintenance or they might break, causing flooding.

**No levees**

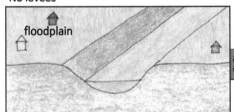

The stream at a normal level, and houses are built on the floodplain.

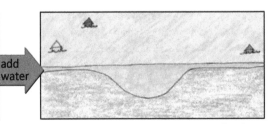

Discharge increases, and the stream floods the floodplain.

**With levees**

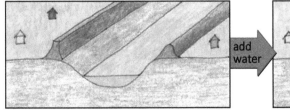

The stream at a normal level.

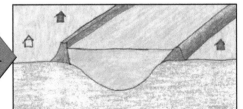

The levees increase the amount of water a stream channel can hold and contain the flood water in the channel.

# 3 Changing the stream channel

The stream channel can be modified to increase the amount of water that can flow through it. It can be deepened and widened to increase the cross sectional area. It can also be straightened and smoothed to increase the speed of the water, since discharge increases as the water speed increases. There are many ways to change the channel of a stream. In the photo, the stream was lined with smooth cement, dug out deeper, and straightened.

**Advantages:** A deeper, straighter channel is better for navigation. Additional land is not needed to control floods.

**Disadvantages:** Changing the stream channel affects the natural ecosystem of plants and animals around the stream. Since the water moves faster, it increases the potential for flooding downstream, where the stream channel has not been modified.

**No changes to the stream channel**

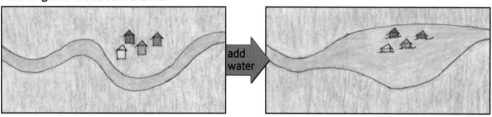

The stream at a normal level.

Discharge increases, and the stream floods the floodplain.

**With changes to the stream channel**

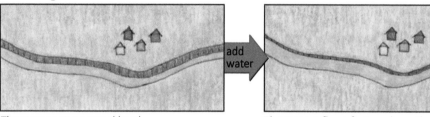

The stream at a normal level.

The stream flows faster where the channel has been straightened and deepened, quickly transporting the extra water downstream.

# 4 Retention ponds

Retention ponds are low areas that hold and store rain water before it reaches a stream. The water then gradually infiltrates into the ground, slowly making its way to the stream. In a similar way, water can be temporarily diverted into another channel, for infiltration or slow flow back into the river. Wetlands like swamps or marshes are natural retention ponds. Some parking lots and roads, like this one, are built with retention ponds next to them to trap the runoff of rain water and prevent it from quickly reaching streams.

**Advantages:** Retention ponds do not alter the stream channel, so they do not dramatically disrupt the ecosystem of plants and animals around the stream or require expensive maintenance.

**Disadvantages:** Retention ponds need space, which may be difficult if the land is already developed.

**No retention pond**

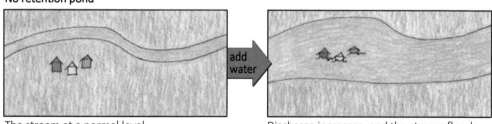

The stream at a normal level.

Discharge increases, and the stream floods the floodplain.

**With retention pond**

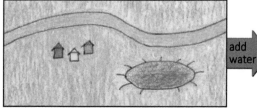

The stream at a normal level.

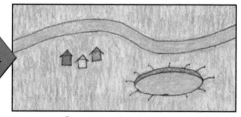

Rainwater flows into the retention pond, delaying it from reaching the stream.

Retention area

# 5 Flood-control dams

Dams can be built across streams with the purpose of trapping extra flood water in streams behind them. The water is then released slowly over time. Dams are made of a variety of materials, including soil or concrete, as shown here. Upstream is to the left.

**Advantages:** Dams can help keep large areas safe from floods. The reservoir behind some dams may be used for recreation.

**Disadvantages:** Dams affect natural ecosystems when trapped water drowns land upstream and the slow release of water reduces the natural variance in water flow downstream. Dams also trap sediment, preventing them from being transported downstream. Dams are costly to build and maintain.

**No flood-control dams**

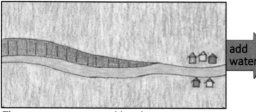

The stream at a normal level.

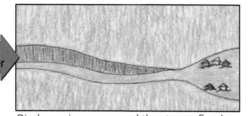

Discharge increases, and the stream floods the floodplain.

**With flood-control dams**

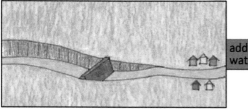

The stream at a normal level.

The dam traps extra flood water behind it, releasing it slowly over time.

# 6 Restrict development

If there are no buildings in a floodplain, then floods will not cause damage. Since all streams naturally flood, geologists make maps showing the heights of large floods. The map to the right shows the area that has a 1% chance of flooding each year in blue. These maps may be used by the government to restrict development and require homeowners to buy flood insurance.

**Advantages:** Restricting development does not disrupt the natural ecosystem of a stream or require expensive maintenance.

**Disadvantages:** Restricting development generally applies to new buildings only and may be difficult to enforce when people want to build on desirable land in floodplains.

**No restricted development**

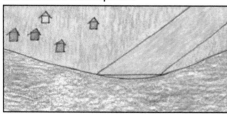

The stream at a normal level.

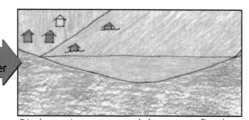

Discharge increases, and the stream floods the floodplain.

**With restricted development**

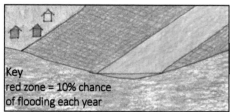

Key
red zone = 10% chance
of flooding each year

The stream at a normal level.

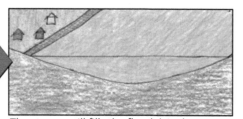

The stream still fills the floodplain, but buildings are not affected because they are built above the area that floods.

## Check
☐ Describe and give examples of the two general principles used to control floods.
☐ List five methods for reducing flood damage, and explain how each works.
☐ Compare and contrast advantages and disadvantages of five different methods of flood control

## End of Chapter Questions: Student Debates

For each of the following questions, determine which student you agree with and explain why.

1. Two students are discussing the path water takes through the water cycle.

   **Student 1:** Water can take different paths as it travels through the water cycle, traveling through different reservoirs.

   **Student 2:** It is called a cycle because the path the water takes is like a circle, with nearly the same path through the reservoirs each time around.

2. Two students are discussing how stream channels form.

   **Student 1:** Water moves downhill through channels that are already in the bedrock.

   **Student 2:** Water erodes sediment and bedrock, carving it into channels it flows through.

3. Two students are discussing what a 100-year flood means.

   **Student 1:** It refers to how long it is between floods on a river, with a 100-year flood happening once every 100 years.

   **Student 2:** It is related to the discharge of a flood that has a certain percent chance of happening, in this case a 1% chance.

4. Three students are discussing how people affect floods.

   **Student 1:** People affect floods by changing the characteristics of a stream, such as making it deeper or straighter.

   **Student 2:** People affect floods by altering areas that drain into streams, such as by building houses and roads.

   **Student 3:** People can't affect floods. Floods are caused by rain, and people cannot influence the rain.

5. Two students are discussing when regional floods happen.

   **Student 1:** Regional floods tend to happen during the most intense part of a rainstorm. When it is raining the most, that is also when the floods are their worst because that is when there is the most water.

   **Student 2:** Regional floods tend to happen after a rainstorm, often by hours or days. Infiltration delays water from reaching a stream quickly because water flows more slowly when it is in the ground.

6. Two students are discussing how often floods happen.

   **Student 1:** Floods happen often when there is lots of rain, since the water level in streams rises above normal levels frequently. They are common events.

   **Student 2:** I almost never hear about flash floods in the news, and I only rarely hear about regional floods, so I think floods in the U.S. happen once every few years.

## End of Chapter Questions: Short Answer

Using your own words or sketching and labeling a diagram, answer the following questions.

7. Create a five step sequence showing one path water may have taken on its journey to become your drinking water.

8. A friend filled a pail with sediment from a stream channel. Explain how you would determine the type of stream channel from which the sediment was most likely collected. Include both observations you could make of the sediment (such as size and shape) as well as information you could get from your friend.

9. Two towns are built near two different streams. Town A is more frequently and severely damaged by floods than Town B. Hypothesize at least three distinct explanations why there is a difference.

10. Engineers are developing pavement that is permeable, which means that water can soak into it. Explain how using permeable pavement would affect flooding in nearby streams in terms of the flood frequency, discharge, and duration.

12. A stream near your school experiences a 100-year flood. Explain what flood control method(s) you think would best prevent damage from future floods, justifying your choice based on characteristics of your area.

**Hints:** For each question, see the sections listed here for information relevant to answering it.

**1.** (13.1, 13.2) **2.** (13.3, 13.4) **3.** (13.6) 4. (13.6, 13.7, 13.8) **5.** (13.2, 13.6) **6.** (13.5, 13.6) **7.** (13.1, 13.2) **8.** (13.3, 13.4) **9.** (13.3, 13.4, 13.5, 13.6, 13.7, 13.8) **10.** (13.2, 13.6, 13.7) **11.** (13.6, 13.7, 13.8)

# Chapter 14: Groundwater

## Chapter Objectives

When you are finished reading this chapter, you should be able to …

• explain the relationship between groundwater, porosity, permeability, and the water table (14.2–14.3).

• summarize how groundwater fits into the water cycle and rock cycle (14.1, 14.4–14.5).

• explain how characteristics of the bedrock affect groundwater, and how groundwater affects the bedrock (14.2, 14.5–14.6).

• describe how people affect groundwater (14.7–14.10).

# 14.1 – 14.6 Groundwater Characteristics

In this section, you will learn how geologists describe groundwater, in terms of its abundance as well as how it moves underground. Groundwater in areas of limestone bedrock behaves and affects people differently than bedrock in other areas.

## Frequently Used Terms

The terms listed here are used repeatedly throughout this section, so by learning them before you read this section, you can focus your mental energy on the concepts presented.

**chemical weathering** Processes that break down rock through breaking or rearranging the bonds between atoms in minerals, resulting in dissolved ions or minerals that have a new composition.

**groundwater** Water that resides underground in pore spaces within bedrock or overlying sediments.

**infiltration** Water soaking into the ground from the surface.

**karst landscape** An area with landforms such as abundant sinkholes and few streams that forms as a result of groundwater chemically weathering limestone bedrock.

**permeability** How well water flows through the pore spaces in rock; a rock with a high permeability allows water to flow through quickly.

**pore spaces** The empty spaces in rock or sediments; they are generally very small spaces between sediments or in cracks in rock.

**porosity** The percentage of pore spaces that are in rock or sediments; higher porosity means more pore spaces.

**recharge** The process of water infiltrating and becoming groundwater.

**water table** An underground boundary that separates pore spaces completely filled with water below it and pore spaces containing air above it.

This dramatic karst landscape painted hundreds of years ago in China was created by erosion by groundwater.

# 14.1 Groundwater and the Water Cycle

**Key Concept:** Surface water infiltrates into the ground and becomes groundwater, flows underground, and leaves the ground in a variety of ways as part of the water cycle. You may recall that water moves through different reservoirs as part of the water cycle (see 13.1). Underground water that is in the small spaces within bedrock and between sediments is part of the groundwater reservoir. Groundwater is an important reservoir to people because it is a major source of water **1**. The main input to the groundwater reservoir is water input when surface water infiltrates, or soaks into, the ground **2**. There are several ways water leaves the groundwater reservoir and enters other reservoirs **3**.

## **1** Groundwater

Groundwater is water that has infiltrated into the ground and fills the empty spaces in rock or sediments, called pore spaces. Most groundwater is similar to water in a sponge in that it flows slowly through tiny pore spaces and not through large underground lakes or rivers. The groundwater reservoir in the water cycle is the largest reservoir of liquid, fresh water, making it useful to people. Groundwater is the source of nearly half of all drinking water worldwide, and it is a particularly valuable source of water for agriculture.

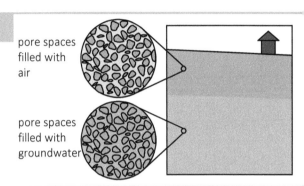
pore spaces filled with air

pore spaces filled with groundwater

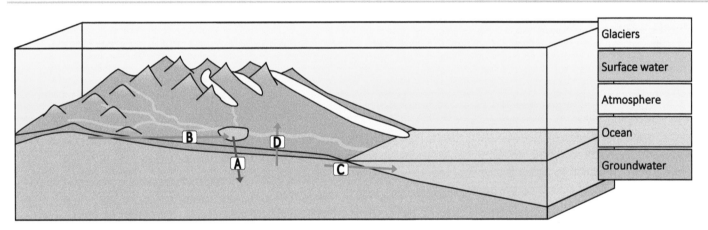

Glaciers

Surface water

Atmosphere

Ocean

Groundwater

## **2** Groundwater reservoir inputs

As water moves through the water cycle, it enters the groundwater reservoir mainly through surface water that infiltrates into the ground, a process called recharge. Water may flow through the ground for tens to thousands of years and is not as dependent on short-term changes to weather as streams are.

### **A** From the Surface water reservoir
Water at the surface (from streams, lakes, swamps, fallen rain, glacier melt, etc.) infiltrates into the ground. People play a role in decreasing this input through construction that reduces infiltration (such as parking lots). However, people can also increase inputs, although to a lesser extent, by creating ponds with water that infiltrates into the ground, recharging the groundwater.

## **3** Groundwater reservoir outputs

As water moves through the water cycle, much of it leaves the groundwater reservoir naturally. Groundwater is an essential source of freshwater for people and for natural ecosystems because it is not dependent on short term weather.

### **B** To the Surface water reservoir
Water seeps out of the ground to the surface forming natural springs, which can feed streams, lakes, swamps, etc.

### **C** To the Ocean reservoir
Groundwater flows directly from the pore spaces in the ground into the ocean, to become part of the ocean water.

### **D** To People
People directly remove groundwater by drilling wells into the ground (see 14.7).

**Check** Before you continue, you should be able to answer each check without looking at the page.
- Draw a simple sketch and use it to explain what groundwater is.
- Describe how most water enters the groundwater reservoir and where it comes from.
- Describe three ways that water leaves the groundwater reservoir and where it goes.

# 14.2 Porosity and Permeability

**Key Concept:** Porosity and permeability of bedrock are the two key characteristics in determining the amount and flow of groundwater. The amount of groundwater present is determined by the porosity of bedrock, which is the amount of empty space in a rock. The higher the porosity, the more groundwater a rock can hold **1**. The flow of groundwater is determined by the bedrock's permeability, which is how well water flows through the pore spaces. The higher the permeability, the more quickly groundwater can flow through the rock **2**. Different rocks have different porosities and permeabilities **3**. Bedrock layers with high porosity and high permeability are essential sources of groundwater used by people.

## 1 Porosity

Porosity is the amount of pore spaces in bedrock or sediments. Pore spaces, either as spaces between sediments or as cracks in rock, can be filled with water or air. The higher the percentage of pore spaces, the higher the porosity, and the more water or air it can hold. An example of something with high porosity is a sponge, since it can hold a lot of water.

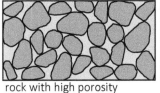 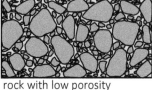

rock with high porosity        rock with low porosity

## 2 Permeability

Permeability is how easily water can flow through rock or sediment. Highly permeable rock lets water flow from pore space to pore space easily, with a rate as fast as 30 cm (1 ft) per day. Water may flow slower than 0.01 cm (0.0001 inch) per day through rock with low permeability. An example of something with extremely high permeability is rice or cereal, since water or milk flows quickly through it.

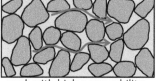 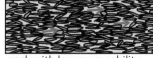

rock with high permeability        rock with low permeability

## 3 Example bedrock

Rock and sediments with high permeability have a high porosity, with the abundant pore spaces connected to each other to allow flow. Groundwater that people can easily remove is found in rocks with both a high porosity, so there is enough groundwater, and a high permeability, so it can flow to where people remove it.

**Sandstone**
Porosity: high
Permeability: high
Sandstone has a lot of pore spaces that are well connected. It can contain a lot of water that will also easily flow through it.

**Shale**
Porosity: high
Permeability: low
Shale has a lot of pore spaces, but they are very small and poorly connected. It can contain a lot of water, but the water will not flow through it.

**Limestone with cracks**
Porosity: high
Permeability: high
Chemical weathering of limestone results in large, well-connected pore spaces. It can contain a lot of water that will also easily flow through.

**Granite**
Porosity: low
Permeability: low
Granite has few pore spaces because it has interlocking minerals. If granite has many interconnected cracks, then it may contain groundwater.

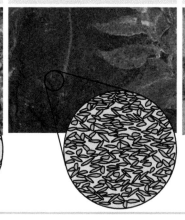 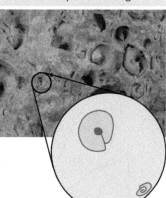 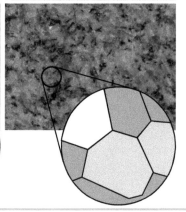

## Check

☐ Draw a sketch and use it to explain the difference between porosity and permeability.
☐ Categorize four rocks by how well they move groundwater and explain your choices.

# 14.3 The Water Table

**Key Concept:** The water table is the boundary underground that separates pore spaces completely filled with water and pore spaces filled with air. Water from Earth's surface moves downward until it reaches the water table. At that point, the pore spaces are fully filled with water **1**. The height of the water table can change **2**. For example, if the amount of water added to the groundwater is less than what is being removed, then the amount of groundwater will be reduced and the water table lowers. However, if the added water is more than what is being removed, the water table rises.

## **1** Understanding the water table

The water table is the top of where pore spaces are completely filled with water. Above the surface of the water table, pore spaces are filled with air along with some moisture. In the analogy below, the spaces between the marbles are pore spaces. The bottom of the cup represents deep bedrock that is low porosity and low permeability, so the water cannot travel downwards.

### Water table and groundwater

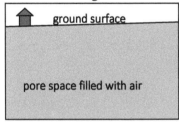
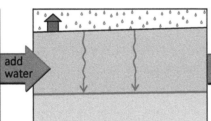
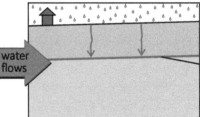

This ground has high porosity and high permeability, such as sediment.

When water is added to the surface, the water trickles down into the ground.

The water table is the top surface where the pore spaces are filled with water.

### Water table analogy

This cup of marbles has high porosity and high permeability.

When you pour water in the cup, the water trickles down between the marbles.

The water table is the top surface where the pore spaces are filled with water.

## **2** Height of the water table

The height of the water table is measured relative to a fixed point, such as sea level. It is not constant over time. When inputs to the groundwater are more than the outputs, more water will be added to the groundwater, and the water table level will rise. Conversely, when inputs are less than outputs, the water table level will lower.

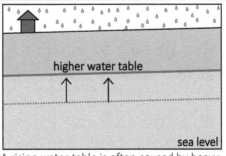
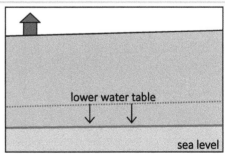

A rising water table is often caused by heavy or prolonged rain increasing the inputs.

A lowering water table is often caused by a draught or by people pumping water out.

## Check

☐ Draw a sketch and use it to explain what the water table is.
☐ Explain what might cause the water table level to rise or lower.

# 14.4 Groundwater Flow

**Key Concept:** The water table is not flat, and groundwater flows slowly along the downward slope of the water table. Water from the surface moves downward until it reaches the water table. The water table is not flat, like a table in your kitchen. Instead, its shape will generally mirror the shape of the land surface **1**. In places where the water table slopes, the groundwater flows downhill to follow that slope surface **2**.

## **1** The shape of the water table

After water infiltrates into the ground, it flows downward until it hits the water table. The height of the water table is not the same everywhere, since it approximately follows the shape of the land. In some places the water table is right at the surface, but in other places it can be hundreds of meters (hundreds of feet) below the surface.

The height of the water table approximately mirrors the shape of the land. A hill has a high water table elevation while a valley has a low water table elevation.

Stable surface water, such as lakes, swamps, or streams, exists where the water table is higher than the land surface. The surface water cannot soak into the ground because the pore spaces are already filled with water. Unlike the water table, the lake's surface is flat because the water flows freely and is not slowed by moving through pore spaces.

Geologists determine the depth to the water table by drilling wells into the ground. The well hole itself acts as a giant pore space and fills with water up to the level of the water table. Geologists can measure this depth of water in the well.

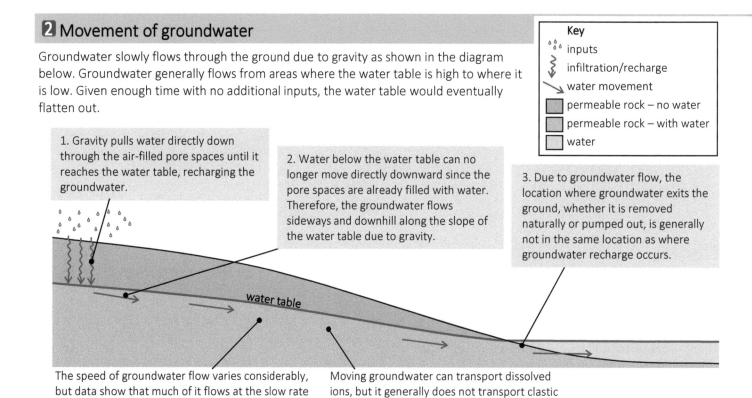

## **2** Movement of groundwater

Groundwater slowly flows through the ground due to gravity as shown in the diagram below. Groundwater generally flows from areas where the water table is high to where it is low. Given enough time with no additional inputs, the water table would eventually flatten out.

**Key**
- inputs
- infiltration/recharge
- water movement
- permeable rock – no water
- permeable rock – with water
- water

1. Gravity pulls water directly down through the air-filled pore spaces until it reaches the water table, recharging the groundwater.

2. Water below the water table can no longer move directly downward since the pore spaces are already filled with water. Therefore, the groundwater flows sideways and downhill along the slope of the water table due to gravity.

3. Due to groundwater flow, the location where groundwater exits the ground, whether it is removed naturally or pumped out, is generally not in the same location as where groundwater recharge occurs.

The speed of groundwater flow varies considerably, but data show that much of it flows at the slow rate of several centimeters (one inch) per day.

Moving groundwater can transport dissolved ions, but it generally does not transport clastic sediments because the water moves too slowly.

## Check

☐ Describe the shape of the water table.
☐ Explain in what direction groundwater moves underground.

# 14.5 Groundwater in Caves and the Rock Cycle

**Key Concept:** Groundwater can dissolve bedrock forming caves and transport and precipitate the resulting dissolved ions as part of the rock cycle. Chemical weathering happens as groundwater flows through pore spaces and slowly dissolves bedrock, removing and transporting the resulting ions. Chemical sediments can precipitate out of groundwater to form new rock as part of the rock cycle **1**. Cave formation and decoration are examples of these processes in limestone bedrock **2**.

## **1** Rock cycle processes related to groundwater

Groundwater weathers bedrock, transports the dissolved ions, and later may precipitate them as chemical sediments. These are all steps in the rock cycle to break down old rock and form new rock.

| Weathering | Transportation | Precipitation |
|---|---|---|
| As groundwater flows through pore spaces in bedrock, it chemically weathers the rock. Groundwater cannot mechanically weather bedrock because of its slow movement. | Groundwater transports the dissolved ions. Groundwater cannot transport clastic sediments such as sand and mud because of its slow movement through tiny pore spaces. | Groundwater may precipitate dissolved ions as chemical sediments, forming new minerals that form chemical sedimentary rocks. When groundwater flows through clastic sediments, minerals may be precipitated within the pore spaces between clastic sediments forming clastic sedimentary rocks (see 8.10). |

## **2** Caves as an example

Caves form through the rock cycle processes of weathering and transportation described above. Bedrock that easily chemically weathers by dissolving, such as limestone that is made of the carbonate mineral calcite, is necessary for forming large caves. Later, the cave may be decorated if new minerals form as dissolved ions precipitate out of the groundwater.

### Cave Formation

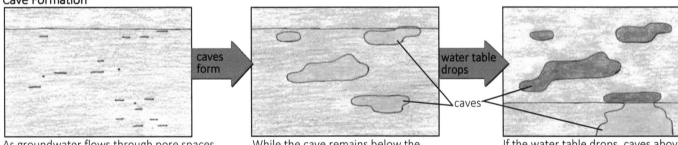

As groundwater flows through pore spaces in bedrock, it dissolves the rock, enlarging the small pore spaces into caves.

While the cave remains below the water table, the cave continues to grow.

If the water table drops, caves above the water table stop growing.

### Cave Decoration

When groundwater infiltrates down to a dry cave, some ions may precipitate out in the cave, forming new minerals that make up limestone rock that decorate the caves. The photo shows stalactites and stalagmites in Carlsbad Caverns, New Mexico as examples of cave decorations.

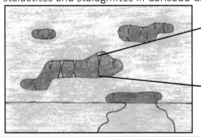

Stalactites form when water with dissolved ions drips from the top of the cave, leaving a small amount of carbonate minerals behind.

Stalagmites form when water drops onto the cave floor, and some carbonate minerals are deposited.

## Check

☐ Explain how groundwater fits into the rock cycle, in terms of weathering, transportation, and deposition.
☐ Describe the characteristics of bedrock in which caves tend to form.
☐ Summarize how caves change over time.

# 14.6 Karst Landscapes

**Key Concept:** Karst landscape is an area with landforms that result from limestone bedrock chemically weathered by groundwater. Although chemical weathering of bedrock occurs underground, the results can be seen at the surface as karst landscape. Karst landscapes usually form where there is limestone bedrock in wet climates because that rock type and water is necessary for extensive chemical weathering **1**. Some underground caves may collapse to form sinkholes at Earth's surface, and some streams on the surface flow into caves, resulting in few streams flowing at the surface **2**. Unique issues facing people living in karst landscapes include sinkholes and easily contaminated groundwater because of the lack of slow infiltration into the ground of groundwater and its contaminants **3**. Karst landscapes develop primarily in areas with limestone bedrock, so some areas of the United States are more likely to have karst landscapes than others **4**.

## **1** Karst landscape formation

Karst landscapes form where bedrock is being dissolved by groundwater, forming caves. Over time, this impacts visible landforms. These landscapes develop over time. However their requirements and characteristics are similar at all stages.

### Requirements for karst landscapes
Based on observations, geologists have determined that karst landscapes form when underground caves affect surface landforms. Karst landscape requires:

1. Extensive limestone bedrock, generally with cracks. Limestone easily dissolves through chemical weathering, and the cracks enlarge to become well-connected caves. The bedrock in the photo is limestone, and caves are visible throughout.

2. A wet climate because a lot of water is needed to dissolve the limestone bedrock.

3. Enough time and flow of groundwater for the rock to dissolve into large caves.

## **2** Characteristics of karst landscapes

Karst landscapes have many caves underground, which cause landforms such as sinkholes and disappearing streams, the formation of which is described below. In comparison with most landscapes in which water flows along the surface as streams, in karst landscapes water often flows underground through connected caves and pore spaces enlarged by chemical weathering. Being able to identify karst landscapes through their distinctive characteristics allows geologists to determine where karst landscapes may impact people.

### Disappearing streams
Disappearing streams are streams that suddenly stop flowing at the surface as surface water. They form when the stream water flows into a sinkhole or cave allowing it to flow quickly down to the water table. As a result, there are relatively few streams that flow through karst landscape.

### Sinkholes
Sinkholes are depressions in the land surface that are generally circular. They form when caves underground enlarge to the point that they become unstable and the ground above them collapses down.

### Caves
Caves are large, empty pockets underground in bedrock. Both caves and pore spaces enlarged by chemical weathering increase the amount of and speed at which groundwater flows.

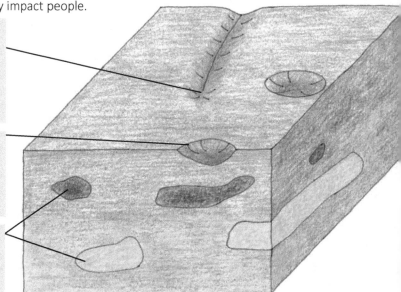

# 3 Karst landscapes and people

Karst landscapes can impact the people living in the area. One impact is that sinkholes destroy buildings and roads. The photo to the right shows a large sinkhole in Oregon in 2016 that destroyed a road, and the aerial photo below shows a sinkhole that destroyed several buildings in Florida in 1981. Another concern is the cleanliness of groundwater used for drinking and irrigation. Unlike typical landscapes where groundwater infiltrates through small pore spaces that filter it naturally, groundwater that flows through the large, underground spaces in karst landscapes is not naturally filtered. Therefore, it often contains more contaminants directly from the surface.

# 4 Locations of karst landscapes

Some locations in North America are more prone to karst topography than others, primarily because they have all three requirements for karst topography. For example, areas like Indiana, Kentucky, and Florida have bedrock with thick layers of limestone and relatively wet climates. Geologists cannot prevent sinkholes from forming in these areas, but the enforcement of clean water laws and public education of people living in karst landscapes may reduce the contamination of groundwater.

This map created by the United States Geological Survey shows the areas of the United States that have the potential to have karst landscapes based on the types of bedrock found in the area.

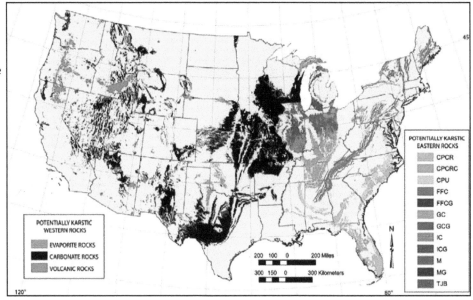

# Check

☐ Discuss two landforms used to identify karst landscapes.
☐ Explain how karst landscapes form.
☐ Summarize two ways that karst landscapes affect people.

Ch 14: 2<sup>nd</sup> Section

# 14.7 – 14.10 People and Groundwater

In this section, you will learn that groundwater is an important source of water for people across the United States. However, if we are not careful with groundwater, it may not be useable in the future.

## Frequently Used Terms

The terms listed here are used repeatedly throughout this section, so by learning them before you read this section, you can focus your mental energy on the concepts presented.

**aquifer** Bedrock or sediments that contains enough flowing groundwater to be a useful source of water for people.

**subsidence** The shifting downward of the ground surface due to the compaction of underground pore spaces.

**well** A hole dug in the ground to remove water from an aquifer.

Groundwater can be contaminated by a wide variety of sources, including underground tanks that leak.

# 14.7 Using Groundwater

**Key Concept:** People remove groundwater from porous, permeable rock or sediment, called aquifers. Groundwater is an important source of water for many people. The best bedrock and sediment to use as a source of water have high porosity and permeability. These useful sources of water for people are called aquifers **1**. People remove groundwater out of the ground using wells, which are holes in the ground that reach below the water table **2**.

## **1** Aquifers

An aquifer is a useful source of groundwater for people. Aquifers are bedrock or sediments that have high a porosity to contain groundwater and a high permeability so groundwater flows through. Geologists study bedrock and sediment layers to determine where and how deep aquifers are found.

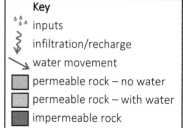

Key
- inputs
- infiltration/recharge
- water movement
- permeable rock – no water
- permeable rock – with water
- impermeable rock

Unconfined aquifer: An aquifer with only permeable layers above it. Surface water infiltrates directly into the aquifer, recharging it.

Perched aquifer: A type of unconfined aquifer that is above the main aquifer, separated by an impermeable layer through which the groundwater cannot travel.

Confined aquifer: An aquifer with an impermeable layer above it, confining it. Surface water recharges the aquifer only in the location where it reaches the surface.

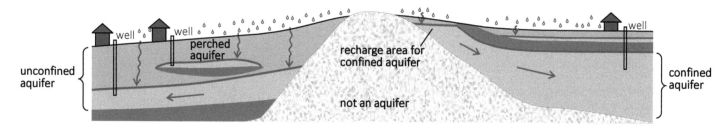

## **2** Groundwater wells

A well is a deep hole dug or drilled into the ground to reach an aquifer. To bring water from the aquifer to the surface, most wells have a pump at the surface to pull water up from below the water table. In addition to using the removed groundwater for drinking and irrigation, geologists use wells to determine the depth to the water table and to check for groundwater pollutants.

A well will contain water as long as the well reaches below the water table. If the water table lowers and the well is no longer deep enough to reach it, then the well will run dry.

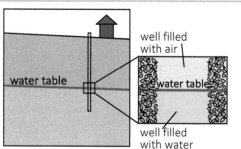

When groundwater is being removed through an active well, the nearby groundwater slowly flows toward the well, replacing the groundwater that was removed. This flow creates a cone-shaped depression in the water table, locally lowering the water table.

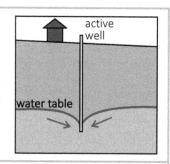

Artesian wells are wells into a confined aquifer where the water in the well rises to the surface without a pump. Artesian wells occur where the elevation of the water table of the recharge area of the confined aquifer is higher than the elevation of the well, as shown in the diagram. That higher water weighs down on the water on the confined aquifer, and the extra pressure pushes the water in the well to the surface. The water itself is not different from other groundwater.

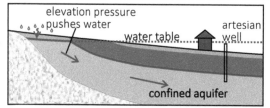

## Check

☐ Summarize the two characteristics of an aquifer and how aquifers relate to impermeable layers.
☐ Describe how people withdraw groundwater using wells.

# 14.8 Benefits of Using Groundwater

**Key Concept:** There are many reasons to use groundwater instead of surface water. Groundwater is available to and used by people across the United States **1**. Amongst the many reasons to use groundwater instead of surface water are that it tends to be located nearly everywhere **2**, naturally clean **3**, and relatively consistent year-round **4**. People choose to use groundwater depending on the availability of useable surface water compared to groundwater.

## **1** Who uses groundwater

Nearly one-quarter of water in the United States used comes from groundwater, and about half of the population depends on groundwater for drinking. Each color on this map made by the United States Geological Survey (USGS) shows the location of a major aquifer. For example, the large aquifer in blue ( ▪ ) is the High Plains Aquifer discussed on the next page. If public water supplies do not have easy access to abundant and clean surface water, then they use groundwater. Alternately, the vast majority of individuals not connected to the public water supply, such as in rural areas, pump their own local groundwater.

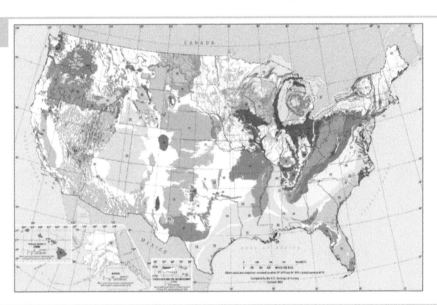

## **2** Widespread locations

Most places across the United States have access to groundwater aquifers. The most widely used aquifers are ones that are made up of sediments, such as sand and gravel, deposited on bedrock. Depending on location, these sediments tend to have been deposited by rivers or glaciers in the past in flat areas and valleys.

**Where it is not widespread:**
Groundwater is less abundant in areas where sediments do not cover the bedrock and in areas with bedrock with low porosity and permeability.

## **3** Naturally cleaned

Most groundwater does not have clastic sediments like mud in it because groundwater moves very slowly and is naturally filtered as it flows through tiny pore spaces. As a result, groundwater is not muddy.

**What is not naturally cleaned:**
Groundwater may still contain bacteria, chemicals, and dissolved ions. Areas of karst landscapes do not tend to filter water because of the larger pore spaces. As with all water, groundwater can also be contaminated as it is transferred to homes through pipes.

## **4** Consistent

If surface water dries up, groundwater is often still available, even for people living in dry climates or during droughts. Groundwater flows from its recharge area and tends to reside underground for hundreds to thousands of years, which means that temporary surface conditions often do not affect its availability.

**When it is not consistent:** If surface conditions change long term (e.g. a long drought) or if groundwater removal is permanently higher than recharge, then areas can run out of groundwater.

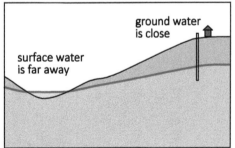

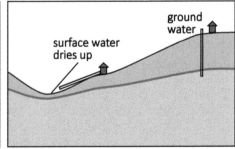

## Check

☐ Summarize three benefits of using groundwater.
☐ Explain under what conditions groundwater may not be available and useable.

# 14.9 DATA AND DIAGRAMS: High Plains Aquifer

**Key Concept:** Maps can compile information from different locations to compare locations and how they change.

This map outlines the High Plains aquifer, a major aquifer located in the central United States from South Dakota to Texas, as can be seen on the map on 14.8. This aquifer is used primarily for irrigation 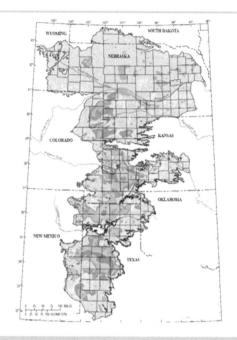. To create a map like this, geologists compile information about water table levels from a large variety of national, state, and local entities. Tips on how to read this map are below . Use the questions to practice interpreting maps .

**Key**
Water-level change from predevelopment to 2015, in feet

- more than -150
- -100 to -150
- -50 to -100
- -25 to -50
- -5 to -25

- -5 to 5

- 5 to 10
- 10 to 25
- 25 to 50
- more than 50

## 1 How to read the diagram

Figure out what data or information the map was designed to communicate. In this case, the map indicates how the water table is changing in the High Plains Aquifer. Relate the information in the key to the map, looking for patterns and how different areas are related.

## 2 An example of what you might interpret

The key indicates that the color green indicates a rising water table level, and these areas with a rising water table are mostly in the northern part of the aquifer.

## 3 Questions

**1. What does the map show?**
a. the volume of groundwater removed from different parts of the aquifer
b. the height of the land in different parts of the aquifer
c. areas that have the highest populations removing water from the aquifer
d. how much the water table height has changed in different parts of the aquifer

**2. What do negative numbers mean for some of the colors?**
a. there is more water added (input) to the aquifer than removed (output)
b. there is more water removed (output) from the aquifer than added (input)
c. the locations that have the highest amount of water being removed
d. the locations that have the lowest amount of water being removed

**3. What color indicates the maximum decrease in the height of the water table?**
a. red
b. grey
c. blue

**4. What might be causing the general trend over time for the water table level in the aquifer?**
a. it is increasing overall, likely due to an increase in rainfall
b. it is declining overall, likely due to water removed by people
c. it is relatively stable overall, likely due to a balance of inputs and outputs

**5. This map gives information only about the change in the level of the groundwater, which is a balance of the inputs and outputs. What additional information would you need to determine in which areas populations are removing water the fastest?**
a. the amount of rainfall, since it adds water to the aquifer
b. the locations of the cities, towns, and farms, since they remove water from the aquifer
c. you don't need any additional information—all the information is in the map

# 14.10 Problems When Using Groundwater

**Key Concept:** Using groundwater becomes problematic when it is used too quickly or becomes contaminated. Although groundwater is the source of drinking water for about half of the population of the United States, many people do not realize that there are issues associated with groundwater that can affect its reliability and usefulness. For example, using groundwater too quickly can lower the water table to the point that it is difficult to drill wells that deep **1**, or to the point that the pore spaces compact, and the ground surface shifts downward causing subsidence **2**. Groundwater can also become contaminated, although it is often difficult to detect **3**. Removing too much groundwater near the ocean can result in the drawing in of salt water. This process, called saltwater intrusion, reduces the usability of the groundwater **4**.

## **1** Lower water table

If people remove water out of an aquifer faster than rainfall can recharge it with new groundwater, the water table lowers. If the water table lowers too much, current wells may no longer be able to supply water to the people who need it for their households, agriculture, or industry.

To prevent the water table from lowering, people must balance the inputs and outputs to the groundwater reservoir, either by increasing the recharge or removing less groundwater.

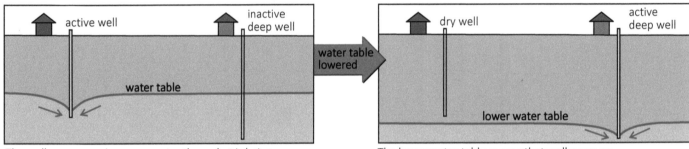

The wells are removing more water than what is being replaced by recharge. Therefore, there are more outputs than inputs to the groundwater reservoir.

The lower water table means that wells may no longer reach the water table and cannot supply water to the people who need it.

## **2** Subsidence

If the water table drops, pores spaces compact because water no longer holds them open. This compaction results in subsidence, where the ground surface shifts downwards, as can be seen in this photo from California. The ground level was at the 1965 sign but fell 7.3 feet over 48 years by 2013. The lowered surface elevation destroys roads and buildings if it is not uniform, changes flow direction at the surface, and makes areas more prone to flooding. Subsidence permanently reduces the porosity, which reduces the size of the aquifer.

To prevent subsidence, people must prevent the water table from lowering, because once subsidence occurs, it cannot be reversed.

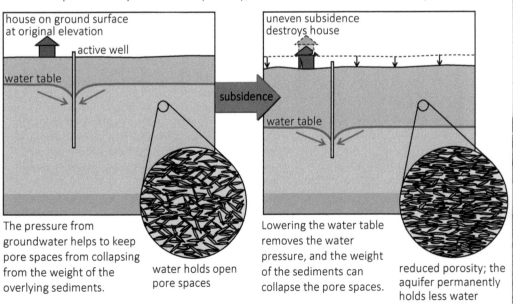

The pressure from groundwater helps to keep pore spaces from collapsing from the weight of the overlying sediments.

water holds open pore spaces

Lowering the water table removes the water pressure, and the weight of the sediments can collapse the pore spaces.

reduced porosity; the aquifer permanently holds less water

# ❸ Contamination

Contaminants can leak into the groundwater from the surface or from sources that may be buried underground. Some contaminants may be filtered out as the water goes through small pore spaces, but many contaminants will get carried with the groundwater, making it undrinkable if no treatment takes place to clean it.

To prevent contamination, people must follow laws for disposing of harmful chemicals and clean it up before contaminants reach wells for drinking water. Environmental geologists and governments work to clean up contaminated water.

### Contaminant sources
Contaminants may leak into the groundwater if they are not disposed of correctly. For example, gas and oil tanks frequently leak. Other common sources are industrial chemicals, military operations, landfills, pesticides, and fertilizers. Cleanup methods include removing the leaking source and contaminated soil, but the flowing groundwater needs to be cleaned as well.

### Flowing contamination
Once contaminants enter the groundwater, they are carried along as it flows down slope. As a result, contaminated groundwater can be found a distance away from the source. Cleanup methods include removing groundwater to treat it, blocking the groundwater from traveling to certain areas, and adding chemicals to the groundwater to treat it underground.

### Natural contaminant sources
Sometimes the bedrock or sediments themselves can cause hazardous levels of dissolved ions in ground water. For example, iron and calcium can be dissolved, causing undesirably hard water. Arsenic in groundwater can be poisonous, and radon is radioactive.

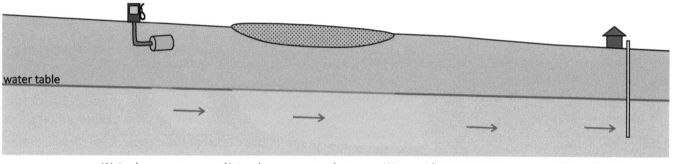

| Water becomes contaminated. | Natural sources may also contaminate water. | Water with contamination flows down slope. | This well will soon have contaminated water. |

# ❹ Salt water intrusion

The salt water in the ocean is denser than fresh water. Near the ocean, salty ocean groundwater can be drawn into a well, replacing the fresh water and making the water undrinkable.

To prevent salt water intrusion, people must increase the recharge of fresh water or remove less groundwater.

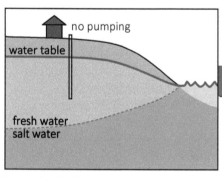

Lower density fresh groundwater sits on top of denser salty groundwater near the coast, much like oil floats on top of water.

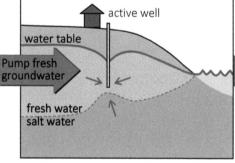

As fresh groundwater is pumped out of the ground, the salt water moves towards the well.

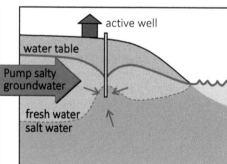

Eventually, if fresh groundwater is pumped out faster than it is recharged, the well will start pumping salty groundwater.

## Check

☐ Explain situations that might cause four different problems associated with groundwater use.
☐ Describe ways to prevent problems associated with groundwater use.

## End of Chapter Questions: Student Debates

For each of the following questions, determine which student you agree with and explain why.

**1. Two students are discussing how easy it would be to see groundwater beneath the surface.**

**Student 1:** Groundwater in most areas is in mostly tiny pore spaces in rock and sediment, so it is not easy to see underground.

**Student 2:** Groundwater in most areas flows through underground lakes and rivers, so once you find them, groundwater is easy to see.

**2. Two students are discussing whether groundwater is muddy.**

**Student 1:** The small pore spaces and the very slow movement of groundwater do not allow it to transport mud-sized sediments, so groundwater is not muddy.

**Student 2:** Groundwater is underground so it is in contact with soil and mud-sized sediments, which make it muddy.

**3. Two students are discussing whether groundwater is part of the water cycle.**

**Student 1:** Once water soaks into the ground, it leaves the water cycle for a while, but comes back again when it makes its way back up to the surface.

**Student 2:** Water in the ground is still part of the water cycle, although you cannot see it. It enters, flows through the ground, and then leaves.

**4. Two students are discussing groundwater flow.**

**Student 1:** Groundwater flows uniformly through the ground at a predictable rate, similar to how the speed of water flowing in streams is predictable.

**Student 2:** Groundwater flows at different speeds, depending on the permeability, so it is difficult to predict and model groundwater flow in an unknown area.

**5. Three students are discussing the formation of caves.**

**Student 1:** Caves form as groundwater erodes and carves bedrock similar to streams eroding valleys.

**Student 2:** Caves form as water in the ground dissolves bedrock through chemical weathering.

**Student 3:** Caves form at the same time as the bedrock forms, so the newly formed rock has holes and gaps in it.

**6. Two students are discussing if people affect the water cycle.**

**Student 1:** People affect the water cycle because we are removing a significant portion of groundwater in some areas and moving it from one reservoir to another.

**Student 2:** People do not affect the water cycle because the processes in the water cycle that move water between reservoirs are natural, like rain and evaporation.

## End of Chapter Questions: Short Answer

Using your own words or sketching and labeling a diagram, answer the following questions.

7. Oil and gas are traditionally pumped out of permeable bedrock. Companies have found oil and gas in shale bedrock and would like to pump it out. Using the concepts of porosity and permeability, explain why this is or is not an easy task.

8. Your grandmother wants to install a groundwater well on her property. Identify and explain three geologic factors she should consider beforehand to help ensure that she is able to pump water out of her new well.

9. Two towns are built in two different areas. Town A has enough groundwater to use for drinking while Town B does not. Hypothesize at least three distinct explanations why there is a difference.

10. Imagine you are on a road trip with friends. Describe to them what to look for to identify karst landscapes.

11. Draw a table to compare at least 6 separate aspects of groundwater in karst landscape and groundwater in sandstone. Things to consider include bedrock type, porosity and permeability, effect on the surface, effect underground, dissolved ions, and people's ability to use the water.

12. A friend tells you that their well is no longer useable. After making sure the pump works, identify a hypothesis explaining what might be the cause. To test your hypothesis, describe two observations, measurements, or actions you can take by visiting the area near the well and what each would tell you about your hypothesis.

13. A friend says "Groundwater is an excellent source of water because people cannot have much of an effect on it." Do you agree or disagree with your friend? Justify your response with at least 3 lines of supporting evidence.

**Hints:** For each question, see the sections listed here for information relevant to answering it.

**1.** (14.2, 14.3) **2.** (14.5, 14.8) **3.** (14.1) **4.** (14.2, 14.4, 14.6) **5.** (14.5) **6.** (14.1, 14.7, 14.9, 14.10) **7.** (14.2, 14.7) **8.** (14.2, 14.3, 14.4, 14.7) **9.** (14.1, 14.2, 14.3, 14.4, 14.6, 14.7, 14.8, 14.9, 14.10) **10.** (14.5, 14.6) **11.** (14.2, 14.5, 14.6, 14.8) **12.** (14.1, 14.2, 14.9, 14.10) **13.** (14.7, 14.8, 14.9, 14.10)

# Chapter 15:
# Oceans and Coasts

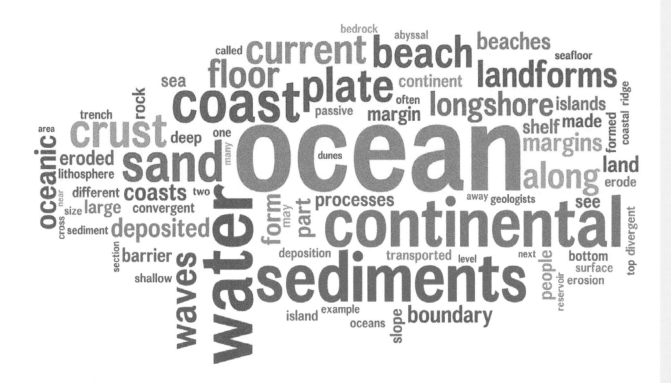

## Chapter Objectives

When you are finished reading this chapter, you should be able to ...

• compare landforms on the ocean floor and explain how they formed (15.1–15.5).

• describe processes that happen along coasts, landforms they create, and impacts on people (15.6–15.10).

# 15.1 – 15.5 Ocean Basins

In this section, you will learn that the ocean floor has many landforms, and geologists have determined that most of them formed as a result of plate tectonic processes.

## Frequently Used Terms

The terms listed here are used repeatedly throughout this section, so by learning them before you read this section, you can focus your mental energy on the concepts presented.

**landforms** Natural features with a distinctive shape on Earth's surface, such as mountains, volcanoes, valleys, ridges, and trenches.

**ocean ridge** A range of undersea mountains; ocean ridges form in oceans at divergent plate boundaries.

**ocean trench** A long, deep depression on the ocean floor; ocean trenches form at convergent plate boundaries where subduction occurs.

**abyssal plain** Deep seafloor that is flat because it is covered by sediment.

**continental shelf** Part of the continental margin next to the continent.

**ocean floor** Also called the seafloor, it is the bottom of the ocean.

**continental margin** The relatively shallow ocean floor near the coast where ocean water covers continental crust instead of oceanic crust.

**oceanic crust** Crust made up of the igneous rock basalt that is thinner and denser than continental crust.

The *Titanic* sank in 1912 to the abyssal plain on the deep ocean floor. It remained undiscovered for over 70 years.

Chapter 15: Oceans and Coasts    Section 1

# 15.1 The Ocean and the Water Cycle

**Key Concept:** **The ocean is the largest reservoir of water in the water cycle.** Ocean water fills the areas of low elevation on Earth **1**. All freshwater, such as rainfall and streamflow, add to the ocean as inputs **2**. The main output from the ocean is evaporation of water **3**. Ocean water is salty because streams and groundwater have slowly added small amounts of dissolved ions to the ocean. Water evaporates out during the water cycle, but the dissolved ions are left behind, making the water salty.

## **1** The ocean covers most of Earth's surface

The ocean is the vast body of salt water that covers about 70% of Earth's surface. Although we give names to different areas, such as the Pacific Ocean, water flows between those areas, resulting in one shared ocean. The ocean has a profound influence on wind patterns, climate, and weather.

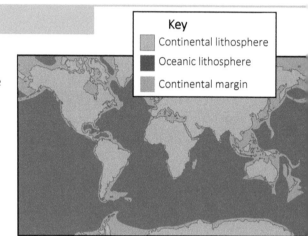

| Key | |
|---|---|
| | Continental lithosphere |
| | Oceanic lithosphere |
| | Continental margin |

### Ocean basins
Ocean basins are the areas filled by ocean water. Water collects in these basins because they are lower in elevation than the continents. They are low-lying because they are composed mostly of thin oceanic lithosphere. The edges of the ocean basin also include less deep continental margins, where ocean water covers thicker continental lithosphere. The shape of ocean basins is a result of plate tectonics. Divergent plate boundaries form growing oceans, and convergent plate boundaries subduct oceanic lithosphere, often near the edges.

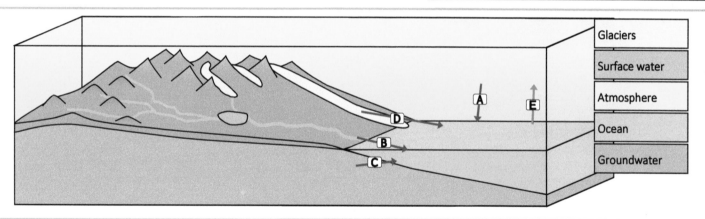

## **2** Ocean reservoir inputs

Water stays in the ocean for an average of several thousand years, so the total amount of water in the ocean is not dependent on short-term changes to weather.

**A** **From the Atmosphere reservoir**
Rain or snow falls directly into the ocean.

**B** **From the Surface water reservoir**
Water at the surface flows through streams into the ocean.

**C** **From the Groundwater reservoir**
Groundwater flows directly from pore spaces into the ocean.

**D** **From the Glacier reservoir**
Glaciers can melt directly into the ocean. Large pieces of glacier ice that fall into the ocean are icebergs, which also melt into the ocean.

## **3** Ocean reservoir outputs

The Sun is the source of energy that causes evaporation and allows water to move upward versus gravity out of the oceans.

**E** **From the Atmosphere reservoir**
Ocean water evaporates to become part of the atmosphere reservoir. The motion of the atmosphere may carry the water over the land, or it may remain to rain or snow back into the ocean.

### Salt water
Salt water is water with a large amount of dissolved ions. The inputs to the ocean are fresh water, but they have small amounts of dissolved ions that remain when water evaporates, resulting in salty ocean water. The dissolved ions built up in the ocean over hundreds of millions of years until a balance was reached as extra salts began precipitating out and forming minerals.

## Check    Before you continue, you should be able to answer each check without looking at the page.

☐ Explain why oceans are the location and shape that they are.
☐ Summarize how water enters and leaves the ocean reservoir.

# 15.2 Formation of Oceanic Crust

**Key Concept:** Oceanic crust is composed of igneous rock that formed at ocean ridges at divergent plate boundaries.
The ocean floor is made of rock beneath the accumulated sediment. The deep ocean floor is made of oceanic crust.
This composition is in contrast to continental margins at the edge of the ocean, since these are made of continental
crust and discussed next. Oceanic crust is created as magma cools in a magma chamber, in dikes, and as erupted lava
at divergent plate boundaries to form a particular sequence of igneous rocks ❶. This structure making up the oceanic
crust is not visible on the ocean floor surface. Therefore, geologists initially identified the pattern by studying rocks on
the continent that they interpreted were part of ancient oceanic crusts ❷.

## ❶ Oceanic crust forms at ridges

Rock that composes the oceanic crust forms at ocean ridges at divergent plate boundaries
as the plates move apart and the magma cools. See 3.8 to review the processes at
divergent plate boundaries in the ocean.

1. Hot mantle rock melts, rises, and forms a magma chamber. The igneous rock gabbro forms as the mafic composition magma chamber cools slowly underground, forming the bottom of the oceanic crust.

2. Basalt dikes form where mafic magma moves upward from the magma chamber through cracks and then cools in place to form new oceanic crust.

3. Basalt lava that erupts from the dike into ocean water does not generally form long lava flows. It instead cools quickly and forms ball shapes called pillow basalt.

4. Sediments are deposited onto the ocean floor on top of the pillow basalt. These sediments slowly build up in thickness over time.

5. Ultramafic composition igneous rock, called peridotite, is the mantle rock beneath the magma chamber. Combined with the crust above, it makes up the oceanic lithosphere.

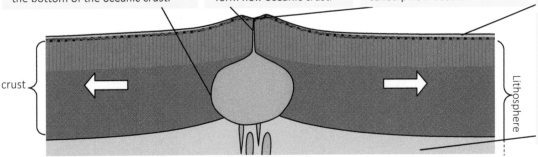

## ❷ Evidence

Geologists have learned the structure of the oceanic crust described above because, in
some rare cases at convergent plate boundaries, oceanic crust had been pushed on top of
continental crust where geologists can make observations of it. These sections of ocean
lithosphere on land are called ophiolites.

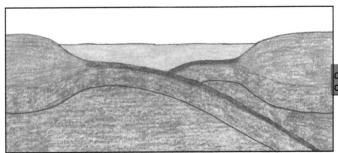

An ocean-ocean convergent plate boundary becomes an
ocean-continent convergent plate boundary but leaves some
oceanic crust on the same plate as the continental crust.

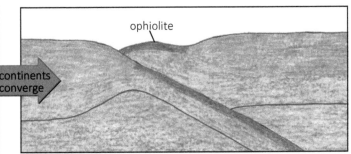

The small part of the oceanic crust is pushed upwards onto the
colliding continent as the plate boundary becomes a continent-
continent convergent plate boundary. These locations allow
geologists to study the rock that once made up the oceanic crust.

## Check
□ Describe the sequence of rocks that form the oceanic crust.
□ Summarize how oceanic crust may end up on the continent so geologists are able to study it.

# 15.3 Active and Passive Continental Margins

**Key Concept:** Continental margins are active if they are located on a plate boundary or passive if they are within a tectonic plate. Continental margins are the area offshore of a continent where ocean water covers continental crust **1**. A continental margin is made up of the continental shelf and continental slope. Continental margins can be classified into two types: passive margins are not currently on a plate boundary **2** and active margins are on a plate boundary **3**.

## **1** Continental margins

The deep ocean basin floor is composed of oceanic crust. In comparison, the continental margin is where continental crust composes the ocean floor. Continental margins have shallow ocean water above them compared to the deep ocean because the continental crust is thicker and therefore sits at a higher elevation. Continental margins are under water because of the current sea level, and they can grow or shrink if the sea level changes. The part of the continental margin that is next to land is called the continental shelf. The continental slope is the transition from continental crust to oceanic crust.

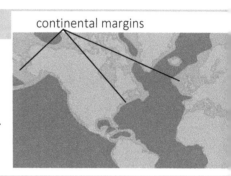
continental margins

## **2** Passive margins

Passive margins occur along the edges of continents that are not near a plate boundary. These wide margins tend to end on deep, flat ocean floor called the abyssal plain. Abundant sediments eroded from the land are deposited on passive continental margins. Passive margins are important for geoscientists to study because they are productive fishing grounds and locations where oil rigs can drill fossil fuels from the ocean floor sediments.

Continent: Not considered part of the margin because it is land.

Continental shelf: The shelf is covered by shallow water (usually less than 100 meters (300 feet) deep). On the East Coast of North America, a typical passive margin, the continental shelf is more than 120 km (75 miles) wide.

Continental slope: The slope is the continental crust that thinned when the ocean first formed as a previous continent broke up. Although it looks steep on the diagram, the slope of the continental slope is actually only about 4°, which is flatter than the steepest train tracks in the United States.

Abyssal plain: Not considered part of the margin because it is oceanic crust.

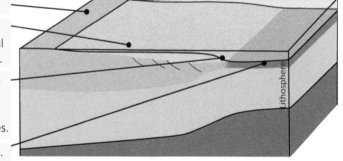

## **3** Active margins

Active margins occur where there is subduction, resulting in an ocean trench next to the margin. The shelf and slope tend to be narrower than those of a passive margin. Active margins are important for geoscientists to study because the convergent plate boundary can generate large earthquakes that can cause extensive damage due to shaking and tsunami.

Continent: Not considered part of the margin because it is land.

Continental shelf: The shelf is narrower than at a passive margin, and sediments are often transported off the shelf into the trench. On the West Coast of North America, the continental shelf is about 30 km (20 mi) wide.

Continental slope: The slope tends to be steeper than the slope at passive margins. It often ends in an ocean trench.

Ocean trench: Not considered part of the margin because it is oceanic crust.

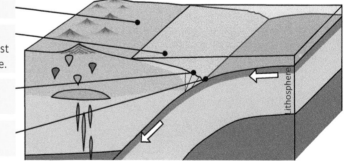

## Check

☐ Sketch the components of a continental margin.
☐ Compare and contrast a passive margin and an active margin.

# 15.4 Landforms on the Ocean Floor

**Key Concept:** The ocean floor is not flat but instead has many landforms. A variety of landforms is found throughout the world's oceans **1**. Ocean ridges, volcanic islands, and seamounts mostly form in the middles of oceans and are surrounded by the flat, deep abyssal plains. Ocean trenches are the deepest part of the ocean floor and are generally found around the edges of oceans. The continental margins are shallow ledges next to the coasts that slope down to the deeper ocean floor. These ocean floor landforms are created through different processes, many of them relating to plate tectonics **2**. Only the shallowest parts of the continental margins, right next to the coast, are related to the coastal processes discussed later in this chapter.

## **1** Map of the ocean floor

The ocean floor is any part of Earth's crust that is covered by ocean water, regardless of the type of crust it covers, although most ocean floor is made up of oceanic crust. The ocean floor has a variety of landforms, each created by different processes as described to the right. Environments throughout the oceans are very different, as illustrated by the two photos at the bottom of the page. Fish in sunlit, shallow water of continental margins are on the left. In comparison, an angler fish living in deep water where sunlight does not reach is on the right. The different ocean environments influence people in a variety of ways. For example, we fish and drill for oil on continental margins, we feel earthquakes created at ocean trenches, and our lives may be interrupted by volcanic eruptions on volcanic islands.

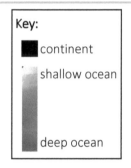

Key:
■ continent
shallow ocean
deep ocean

ocean ridge        continental margin        ocean trench        abyssal plain        islands and seamounts

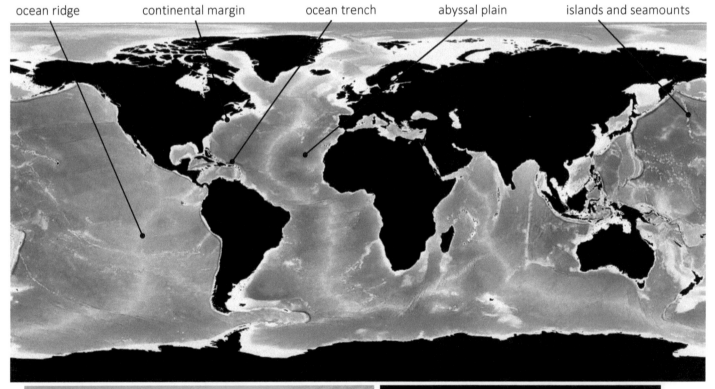

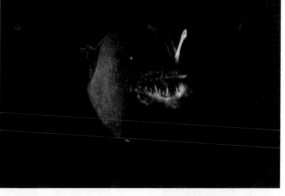

# ❷ Descriptions of ocean floor landforms

Each ocean floor landform can be recognized based on what it looks like, which give clues as to how it formed.

| Landform | What it looks like | How it formed |
|---|---|---|
| Ocean ridge | Long, rugged, higher area of seafloor. Example: Mid-Atlantic Ridge | At divergent plate boundaries, low-density lithosphere above the hot rising mantle is higher in elevation than the surrounding lithosphere (see 3.8). The ridge is made of newly formed ocean crust (see 15.2). |
| Continental margin (made up of the continental shelf and continental slope) | The flat, shallow part of the ocean next to the continent and the slope to the deep ocean Example: shallow water off of Australia | An ancient divergent plate boundary on land thinned the continental crust until the continent splits apart, forming the edges of an ocean (see 3.7 and 3.8). The continental slope is the thinned continental crust that transitions to oceanic crust. Sediments, particularly mud-sized sediments, transported by rivers on the continent are deposited in thick layers on the continental shelf (see 8.14 and 15.3). As sea level rises and falls through geologic time, different amounts of the continental shelf are under water. |
| Ocean trench | Long, very deep area of seafloor Example: trench off the coast of Indonesia | A subducting oceanic plate bends down beneath another tectonic plate at a convergent plate boundary creating a deep area on the seafloor (see 3.9 and 3.10). |
| Abyssal plain | Flat, deep seafloor Example: middle of the Pacific Ocean | Sediment slowly buries small landforms on the ocean crust, creating a flat sediment blanket (see 8.14). The sediments are very tiny, generally made up of dust from the atmosphere, mud from distant rivers, or microscopic shells. These microscopic shells come from single-celled organisms that live near the ocean's surface, and they sink to the deep ocean floor after the organisms die. |
| Volcanic islands and seamounts | Volcano on the seafloor; islands reach above sea level and seamounts do not Example: Hawaiian Islands | These form where volcanoes form on the ocean floor. A mantle plume results in hotspot volcanoes, and tectonic plate motion results in a chain of volcanoes (see 3.17 and 7.5). In addition, volcanic islands form at convergent plate boundaries (see 3.10). Seamounts occur if the volcano in either situation does not get large enough to reach the surface, or if it was an island that eroded below sea level. |

## Check

☐ Describe the characteristics of five different landforms on the ocean floor.

☐ Explain how landforms on the ocean floor formed.

# 15.5 DATA AND DIAGRAMS: Interpreting Ocean Floor Landforms

**Key Concept:** Profiles and cross sections can show landforms on Earth's surface and allow interpretations about how they form. These diagrams show two different views of the same ocean basin **1**. To create a diagram like this, geologists first need to interpret data collected by sonar on ocean ships to determine the shape of and depth to the ocean floor. They then use the theory of plate tectonics to interpret what these landforms are and explain how they form. Tips on how to read this diagram are below **2**. Use the questions to practice interpreting profiles and cross sections **3**.

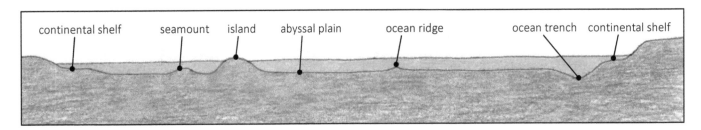

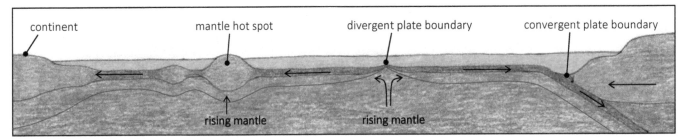

## **1** How to read the diagram

Analyze the top profile that shows the heights and depths of the ocean floor as if you were looking at it from the side. Compare the top profile with the bottom cross section that shows the interpretation of what is happening beneath the surface to form the different landforms.

## **2** An example of what you might

The characteristics shown in the profile are landforms making up the ocean floor. The ocean ridge in the middle of the ocean on the top profile is interpreted to be formed by a divergent plate boundary as shown in the bottom cross section.

## **3** Questions

**1. What is shown in this diagram?**
a. Ocean currents caused by topographic differences in the ocean floor
b. The view from above of an underwater river system
c. Landforms on the seafloor and explanations of how they form

**2. What do the arrows indicate?**
a. ocean currents
b. labels on the diagram
c. magnetic field direction
d. movement of rock

**3. If you wanted to explore the deepest part of the ocean, where would you go?**
a. divergent plate boundary
b. convergent plate boundary
c. hotspot in the ocean

**4. If you are exploring the floor of a new ocean, and you observe an ocean ridge, what interpretations can you make?**
a. There are two tectonic plates moving away from each other.
b. There are two tectonic plates moving towards each other.
c. There is a single tectonic plate over a mantle plume forming a hotspot volcano.

**5. What is the relationship between the top profile and the bottom cross section?**
a. The top is a map view from overhead and the bottom is a cross section.
b. The top is observations and the bottom is interpretations.
c. The top is zoomed out and the bottom is zoomed in to show detail.

# 15.6 – 15.10 Coastal Processes

In this section, you will learn that the variety of appearances of coasts are a result of the various processes shaping them. People use many techniques to try to protect what they build along coasts.

## Frequently Used Terms

The terms listed here are used repeatedly throughout this section, so by learning them before you read this section, you can focus your mental energy on the concepts presented.

**beach** A coast where there are sand- or gravel-sized sediments.

**coast** Land near the ocean.

**deposit** When sediments that were being transported are no longer moving and are left in place; deposition tends to happen when there is not enough transportation energy to continue moving the sediment.

**erode** To initially move sediments away from the soil or bedrock from which they weathered.

**longshore current** Movement of the water along the coast, parallel to it.

**transport** The movement of sediments.

The erosion of the coast in the Isla Vista area of Southern California has reached the point where buildings are no longer habitable.

# 15.6 Waves and the Longshore Current

**Key Concept:**  When waves hit the coast, they can cause a current along the coast that transports sediments.  As wind blows across an ocean, it forms waves at the surface. The waves slow down and become steeper as they move into the shallow water of the coast, eventually breaking on the shore ❶. One of the ways that waves affect a coast is by creating a current that transports sediments. Where wind-blown waves approach the coast at an angle, the water flows in a zigzag pattern along the coast, resulting in a current called the longshore current ❷. This current shapes the coast and landforms along it, as described in 15.8.

## ❶ Wave formation

Waves form at the ocean's surface as wind blows across the water. When the waves move into the very shallow water near the shore, they begin to drag on the bottom, slowing them down. They become narrower and taller until they eventually topple, or break, on the coast. Similar changes, although on a larger scale, happen to tsunami when they approach the coast (see 10.11). Where the waves drag on the bottom, they move sediment.

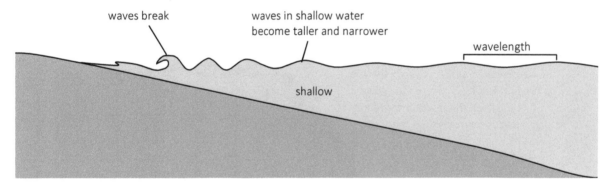

## ❷ Longshore current

Wind-blown waves that approach a coast at an angle create the longshore current that transports sediments along the coast, parallel to it. This current only affects the coastal environment and does not relate to deep ocean currents. You may have experienced the longshore current at a beach, either by watching people in the water drift past you or coming out of the water and finding that you are no longer near your towel.

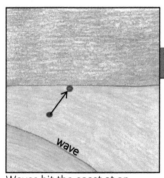

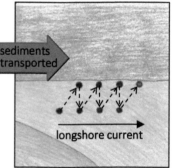

| Waves hit the coast at an angle, pushing the water transporting sediments up the beach at an angle. | When the wave recedes, the water and sediments are carried straight back down the slope of the beach. | The next wave again pushes the water and sediments at an angle. The water and sediments move in a zigzag motion along the coast. | The resulting longshore current transports sediments along the coast. |

## Check

☐ Contrast waves in deep ocean with waves as they arrive near the coast in terms of speed and height.
☐ Explain how the longshore current transports sediments.

# 15.7 Coasts and the Rock Cycle

**Key Concept:** Sediments are eroded from, transported along, and deposited on a coast as part of the rock cycle. Rivers weather, erode, transport, and deposit rock and sediments as part of the rock cycle, and coastal processes play a similar role **1**. Some coastal environments are dominated by processes related to waves. In comparison, there are other environments along the coast where the processes are strongly influenced by the flow of river water and the sediments carried by it **2**.

## **1** Rock cycle processes related to coasts

The movement of ocean water as waves can erode bedrock to create sediments or erode previously-deposited sediments. Ocean currents then transport those sediments and deposit them where the speed of the water slows down.

**Weathering and Erosion**
Sediments along the coast initially come from weathered and eroded bedrock on land. These sediments may be formed locally at an eroding cliff or formed distantly and transported to the coast by rivers.

**Transportation**
Sediments are transported along the coast by the longshore current, produced by ocean waves. This transportation results in sediments that are generally well-rounded. The energy of the waves transports and deposits only particular sediment sizes, most often the size of sand, so the sediments are well-sorted (see 8.9).

**Deposition**
After transportation, sediments are deposited where the current slows down, either along the beach or in deep water. If these sediments become sedimentary rock, they will typically form layers of well-rounded, well-sorted sandstone or shale, giving geologists clues to the ancient environment of the area.

## **2** Coastal environments

While some environments along the coast are being weathered and eroded, others are primarily environments of deposition.

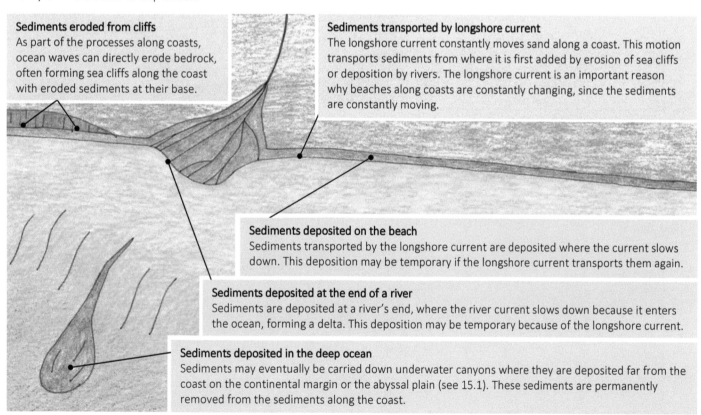

**Sediments eroded from cliffs**
As part of the processes along coasts, ocean waves can directly erode bedrock, often forming sea cliffs along the coast with eroded sediments at their base.

**Sediments transported by longshore current**
The longshore current constantly moves sand along a coast. This motion transports sediments from where it is first added by erosion of sea cliffs or deposition by rivers. The longshore current is an important reason why beaches along coasts are constantly changing, since the sediments are constantly moving.

**Sediments deposited on the beach**
Sediments transported by the longshore current are deposited where the current slows down. This deposition may be temporary if the longshore current transports them again.

**Sediments deposited at the end of a river**
Sediments are deposited at a river's end, where the river current slows down because it enters the ocean, forming a delta. This deposition may be temporary because of the longshore current.

**Sediments deposited in the deep ocean**
Sediments may eventually be carried down underwater canyons where they are deposited far from the coast on the continental margin or the abyssal plain (see 15.1). These sediments are permanently removed from the sediments along the coast.

## Check

☐ Explain how waves and the longshore current affect erosion, transportation, and deposition along a coast.
☐ Compare and contrast the environments in which coastal sediments are deposited.

# 15.8 Landforms at Coasts

**Key Concept:** **The landforms along a coast are mainly dependent on the balance between erosion and deposition.** As you may have noticed, coasts have a variety of appearances. Many landforms along a coast are a result of deposition of sediments. For example, landforms that result from the longshore current transporting and depositing sediments along a coast are beaches **1**, spits **2**, and barrier islands **3**. Deltas occur where large amounts of sediments are deposited where rivers reach the coast, and they extend out onto the continental shelf **4**. Other landforms along a coast result if there is more erosion than deposition. For example, sea cliffs often form as ocean waves erode bedrock **5**. In addition, along warm coasts where there are few sediments from land, reefs will grow in the clear water **6**.

## **1** Beach

Sediments deposited along a coast form a beach. A beach is stable if the input of sediments to the beach is the same as the output of sediments from that beach. The longshore current plays a large role in this balance, as it is the main mode of transportation for the sediments. Sand-sized sediments are deposited to form this beach in Australia.

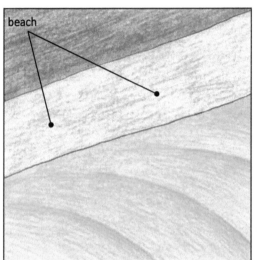

beach

## **2** Spits

Spits form where the coastline bends, and sand is carried away from land and deposited by the longshore current. The new land that formed juts away from mainland in the direction of the longshore current. In the photo, sand is being deposited as a spit off the coast in Alabama.

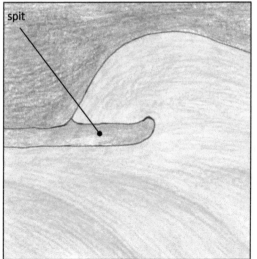

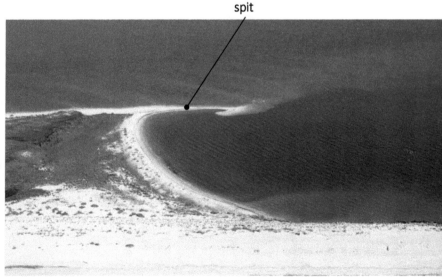

spit

# 3 Barrier islands

Barrier islands are long, narrow islands made of deposited sand that run parallel to the coast. They form near land on the continental shelf, where there is a large supply of sediments and where there is a strong longshore current. Barrier islands are popular places to build houses, despite being composed of easily eroded sand and being strongly affected by rising sea levels and large storms (see 15.9). In this photo of Dauphin Island, Alabama, the ocean is to the left of the barrier island, and the mainland is to the right and parallel to the barrier island.

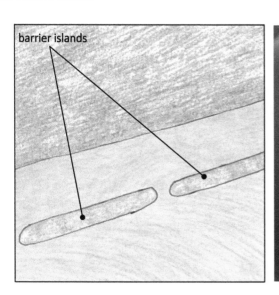

barrier islands

barrier island

# 4 Delta

A delta forms where a river deposits sediments on the continental shelf when it reaches the ocean (see 13.4). Deltas have many different shapes, depending on factors such as the amount of sediments deposited by the river, the amount of river water, and the strength of the longshore current. This delta in Kachemak Bay, Alaska, exists because a river from a melting glacier carries abundant sediments and deposits them where it reaches the ocean.

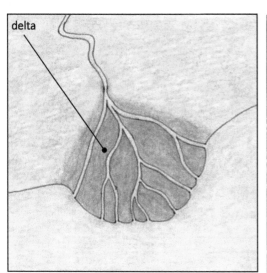

delta

delta

# 5 Sea cliffs

Sea cliffs form in areas where bedrock or sediments are being eroded by ocean waves. They often form where land has been raised through plate tectonic processes. These large cliffs of bedrock near San Francisco, California are being mechanically weathered by waves into smaller pieces, forming the beach in the foreground.

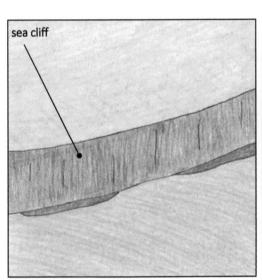

# 6 Reef

Under certain conditions, reefs may form along a coast. Reefs require a warm climate and clear water with few clastic sediments, such as mud. The shells of coral and other animals form large mounds, creating a coral reef. These growing coral and other animals create their shells using dissolved ions in the water. The photo shows Heart Reef, a coral reef that is part of the Great Barrier Reef, Australia. It is slowly growing in the clear, warm, shallow water, protecting the land from the full erosive power of ocean waves.

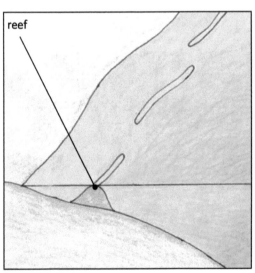

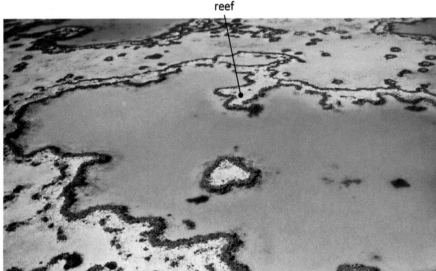

# Check

☐ List six landforms along coasts and describe how each of them forms.
☐ Compare landforms along a coast that form where there are abundant sediments deposited with landforms that form where there are few sediments deposited.

# 15.9 DATA AND DIAGRAMS: Barrier Islands

**Key Concept:** Before and after photographs allow geologists to make observations about how landforms change during an event. These two photographs were taken of the same barrier island off the coast of New Jersey before and after Hurricane Sandy in 2012. **1**. For photos like this to be most useful, geologists need to take photographs of areas well before a natural disaster happens, so they have something to which to compare the photographs taken after the event. Tips on how to interpret these photos are below **2**. Use the questions to practice interpreting before and after photos **3**.

May 21, 2009

November 5, 2012                    ≋USGS

## **1** How to read the diagram

When comparing two photographs, it is helpful to first determine the scale by looking at a scale bar or at a feature of known size. Next, make observations about the shapes of the features and landforms present. Finally, determine what changed, and make interpretations about what happened between the photographs.

## **2** An example of what you might interpret

The mainland is on the far side of the photo, and the size of roads and houses can help determine that the photo is about 300 meters (1,000 feet) across. The building the yellow arrow is pointing to and the bridge can be used as reference points to help with comparisons.

## **3** Questions

1. What do these photographs show?
a. a map of the changes resulting from a hurricane
b. the maximum height of the sea level because of a hurricane
c. how a barrier island changed because of a hurricane
d. the effect of sea level rise on barrier islands

2. What is NOT a clue for determining that this is a barrier island?
a. It is longer in one direction than another.
b. It has one side with ocean waves and the other with peaceful water.
c. It is relatively flat, with no large hills or mountains.
d. It has trees, roads, and buildings.

3. Which of the following is an observation, not an interpretation, made from these photographs?
a. The hurricane caused water to cross the island washing away houses and sand.
b. The island is a different shape in the before and after photos.
c. It will be difficult to rebuild the houses that were washed away.
d. It was mostly the water that caused the damage to the island, not the wind.

4. What can you interpret from the photos about what the barrier island is made of?
a. sand, because it is easily eroded by water
b. bedrock, because there are houses built on it
c. it is impossible to tell

5. What interpretations would be difficult to make about the hurricane damage seen in the second photograph if first photograph had not been taken before the hurricane?
a. that many houses were destroyed
b. that it is a barrier island
c. where sand was deposited and eroded
d. an estimate of the costs to rebuild

# 15.10 People and the Coast

**Key Concept:** People use a variety of techniques to try to prevent coasts, especially beaches, from eroding. Most coasts around North America are eroding, often due to direct or indirect actions of people **1**. Preventing erosion is particularly important where eroding beaches are endangering buildings, roads, and homes. One method is to preserve natural coastal plants and dunes that help prevent waves from permanently eroding beaches **2**. Additionally, barriers jutting into the water perpendicular to shore, called groins, can block the longshore current, resulting in sediments being deposited **3**. Walls built along the coast, called seawalls, can also prevent waves from reaching and eroding buildings and roads **4**. Finally, more sand can be added to eroding beaches **5**. Each of these techniques has advantages and disadvantages. When you visit a coastal area in the future, look for some of these techniques to prevent coastal erosion.

## **1** Shrinking beaches

Whether or not a beach grows or shrinks depends largely on the balance between the input and output of sand. Beaches are particularly vulnerable to shrinking, as compared to coasts with bedrock, because beaches are made up of sand that can be relatively easily eroded and transported. People, either through direct methods or via indirect consequences, are affecting the balance of sand at beaches, generally causing beaches to shrink.

| Processes that affect the size of a beach | How people affect this process |
| --- | --- |
| Coastal sand dunes are a source of sand for nearby beaches. Removing sand dunes decreases the size of a beach. | People trample or remove plants that hold sand in place in dunes, so dunes blow or wash away. People have also removed sand dunes by bulldozing them. |
| The longshore current erodes, transports, and deposits sand at beaches. Blocking the longshore current changes the pattern of erosion and deposition of beach sand. | People build barriers (such as groins) that slow down the longshore current, so sand deposits in one location but is eroded in another. |
| Small waves carry offshore sand onto beaches, and large waves erode sand, often depositing it in deeper water. Increasing the number and size of large waves decreases the size of a beach. | People build walls along beaches (called seawalls), and when waves bounce off of them, the waves erode more sand than without the seawall. In addition, climate change is causing more large storms that generate large waves that erode beaches. |
| Sand making up many beaches was initially transported to the coast by rivers. Decreasing the sediment carried by rivers to the coast decreases the size of nearby beaches. | People build dams across rivers, trapping sediments and preventing them from being transported to the coast. |
| The sea level affects the location of beaches and how much of them are under water. Increasing the sea level decreases the size of a beach. | Climate change is causing sea level to rise, flooding beaches. Beach sand would naturally migrate inland to keep pace with rising sea level, but in many places, people build structures that prevent the sand from doing so. |

## **2** Preserve coastal plants

Sand dunes protect the beach by preventing storm waves from completely eroding a beach and reaching buildings further inland. In addition, the sand in dunes frequently adds sand back to the beach if it erodes. Roots and stems of plants hold sand in place, so ocean waves are less likely to erode it away. The fences around these dunes in Rhode Island help preserve them by preventing people from walking on them and damaging the plants.

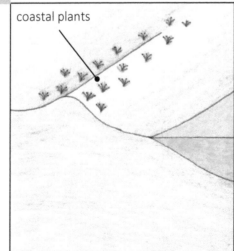

coastal plants

# 3 Build groins

Groins are barriers built to jut out from the coast to reduce the speed of the longshore current. Groins can be wood as shown in the picture or long piles of huge rocks. The slowed current deposits sand on one side of the groin, protecting the beach and buildings on that side. However, the longshore current picks up sand again on the other side of the groin, eroding the beach. This picture of a groin shows trapped sand transported by the longshore current on the right side and eroded beach on the other side.

# 4 Build a seawall

Seawalls are barriers built along a coast to protect the land behind them from erosion by waves. However, when large waves bounce off the seawall, they pick up and carry beach sand to deeper water. This increases the erosion of the beach in front of the seawall and around its edges. The beach in front of this seawall in Hawaii has been eroded away by waves hitting and bouncing off the seawall during storms.

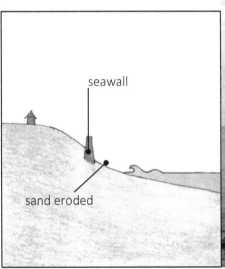

# 5 Add more sand

Adding sand increases the height and size of a beach. However, the protection offered by this increase is usually temporary because the processes that eroded the original beach continue to erode the new beach as well. This barrier island beach in New Jersey has new sand being added to it to make the beach higher and wider.

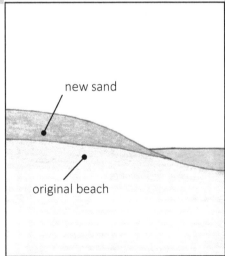

## Check

☐ Explain how four techniques for preventing coastal erosion work.
☐ Compare the advantages and disadvantages of each technique for preventing coastal erosion.

## End of Chapter Questions: Student Debates

For each of the following questions, determine which student you agree with and explain why.

**1. Two students are discussing how an ocean ridge forms.**

**Student 1:** Ridges form as two tectonic plates move apart and the rising hot mantle results in a high seafloor forming a ridge.

**Student 2:** Ridges are high seafloor, so I think they form as two tectonic plates come together and push the seafloor up forming a ridge.

**2. Two students are discussing Earth's crust at coasts.**

**Student 1:** Coasts are on continental crust. The sea level is high enough where oceans cover the low edges of continental crust.

**Student 2:** Coasts are the point where the crust changes from oceanic crust to continental crust. Oceans cover only the oceanic crust.

**3 Two students are discussing the cause of the longshore current.**

**Student 1:** Waves hitting the coast at an angle cause the longshore current. As a result, the direction of the longshore current depends on the direction of the wind that causes waves and the way the coast faces.

**Student 2:** Ocean currents crossing the deep ocean cause the longshore current. As a result, the direction of the longshore current depends on the location of the coast compared to the direction of the deep ocean currents.

**4. Two students are discussing analogies for a continental shelf.**

**Student 1:** A continental shelf is like a shelf on a wall. It extends out over the ocean floor in the same way as a shelf on a wall extends out over the house's floor. There is water directly above it and directly under it, until you reach the solid rock of the ocean-floor crust.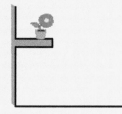

**Student 2:** A continental shelf is not quite like a shelf but actually more like a ledge that is part of a wall. It is made up of the solid ocean-floor crust. There is water only above it, not beneath it, since it is solid rock.

**5. Two students are discussing where sand at a beach forms.**

**Student 1:** Most sand on a beach forms on the beach, as ocean waves break pebbles on the beach apart.

**Student 2:** Most sand forms through weathering on land, and is transported to the beach long after it forms.

## End of Chapter Questions: Short Answer

Using your own words or sketching and labeling a diagram, answer the following questions.

6. Draw a table to compare 4 separate aspects of continental shelves and abyssal plains. Things to consider include formation, relative depth, crust type, and deposition of sediments.

7. Compare the relative abundance of 4 ocean floor landforms in the Pacific Ocean compared to the Atlantic Ocean. Explain how the common landforms present in each ocean are related to plate tectonics and how that affects their abundance.

8. Sketch two cross sections of Earth's lithosphere, one showing an oceanic trench and the other showing an ocean ridge. On the appropriate cross sections, label the following landforms: ocean ridge, ocean trench, abyssal plain, and continental margin. For each landform, use labels and arrows to explain how it formed by illustrating the processes involved.

9. Examine the maps of ocean floor landforms in 15.1 and 15.4. You are designing a submarine cruise for vacationers who want to experience a variety of landforms. Draw the path of your cruise and identify 4 locations where you would stop. Write a short description of each stop, identifying the landforms you would visit and why the landforms are there.

10. Two houses are built near two different coasts. House A has their coast eroding while House B does not. Hypothesize at least three distinct explanations why there is a difference.

11. A friend says "I have a house on the beach, and what I do to my beach is my own business because it affects me and no one else." Do you agree or disagree with your friend? Justify your response with at least 3 lines of supporting evidence.

12. A friend asks you for advice about whether or not she should invest in property on a barrier island. Respond to your friend, and support your response with 3 concerns or recommendations of actions to take.

**Hints:** For each question, see the sections listed here for information relevant to answering it.

**1.** (15.4) **2.** (15.3, 15.4) **3.** (15.6) **4.** (15.3, 15.4) **5.** (15.7) **6.** (15.2, 15.3, 15.4, 15.6) **7.** (15.3, 15.4, 15.5) **8.** (15.2, 15.3, 15.4, 15.5) **9.** (15.1, 15.2, 15.3, 15.4, 15.5) **10.** (15.6, 15.7, 15.8, 15.9, 15.10) **11.** (15.6, 15.7, 15.10) **12.** (15.6, 15.8, 15.9, 15.10)

# Chapter 16:
# Additional Surface Processes

## Chapter Objectives

When you are finished reading this chapter, you should be able to ...

• distinguish a variety of landforms associated with landslides, glaciers, and deserts and identify the processes that form them (16.1, 16.5–16.6, 16.8, 16.11–16.13, 16.16).

• compare the active geologic processes on the rocky inner planets and the resulting landforms (16.1–16.3).

• summarize how a variety of surface processes associated with landslides, glaciers, and deserts fit into the rock cycle (16.4, 16.10, 16.15).

• identify the causes of some surface processes associated with landslides, glaciers, and deserts and how they affect people (16.6–16.7, 16.9, 16.16).

# 16.1 – 16.3 Processes Affecting Planets' Surfaces

In this section, you will learn that geologists study the many processes that affect how the surface of a planet appears.

## Frequently Used Terms

The terms listed here are used repeatedly throughout this section, so by learning them before you read this section, you can focus your mental energy on the concepts presented.

**landscape** Shape of Earth's surface made up of bedrock and sediments.

**landforms** Natural features with a distinctive shape on Earth's surface, such as mountains, volcanoes, valleys, ridges, and trenches.

**surface process** The way that the surface of a planet is changed, such as lava flowing, impacts forming, or sediment being moved by wind or water; different surface processes create unique landforms, such as lava flows or impact craters.

Astronaut Buzz Aldrin's footprint on the Moon changed the shape of the surface in 1969. There are few surface processes that will erase those footsteps.

Chapter 16: Additional Surface Processes    Section 1

# 16.1 Surface Processes Overview

**Key Concept:** A large variety of processes shape Earth's surface. You may think of landscapes as having always been there, but Earth is continually being shaped by many surface processes **1**. In previous chapters we discussed how impact craters, volcanoes, mountain building, streams, and coastal processes affect Earth's surface. In this chapter, we discuss additional surface processes and the landforms that result when landslides, glaciers, and wind in deserts change Earth's surface. Although these processes are discussed separately, they frequently work together to shape Earth's surface.

## **1** Surface processes

Surface processes erode bedrock, transport sediments, deposit sediments, and otherwise move rock to modify Earth's surface. Each process does so differently, resulting in distinct landscapes. A few processes create new rock by rearranging atoms at the mineral level. However, most surface processes rearrange, modify, and move rock and sediments that already exist. How each process shapes the surface is described briefly here.

### Impact Craters
Meteorite impacts create holes, or impact craters, in the ground. They happen randomly everywhere. This photo of the Moon shows what a surface looks like when there are no other processes that change the surface. See 2.7 for more information.

### Volcanoes
Volcanoes build new bedrock and cover previous surfaces when they erupt lava flows like this one. Some volcanoes are so explosive they leave large calderas as massive holes in the landscape. See Chapter 7 for more information.

### Mountain building and faults
Mountains and faults tend to form at plate boundaries. Lithosphere is pushed up at convergent plate boundaries, forming mountains, which is where a lot of faults occur. See 3.9-3.11 and 9.10.

### Streams
Streams like the one shown erode down through bedrock to form stream valleys. They transport eroded sediments and deposit them within the stream valley or where the stream ends. See Chapter 13.

### Coastal processes
Coastal waves erode bedrock and sediments at sea cliffs. Coastal currents transport sediments and deposit them as beaches like this one or further out on the continental shelf. See Chapter 15.

### Landslides
Landslides like the one shown here erode slopes and transport bedrock and sediments downhill, depositing them near the bottom of the slope. See 16.4.

### Glaciers
Glacial ice erodes sediments and bedrock. After transporting them, glaciers deposit the sediments directly as shown or the meltwater deposits sediments. See 16.10.

### Wind in deserts
Wind does not erode bedrock as quickly as water or ice does. In dry climates, wind transports sediments and deposits them as sand dunes like these. See 16.15.

**Check**   Before you continue, you should be able to answer each check without looking at the page.
- ☐ List eight processes that shape Earth's surface.
- ☐ Describe how each process changes Earth's surface.

# 16.2 Surface Processes on Rocky Inner Planets

**Key Concept:** Planet characteristics affect which surface processes occur, which in turn affect what landforms might form.
As described on the previous page, there are many surface processes that may change the shape of a planet's surface. Each planet's unique characteristics determine what surface processes occur **1**. The rocky planets in our solar system each have a unique set of characteristics. Recall from 2.7-2.10 that a rocky, inner planet's size and distance from the Sun can help predict their particular characteristics. These characteristics determine the resulting surface processes and landforms **2**. For example, large planets, like Earth and Venus, have an interior hot enough for volcanoes and plate tectonics, while smaller planets are too cool (see 2.8). Larger planets have enough gravity to hold an atmosphere and have wind-formed landforms (see 2.9). Finally, the surface temperature, as determined by the distance from the Sun and composition of the atmosphere (see 2.10), affects whether there is surface water.

## **1** Processes and required characteristics

For each process listed in the rows, the required planet characteristics are indicated.

## **2** Planets and characteristics

For each planet listed in the columns, their characteristics, including the presence of an atmosphere, hot interior, and liquid water, are indicated.

### **2** Planets and characteristics

| Processes and required characteristics | Mercury — The small size results in no atmosphere and a cool interior. It has no liquid water. | Venus — The large size results in an atmosphere and a hot interior. It has no liquid water. | Earth — The large size results in an atmosphere and a hot interior. It has liquid water and ice. | Mars — The medium size results in an atmosphere and a cool interior. It has ice. |
|---|---|---|---|---|
| **Impact craters** Require a solid surface | Active | Active | Active | Active |
| **Volcanoes** Require a hot interior | -- | Active | Active | Probably not* |
| **Mountains and faults** Require a hot interior | -- | Active | Active | Probably not* |
| **Streams** Require liquid water on the surface | -- | -- | Active | --* |
| **Coastal processes** Require liquid water and shorelines | -- | -- | Active | --* |
| **Landslides** Require slopes such as mountains | -- | Rare | Active | Rare |
| **Glaciers** Require ice on the surface | -- | -- | Active | Active |
| **Wind forming dunes** Require atmosphere and sediment | -- | Active | Active | Active |

*These processes were active on Mars in its early history when it had a hot interior and liquid water on its surface. We can still see the landforms left behind by these processes.

## Check

☐ Discuss the relationship between the size of a planet and the surface processes.
☐ Summarize what surface processes occur on each of the inner, rocky planets (Mercury, Venus, Earth, Mars).

# 16.3 DATA AND DIAGRAMS: Aerial Views of Landscapes

**Key Concept:** Aerial views of landscapes allow geologists to make observations and interpretations about landforms **over a large area.** This aerial view is of Owens Valley in eastern California. Geologists made observations, applied their knowledge of landform appearance, and made interpretations of key landforms in the image, which are labeled. They can then interpret how a landscape formed, which can lead them to formulate hypotheses to test about Earth, such as the history of an area, resources present, and potential hazards **1**. To create a photo like this, geologists take pictures from nearby mountains, helicopters, airplanes, or drones. Tips on how to interpret this photo are below **2**. Use the questions to practice interpreting photographs of landscapes **3**.

glacially sculpted peak        alluvial fan        stream        glacial valley        volcano        mountains        desert lake        evaporite rocks

## **1** How to read the diagram

To view this aerial photograph like a geologist, make observations about the shapes of the features, and relate that information to what you know about landforms. It is important to remember that some landforms may result from processes that are no longer active in the area.

## **2** An example of what you might interpret

Features that have a long and winding shape are likely to be streams which indicate a flooding hazard. Features that are cone-shaped are likely to be a volcano, although it may no longer be active.

## **3** Questions

1. Which of the following observations of the photo is LEAST useful to identify surface processes occurring in this area?
a. The valley has a broad, flat bottom.
b. There are clouds over the mountains.
c. There is not much vegetation growing.

2. Where does water for the stream and desert lake likely come from?
a. water released from the volcano during an eruption
b. rainfall directly into the meandering stream valley
c. rain and snow melt in the mountains feeding mountain streams

3. Based on the observed landforms, what are three potential hazards for people in the area?
a. landslides, tsunami, volcanic eruptions
b. earthquakes, volcanic eruptions, floods
c. floods, hurricanes, rising sea level

4. Based on the observed features, what resources are most likely present in this area?
a. gold
b. salt
c. oil

5. If we use our observations to make interpretations about the geologic history of this area, how do we know that climate has changed?
a. there is evidence of glaciers and a bigger lake in the past
b. there is evidence of volcanoes and lava flows in the past
c. there is evidence of earthquakes along faults in the past

6. Which of the following is an active geologic process that is currently eroding and depositing sediment to form the landscape?
a. impact craters
b. mountain building
c. volcanoes
d. streams

# 16.4 – 16.7 Landslides

In this section, you will learn that geologists study the various types of landslides, determine why they occur, and figure out how to reduce the damage they cause.

## Frequently Used Terms

The terms listed here are used repeatedly throughout this section, so by learning them before you read this section, you can focus your mental energy on the concepts presented.

**debris** A general term for an accumulation of rock, sediments, soil, and plants; a debris flow is a landslide that occurs when debris flows like a fluid.

**landslide** All types of movement of bedrock, soil, or sediment downhill, including sliding land, flowing mud, and falling rocks.

**landslide scar** The mark on the ground's surface resulting from a landslide, both the location where the land started moving and the path along which it traveled.

This deadly landslide in Oso, Washington in 2014 changed the shape of Earth's surface and had a devastating impact on people nearby.

Chapter 16: Additional Surface Processes     Section 2

# 16.4 Landslides and the Rock Cycle

**Key Concept:** Landslides occur when rock and sediments are transported downhill and deposited as part of the rock cycle.
Recall from 5.2 that steps in the rock cycle include weathering and eroding rock to form sediments and transporting and depositing those sediments to become sedimentary rock. Weathering weakens bedrock, making it more likely to move downhill as a landslide because of gravity. This process of moving downhill transports the rock and sediments, and they are usually deposited where the slope becomes flatter **1**. Distinctive characteristics from each landslide help geologists interpret the details of the type of landslide **2**. The type often relates to why it happened.

## **1** Rock cycle processes related to landslides

After bedrock is weathered and therefore weakened, landslides can transport it down slope, usually over short distances.

| **Weathering and erosion** | **Transportation** | **Deposition** |
|---|---|---|
| Often physical and chemical weathering play an important role in weakening bedrock involved in a landslide. Rock and sediments begin moving downhill when the force of gravity is stronger than the resistance of the rock and sediments to movement. | Rock and sediments are transported downhill because of gravity, sometimes as solid blocks and other times as a mixture of water and mud. This process ranges from extremely fast, occurring in minutes, to extremely slow, moving over the course of decades. The next page discusses transportation in more detail. | When the rock and sediments stop moving downhill, often due to a gentler slope, they are deposited. The appearance of these deposited sediments will vary depending on the landslide motion and size of sediments. The next page discusses the appearance of landslides. If these sediments become bedrock, they will typically form layers of the sedimentary rock conglomerate. |

## **2** Landslide characteristics

Landslides have characteristics that result from the processes of erosion, transportation, and deposition. Different types of landslides will have different shapes and will not look exactly like the example here.

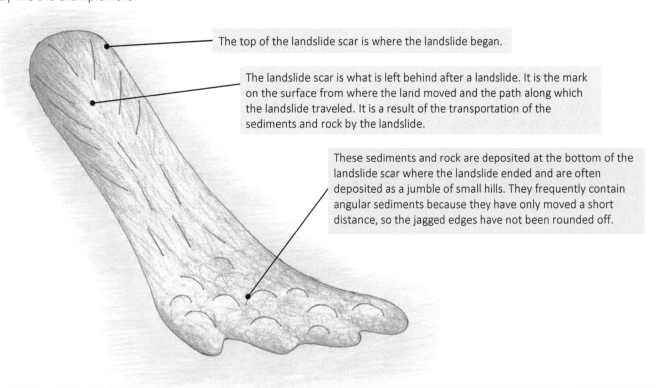

The top of the landslide scar is where the landslide began.

The landslide scar is what is left behind after a landslide. It is the mark on the surface from where the land moved and the path along which the landslide traveled. It is a result of the transportation of the sediments and rock by the landslide.

These sediments and rock are deposited at the bottom of the landslide scar where the landslide ended and are often deposited as a jumble of small hills. They frequently contain angular sediments because they have only moved a short distance, so the jagged edges have not been rounded off.

## Check

☐ Explain how landslides fit into the rock cycle, in terms of erosion, transportation, and deposition.
☐ Describe the landforms you would look for to identify a landslide.

# 16.5 Types of Landslides

**Key Concept:** Landslides are grouped by the type of rock or sediment involved and their downhill motion.

"Landslides" is used here as a general term for bedrock and sediment moving downhill, but there are different types of landslides depending on what is moving downhill and how it is moving. Falls, such as rock falls, occur when the motion is falling, bouncing, and rolling **1**. Slides occur when the motion of an entire block of land is sliding along a weak surface, with slumps being a special case if the surface is curved **2**. Flows occur when the motion is flowing, like a fluid **3**. Mudflows and debris flows are fast-moving flows. Creep is another example of a flow, but it happens so slowly that you cannot observe it. Although you may have pictured a landslide as rock and sediment flowing downhill quickly, landslides have a much greater variety of motions and speeds.

## **1** Falls

A fall is when rocks and sediments fall, bounce, and roll downhill. They often occur because weathering (both physical and mechanical, see 8.1–8.3) has weakened the bedrock along cracks. The free falling motion means that these are generally extremely fast. For example, it is common for falls to move 30 meters per second (70 miles per hour), although it can go even faster if it falls a long distance. Most falls are rock falls, where the main component falling is rock.

### Rock fall characteristics
Rock falls are commonly identified by boulders and jagged pieces of weathered bedrock piled up at the bottom of a cliff or steep rocky slope. It may be difficult to identify the landslide scar because the cliff is often already jagged, and the missing rock does not leave a distinctive shaped scar. This rock fall in Zion National Park, Utah in 2016 occurred after the slope was steepened by a road cut.

## **2** Slides

A slide is when rocks and sediments slide together as a coherent block downhill along a weak surface. Depending on what is sliding, slides can have different names, such as a landslide or rock slide. Slides range in speeds from slow to very rapid. Slower speeds are approximately 1 meter per year (3 feet per year, 0.1 inch per day) over many years, and faster speeds are approximately 1 meter per second (2 miles per hour) over just a few minutes. A particular type of slide is a slump, which happens when the land rotates as it slides because the weak surface is curved.

### Slump characteristics
Slumps are a particular type of slide where the land slides downward as individual blocks along a curved path from the top of the landslide. Therefore, the lower part of the block moves horizontally. Frequently this land that moves horizontally no longer remains as a single block, and the sliding motion changes to a flowing motion. The top of the landslide has curved cliffs, possibly with blocks of ground that have been tilted along the landslide scar below. The bottom is a jumbled, more fluid-like mass of deposited rock and sediments below the cliffs. This slump in Oso, Washington in 2014 shows the curved cliff at the top with land that slide intact with trees below it and jumbled and poorly-sorted sediment below that.

# 3 Flows

A flow is when rocks and sediments are generally mixed with water and flow downhill as a jumbled, fluid-like mixture. Depending on what is flowing and its speed, flows can have different names, such as mudflows, debris flows, and creep. Most flows are very rapid, with speeds often faster than 5 meters per second (10 miles per hour). This speed is faster than most slides and as fast as many people can run. In contrast, a very slow type of flow is creep. Creep occurs when sediments on the surface flow downhill so slowly that they move only centimeters per year (inches per year). Therefore, it would take creeping sediment years to cross this page.

### Mudflow and debris flow characteristics

Mudflows are made up of mostly wet mud, but frequently also include plants and rocks. Debris is a general term that includes rock, sediments, soil, and plants. Debris flows have similar characteristics as mudflows but are made up of less mud. Both tend to flow through and deposit in stream valleys leaving a narrow landslide scar where it flowed along the valley. The deposited sediments may spread out with multiple rounded edges if it flows onto a flat surface. This debris flow in Montana in 2014 occurred after a rainstorm and includes many branches, rocks, and other debris mixed with the mud.

### Creep characteristics

Creep is the very slow flow of sediments down a hill over the course of many years, happening so slowly that you cannot observe it without careful measurements. Although creep cannot be observed directly, its effects can be seen on vertical things in the ground. For example, trees that are in creeping soil have curved trunks because they continue to grow upwards as the slope moves. Other objects like fences or retaining walls that were originally vertical in the ground may tip at an angle as the soil creeps. This hillside shows curved tree trunks, indicating that creep is happening here.

## Check

☐ Summarize the type of motion, the speed, and the type of sediment or rock for each of three types of landslides.
☐ Describe characteristics that can be used to identify each of the three different types of landslides.

# 16.6 Causes of Landslides

**Key Concept:** Landslides often result when slopes are steepened, water is added, plants are removed, or bedrock is weakened. Landslides tend to happen in some areas more than others because of the characteristics of the land. For example, steeper slopes are less stable and more likely to slide **❶**. A large amount of water in the ground reduces friction in rock and sediments and adds weight, both of which increase the chance for landslides **❷**. More plants with strong roots result in fewer landslides because the roots hold sediments together and absorb water **❸**. Finally, weak ground, such as loose sediments or bedrock with cracks or weak layers, can more easily slide **❹**. As you will see, these causes of landslides directly relate to strategies to reduce their occurrences, as discussed next.

## ❶ Steepening slopes

Steeper slopes increase the chance of landslides because they reduce stability. Slopes can be made steeper naturally, such as when a stream erodes its banks (see 13.5), when plate tectonics raises mountains (see 3.9 and 3.11), and when ocean waves erode coastlines (see 15.8). People can also steepen slopes, such as by cutting into the side of a hill to build a road, as seen in this photo of a road cut in Colorado.

Stable                                          Not stable

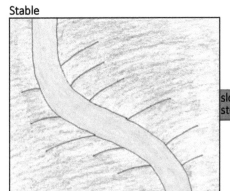
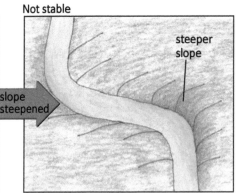

Rivers tend to erode the rock and sediment on the outside curve of a meander.

The steepened slopes are more likely to have landslides.

## ❷ Adding water

Water in pore spaces increases the chance of landslides by pushing sediments apart, which reduces friction, and by adding weight to the sediments. Over the long term water can also increase weathering, which decreases stability. Most water is added through rainfall and melted snow. This 2017 debris flow in Santa Cruz, California happened after a large amount of rain saturated the pore spaces with water.

Stable                                          Not stable

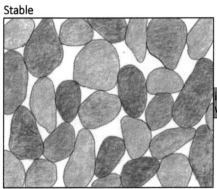
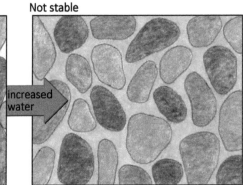

Dry pore spaces allow sediments to touch and increase friction.

Water in the pore spaces reduces friction by pushing sediments apart.

## ❸ Removing vegetation

Trees and other plants with large roots decrease the chance of landslides because roots hold soil in place and remove water from the ground. Removing vegetation can happen naturally, such as during a drought or fire, or people may remove vegetation by cutting down trees and allowing livestock to overgraze. This slope in Idaho was burned by a fire, making it more vulnerable to landslides such as debris flows the next time it rains.

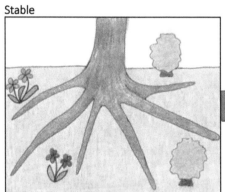

Stable

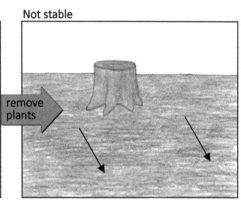

Not stable

remove plants

Tree roots hold the sediment in place and absorbs water.

Without roots, the sediments can move, and water remains in the ground.

## ❹ Reducing ground strength

Weaker ground has a higher chance of landslides. Sediments are weaker than bedrock, so they are more likely to move with gentle slopes. Solid bedrock is strong and will generally only move if the slopes are very steep of if there are weak areas within, such as what is caused through weathering along cracks. Weak layers in bedrock can also result in landslides if the bedrock slides along that weak surface. Layers containing abundant clay minerals are especially weak because clay becomes slippery when wet. The photograph shows strong sedimentary layers with weaker layers between them tilted in the same direction as the slope, which increases the chance of a rock slide.

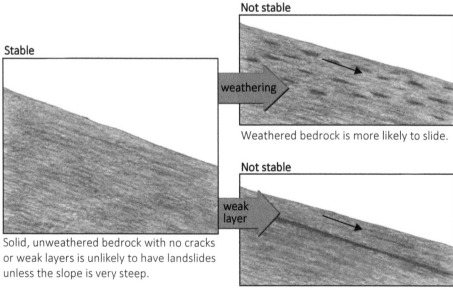

Not stable

Stable

weathering

Weathered bedrock is more likely to slide.

Not stable

weak layer

Solid, unweathered bedrock with no cracks or weak layers is unlikely to have landslides unless the slope is very steep.

The rock above a weak layer is likely to slide.

## Check

☐ Explain four causes of landslides.
☐ Discuss how natural processes and people's activities can each lead to landslides.

# 16.7 Minimizing the Effects of Landslides

**Key Concept:** The effects of landslides can be minimized by preventing their causes or reducing the effects they would have. After learning about causes of landslides in the last section, you probably will not be surprised about many of the ways to prevent them, since some landslides can be prevented by removing or reducing the factors that cause them. For example, slopes can be made less steep **1**, water can be drained from the ground **2**, plants can be added (or not removed) **3**, and the ground can be strengthened **4**. Another strategy beyond preventing landslides is to build barriers to protect structures from small landslides **5**. Although most large landslides cannot be prevented, they cannot cause damage to structures if we avoid building in areas with geologic conditions that make landslides more likely **6**.

## **1** Reduce slope steepness

If possible, reducing the steepness of an unstable slope may prevent landslides or reduce their chance of happening. The photo shows an area near a recent landslide in California where crews are working to reduce the slope of the hillside to prevent another landslide.

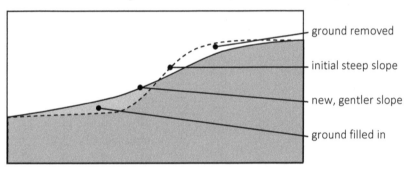

ground removed

initial steep slope

new, gentler slope

ground filled in

## **2** Reduce the amount of groundwater

Techniques that prevent excess water in the ground can help stabilize the slope, since water is a major factor for most landslides. The type of wall shown in the photo lets water through, so it leaves the ground. Water can also be removed from the ground with pipes.

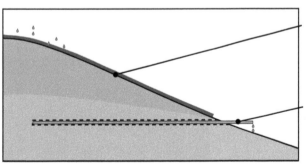

impermeable layer such as plastic or cement, so water cannot infiltrate into the ground

drain for water already in the ground

## **3** Add vegetation

On a slope with little vegetation, adding new plants that have extensive roots can help stabilize the slope preventing landslides. The area shown in the photo is being stabilized with newly planted vegetation.

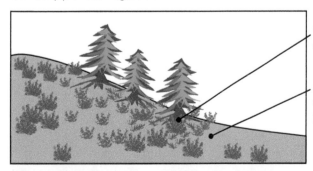

tree roots reduce the chance of deep landslides

small plants reduce the chance of the top sediment moving

# 4 Strengthen sloped ground

Methods to strengthen bedrock with many cracks or sediment can help stabilize a slope and prevent landslides. These methods include bolting unstable rock to underlying solid bedrock to hold it in place and cementing unstable rock and sediments to hold them together. The photo shows rock bolts stabilizing the side of a bedrock cliff.

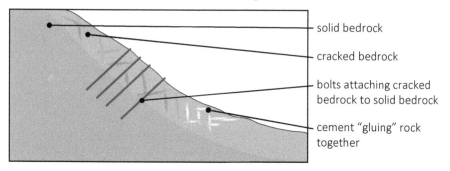

- solid bedrock
- cracked bedrock
- bolts attaching cracked bedrock to solid bedrock
- cement "gluing" rock together

# 5 Build a barrier

Walls, fences, and other barriers can protect structures from damage by small, frequent landslides. The photo shows workers installing mesh on a steep hillside next to a road.

- mesh attached to the slope to stop small rocks from falling

- wall that prevents rocks and small landslides from damaging the road and the cars on it

# 6 Do not live near landslides

Most of the techniques listed can reduce the chance of small- to medium-sized landslides from happening. The action of avoiding areas that are likely to have landslides is the only technique guaranteed to keep most people safe from very large landslides. Geologists can make maps of landslide-prone areas based on landslide causes (e.g. steep slopes and weak ground). Individuals can make their own decision about whether or not to purchase property in these areas, or, in some cases, a community can restrict building in landslide-prone areas.

Percent chance of a debris flow in selected basins in response to a 5-year, 30-minute rainfall of 43.4 mm (1.71 inches)

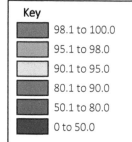

**Key**

| | |
|---|---|
| | 98.1 to 100.0 |
| | 95.1 to 98.0 |
| | 90.1 to 95.0 |
| | 80.1 to 90.0 |
| | 50.1 to 80.0 |
| | 0 to 50.0 |

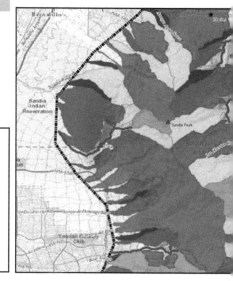

## Check

☐ Describe six ways to prevent landslides or minimize their impact on people.
☐ Explain why each of the six ways to prevent and minimize the impact of landslides works.

Ch 16: 3<sup>rd</sup> Section

# 16.8 – 16.12 Glaciers

In this section, you will learn how glaciers fit into the water and rock cycles and ways that geologists have determined how glaciers affect Earth's surface.

## Frequently Used Terms

The terms listed here are used repeatedly throughout this section, so by learning them before you read this section, you can focus your mental energy on the concepts presented.

**deposit** When sediments that were being transported are no longer moving and are left in place, such as when glaciers melt at their end and leave the sediment there.

**erode** To initially move sediments away from the soil or bedrock from which they weathered; after rock is eroded, the sediments are transported, such as by glaciers.

**glacial budget** The balance between the inputs and outputs of ice from a glacier; glaciers grow if there are more inputs than outputs, and shrink if there are more outputs than inputs.

**glacial till** Sediments deposited directly by glacial ice; characteristics of glacial till is that the sediments are not deposited in layers, have an angular shape, and are poorly-sorted (all sediment sizes).

**glacier** Ice on land that flows downhill due to gravity; it forms from snow.

**ice age** A period in Earth's history when the average temperature is a few degrees cooler than normal, resulting in extensive glaciers covering large parts of Earth's surface; the most recent Ice Age began about 2 million years ago and continues through today, although we are in a warm period within it.

**moraine** The landform made up of glacial till, often deposited at the end or sides of a glacier.

**transport** The movement of sediments; glaciers move sediments of all sizes

**sorting** A description of the variety of sediment sizes in one location; poorly-sorted sediments have a wide range of sediment sizes, whereas well-sorted sediments are all the same size (e.g., all sand).

These glaciers in Greenland flow downhill into the bay shown on the bottom left and are changing the shape of Earth's surface.

# 16.8 Introduction to Glaciers

**Key Concept:** Glaciers are masses of ice that flow on land through valleys or across continents. Glaciers are formed from compacted snow accumulated on land over thousands of years. Glaciers exist where this snow does not fully melt in the summer, so it compresses into ice. When it becomes heavy, it begins to flow downhill under its own weight because of gravity and is considered a glacier **1**. Glaciers can be divided into two categories based on their size and location. Mountain glaciers flow through mountain valleys **2**, while continental glaciers cover vast, continent-sized areas of land **3**.

## **1** What is a glacier?

A glacier is ice on land that flows because of gravity. Glaciers exist on land where it is cold enough for snow and ice to remain year round, either near the poles or high in mountains anywhere around the world. Layers of snow fall on a glacier and compact, recrystallizing into ice. If there is enough ice that it becomes heavy enough to flow, then it is considered a glacier. Glaciers flow slowly, with typical speeds of centimeters to a meter per day (inches to several feet per day). Therefore, it would take most glacial ice about a day to flow across this page. However, some glaciers flow ten times faster because of warm temperatures or the presence of meltwater under the glacier making the bottom slippery on the bedrock.

## **2** Mountain glaciers

Mountain glaciers flow downhill through mountain valleys due to gravity. They are long and narrow like the shape of the valley. Mountain ranges around the world, including near the equator, have mountain glaciers at high elevations where it is cold enough for snow and ice to exist year round.

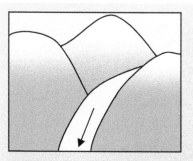

Glacial ice in a mountain glacier flows downhill along a valley, beginning in the mountains. The photo below shows the top of a mountain glacier flowing away from us and down a valley.

## **3** Continental glaciers

Continental glaciers cover large areas of land, and they flow by spreading outward due to gravity from a central thick part of the glacier. The large glaciers covering Greenland and Antarctica are the only continental glaciers on Earth today. However, during the recent Ice Age, a large continental glacier covered parts of North America.

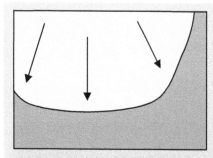

Glacial ice in a continental glacier flows outward towards edges. The photo below taken by a NASA astronaut shows Greenland covered by a vast continental glacier.

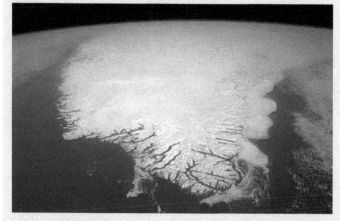

## Check

☐ Describe how a glacier is different than snow.
☐ Compare and contrast mountain glaciers and continental glaciers in terms of area covered, flow direction, and location.

# 16.9 Glaciers and the Water Cycle

**Key Concept:** In a stable glacier, the amount of ice added from snowfall equals the amount of ice removed in the water cycle. Water cycles through different reservoirs as part of the water cycle (see 13.1), and glaciers are the largest reservoir of fresh water. Water is added to the glacier reservoir as inputs **1** and subtracted as outputs **2**. If the outputs are larger than the inputs, the glacier will become smaller, and the opposite will cause a glacier to become larger **3**. The amount of snow and the temperature of the air are important to the balance of inputs and outputs, so the size of glaciers around the Earth is strongly dependent upon climate. Therefore, glaciers are good indicators of climate change (see Chapter 12).

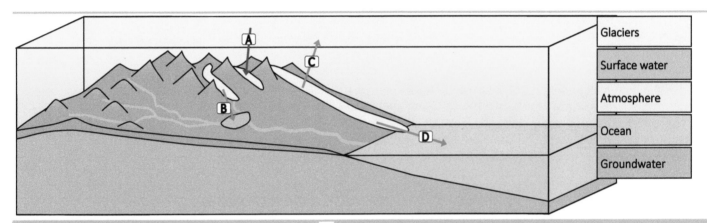

Glaciers

Surface water

Atmosphere

Ocean

Groundwater

## **1** Glacier reservoir inputs

As water moves through the water cycle, it enters the glacier reservoir primarily from compacted snowfall.

### **A** To the Atmosphere reservoir
Snow falls on glaciers. New snow layers compacts older, buried layers, causing the snow to recrystallize into ice without melting.

## **2** Glacier reservoir outputs

Water leaves the glacier reservoir in a variety of ways such as melting, sublimating, and breaking off.

### **B** From the Surface water reservoir
When glaciers melt, the water flows across the surface, forming streams. These streams can be important to people as a source of fresh water.

### **C** From the Atmosphere reservoir
Glacial ice can sublimate into the atmosphere, directly becoming gas.

### **D** From the Ocean reservoir
If glaciers reach the ocean, pieces of the glacier can fall off into the water, forming icebergs that slowly melt.

## **3** Glacier budget

Glacial ice constantly flows downhill, but glaciers remain the same size if the inputs to them at the top are balanced by the outputs from them at the bottom. Therefore, although the ice continues to flow downhill, the location of the bottom end of the glacier will change depending on the budget.

1919

2008

**Inputs versus outputs**
If there are more outputs than inputs, then the amount of ice in the glacier will decrease, and the glacier will become thinner and shorter. The bottom end will move back. In contrast, glaciers will grow and the bottom end will move forward if there are more inputs than outputs. The Toboggan Glacier in Alaska in the photos is an example of a shrinking glacier because the outputs are larger than the inputs.

**Glaciers and climate**
The glacier budget, and therefore glacier size, is sensitive to climate. The outputs from a glacier are largely controlled by melting that is affected primarily by the average local temperature. The inputs to a glacier are largely controlled by the local snowfall.

## Check

☐ Summarize where water comes from that enters the glacier reservoir and where water goes that leaves the glacier reservoir.

☐ Explain why glaciers grow, shrink, or stay the same size.

# 16.10 Glaciers and the Rock Cycle

**Key Concept:** Glaciers erode bedrock, and they transport and deposit sediment as part of the rock cycle. Similar to streams, glaciers erode, transport, and deposit rock and sediments as part of the rock cycle, although the processes and resulting landforms are different. Glaciers scrape along bedrock eroding it into clastic sediments. They transport all sizes of eroded sediments as they slowly flow, and they deposit the sediments where the ice melts and the glacier can no longer carry them **1**. The sediments created by moving glaciers vary greatly in size **2**. The resulting landforms created by glaciers are described in more detail in the following pages.

## **1** Rock cycle processes related to glaciers

Glaciers erode bedrock and may transport sediments of any size before depositing them when they melt.

| **Weathering and erosion** | **Transportation** | **Deposition** |
|---|---|---|
| The freeze-thaw cycle in areas with glaciers increase the mechanical weathering of the bedrock. Pieces of rock within a glacier may scrape along the bedrock, physically weathering and eroding it. As the glacier moves, some of the eroded sediments can be ground into very small mud-sized pieces, while other sediments may be larger sand, gravel, or boulders. | Glacial ice can carry sediments of any size, from tiny mud-sized sediments to large boulders. In addition to sediments they erode, glaciers also transport sediments from other sources, such as landslides that fall on them. Glacial ice is always moving due to gravity, so sediments in or on the glacier are continuously transported toward its end, as shown in the photo of a glacier below. During transportation the sediments generally remain fairly angular in shape because they do not rub against each other. | Many sediments are deposited at the end of the glacier, where the ice melts leaving them behind. Ice is strong enough to move sediments of all sizes, so the deposited sediments may include giant boulders as large as a house. Some sediments are deposited directly when the ice melts, but some are transported by melted glacier ice. |

## **2** Sediments deposited by glaciers

Geologists can identify sediments deposited by glacial ice because they have a unique combination of characteristics. They have an angular shape, are not deposited in layers, and are poorly sorted, ranging in size from tiny mud-sized sediments to large boulders because ice can carry all sized sediment. If these sediments become bedrock, they will typically form conglomerate with angular sediments, called breccia. Sediment deposited directly by glacial ice is called glacial till. The bottom photo to the right is an example of poorly-sorted glacial till. In comparison, melting glaciers may become streams that transport and deposit sediments. These sediments have the characteristics of stream-deposited sediments, with layers of well-rounded, well-sorted, sediment. If these sediments become bedrock, they will typically form layers of shale, sandstone, and conglomerate.

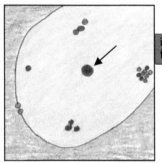
Flowing glacial ice erodes the bedrock forming sediments.

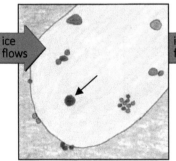
The glacial ice flowing downhill transports the sediments.

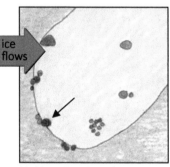
Melting glacial ice deposits the sediments where it melts.

## Check

☐ Explain how glaciers fit into the rock cycle, in terms of erosion, transportation, and deposition.
☐ Describe three characteristics used to identify sediments deposited by glacial ice or by glacier meltwater.

# 16.11 Depositional Glacial Landforms

**Key Concept:** Sediments can be deposited directly by glacial ice or by streams formed when the glacial ice melts. The sediments that glaciers erode and transport, will eventually be deposited. Where ice melts at the end of the glacier, the sediments are deposited as glacial till in a jumbled, poorly-sorted pile called a moraine **1**. Additionally, large boulders deposited in random locations by the melting glacial ice are called glacial erratics **2**. Instead of being deposited by the solid ice, the ice may melt and form streams that can transport and deposit sediments **3**. In the particular case where a large block of ice is surrounded by deposited sediments, the resulting depression in the ground after the ice melts is called a kettle **4**. Different glaciers will form different combinations of these example depositional landforms.

## 1 Moraine

Moraines form where glacial ice melts and leaves behind sediments carried by the glacier. Moraines are hills made up of glacial till that is poorly-sorted, and jumbled together. The moraine that forms at the end of a glacier is called an end moraine. There may also be moraines along the sides of a glacier, as shown in this photo from Washington.

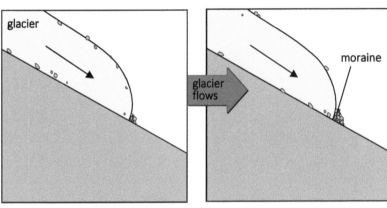

Ice carries many sized sediments as it flows.

The ice melts, depositing the sediments at the bottom ends or sides, forming moraines.

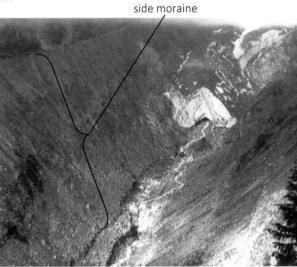

side moraine

## 2 Glacial erratic

A glacial erratic is a boulder left behind by a glacier when it melts. Erratics are frequently too big to have been transported by streams and are often a different type of rock than the local bedrock. Both of these factors indicate it was transported from elsewhere. The glacial erratic in the photo is in Minnesota now, but it likely came from bedrock in Canada.

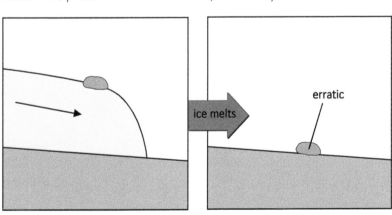

Ice carries a large boulder as it flows.

The ice melts, depositing the large boulder as a glacial erratic.

erratic

## 3 Sediment deposited by braided streams

Braided streams from melted glacial ice may deposit layers of sand and mud-sized sediments beyond the end of the glacier. As discussed in Chapter 13, braided streams form where streams contain a large amount of sediment. The photo shows Red Glacier in Alaska in the distance and glacial moraines at its bottom end. The valley in the foreground is filled with sediment carried there by the meltwater from the glacier.

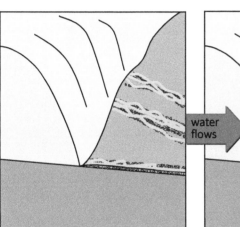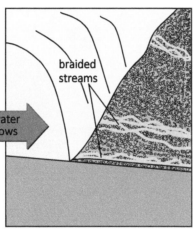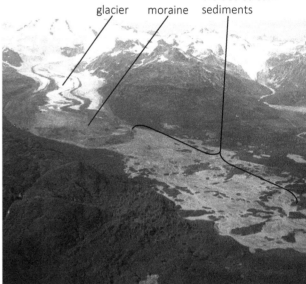

A glacier melts to become water that flows away from the glacier as a stream.

The stream transports and deposits sand- and mud-sized sediments.

## 4 Kettles

Kettles are holes or depressions that form where a large block of glacial ice breaks off the glacier. Sediments are then deposited around the ice, and when the ice melts, it leaves behind a kettle. If the depression is deep enough that it reaches the water table, it fills with water and is called a kettle lake. This photo shows several kettle lakes surrounded by sediments deposited by braided streams related to a glacier in Alaska.

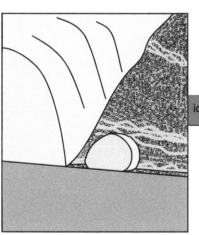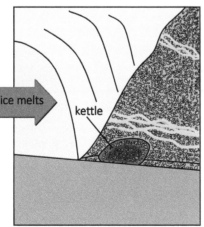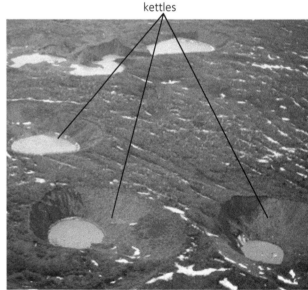

A large block of ice breaks off from the glacier. The area surrounding the ice is covered by sediments from braided streams.

When the ice melts, a depression called a kettle remains because no sediments were deposited there.

## Check

☐ List four landforms formed by deposition by glaciers and describe how they form.
☐ Compare and contrast landforms formed by deposition by glacial ice and glacial meltwater.

# 16.12 Erosional Glacial Landforms

**Key Concept:** Mountain and continental glaciers erode the land to produce a variety of landforms. Glaciers erode the bedrock as they flow, so they change the shape of the land. Both continental and mountain glaciers scratch the bedrock surface **1**. Continental glaciers cover large areas and tend to flatten landscapes **2**. Mountain glaciers tend to flatten valley bottoms and steepen the sides **3**. They also steepen mountain tops, forming jagged ridges and pyramid-shaped peaks **4**.

## 1 Glacial scratches (striations)

Pieces of rock at the bottom of glacial ice scrape along the bedrock, leaving scratch marks and grooves called striations. These glacial striations from Jasper National Park in Canada indicate that the direction of glacier movement was towards or away from the photographer.

## 2 Flat continent

Huge continental glaciers flatten landscapes through erosion, which tends to destroy existing stream valleys. These areas do not have a well-defined "downhill," so there are no well-connected streams to drain the land, resulting in abundant lakes. This flat landscape in Canada resulted from continental glaciers during cold periods during the last Ice Age.

## 3 U-shaped valley

When a mountain glacier erodes a valley, the rigid structure of the ice and the erosion on all sides carves a flat bottom and steep sides. This U-shaped valley in Glacier National Park in Montana was shaped by a glacier that has since melted.

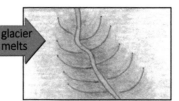

Streams erode valleys into a V-shape with a pointy bottom.　　A glacier flattens the bottom and steepens the sides into a U-shape.　　The glacier melts and the valley's shape is evidence for the glacier.

## 4 Horns and cirques

As mountain glaciers erode mountain tops, the resulting steep-sided, round-shaped basins eroded by the upper end of the glacier are called cirques. Several glaciers that forms cirques that are side-to-side around a mountain may carve sharp, pyramid-shaped peaks called horns. The peak of the Matterhorn in Switzerland is a horn surrounded by three cirques.

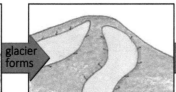

The mountain eroded by water is rounded.　　Glaciers erode bedrock, steepening the sides.　　The glaciers melt and the horn and cirques remain.

## Check

☐ List four landforms formed by erosion by glaciers and describe how they form.
☐ Compare and contrast the landforms formed by erosion by mountain glaciers and continental glaciers.

# 16.13 – 16.16 Deserts

In this section, you will learn why deserts exist, how they fit into the rock cycle, and surface features that are formed in deserts.

## Frequently Used Terms

The terms listed here are used repeatedly throughout this section, so by learning them before you read this section, you can focus your mental energy on the concepts presented.

**alluvial fan** A fan-shaped sedimentary landform formed where sediments are deposited when streams leave mountains and flow onto flatter ground.

**desert** An area with little rain fall.

**desert pavement** A flat surface of gravel formed where wind has blown smaller sediments away.

**playa** The area of a dry, temporary lake in a desert that repeatedly fills with water that evaporates away.

**sand dune** A hill of sand that is transported and deposited by wind.

A sand dune slowly migrates over the landscape as the sand is blown by the wind.

# 16.13 Introduction to Deserts

**Key Concept:**  Deserts are areas with little rain that frequently have bedrock, sand, or gravel at the surface. Deserts have distinctive characteristics compared to other environments because of the small amount of rain they receive, not the high temperatures **1**. Although uncommon, a few deserts are made up of sand dunes covering the bedrock. For sand dunes to form there needs to be a large supply of sand-sized sediments and steady wind that piles the sand into dunes **2**. In contrast, the surface of many deserts is made up of gravel-sized sediments or bare bedrock, where small mud- and sand-sized sediments have been transported away by wind **3**.

## **1** What is a desert?

Deserts are areas without enough rainfall to support the growth of most plants. In general, deserts have less than 25 centimeters (10 inches) of rain or snow a year. Deserts are defined by having low rainfall, so they can actually have a wide range of temperatures. Deserts may look different from each other, but they share certain characteristics that set them apart from other environments.

|  | Characteristics of Deserts | Characteristics of Other Environments |
|---|---|---|
| Plants | Low rainfall cannot support a large number of plants. | Trees, grasses, and other plants grow easily with more water. |
| Erosion | Lack of vegetation allows water and wind to easily erode and deposit sediment. | Plants play a large role in the way sediments are eroded and deposited, essentially eliminating the effects of wind. |
| Soil | Little chemical weathering and few decaying plants result in soils that are poorly developed and sandy. | More water allows chemical weathering and abundant decaying plants, which speeds up the development of fertile soils (see 8.5). |
| Bedrock exposure | Bedrock is more easily accessible, including to geologists. | Much of the bedrock is hidden beneath soil and plants. |

## **2** Sand dune deserts

Although sand dunes are often thought of as the typical landform in deserts, they make up only about one-fifth of desert surfaces around the world. Sand dunes form in a desert where there is an abundance of sand-sized sediments (see 16.16). Sand dunes have a variety of shapes depending on factors such as how much sand there is, the size of the sand grains, and the consistency of the speed and direction of the wind. Sand dunes cover the surface of this sand dune desert in New Mexico.

## **3** Non-sandy deserts

About half of desert surfaces are gravel surfaces. Wind blows away smaller sediments, such as sand and mud, and there is no source of sand or mud to replace them. Where this erosion occurs, it leaves behind a flat, wind-swept gravel surface. Other desert surfaces include bare bedrock, where the bedrock has no covering of soil or sediments on it, and sediments deposited by lakes and infrequent stream flow. This desert in Arizona is an example of a typical desert with gravel surfaces and exposed bedrock.

## Check

☐ Describe how deserts are different from other environments in terms of rainfall, plants, erosion, soil, and bedrock exposure.
☐ Compare and contrast sand dune deserts and non-sandy deserts.

# 16.14 Causes of Deserts

**Key Concept:** **Deserts form where dry air sinks, resulting in little rain.** You may picture deserts as forming exclusively near the equator, but that is actually not the case. Deserts tend to form where dry air sinks in the atmosphere, that results in a climate with little rainfall **1**. There are two main causes of sinking dry air. First, as humid air rises over a mountain, it cools, and the water falls out of it as rain. After going over the mountain, the air that sinks on the other side is dry, which results in a desert called a rain shadow desert **2**. Second, as Earth's atmosphere circulates in a consistent pattern, warm, humid air rises because it has a lower density than cold, dry air. The rising air cools, and the water falls out as rain. The resulting cool, dry air then sinks at 30° latitude north and south of the equator, resulting in latitudinal deserts **3**.

## **1** Deserts are caused by dry air

Deserts form in locations where the air is consistently dry for the reasons described below. Where this dry air sinks from higher in the atmosphere, the climate is dry, resulting in a desert. This global map of deserts shows deserts in red and pink, and dry climates are shown in in orange and yellow. Most deserts do not form near the equator because dry air is not consistent there.

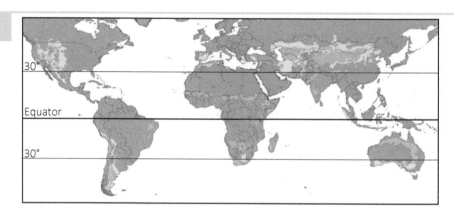

## **2** Rain shadow desert

Rain shadow deserts form where humid air rises up one side of a mountain range causing rain falls on that side. The dry air then continues over the mountains to the other side, resulting in a desert.

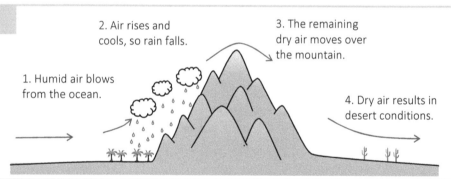

1. Humid air blows from the ocean.

2. Air rises and cools, so rain falls.

3. The remaining dry air moves over the mountain.

4. Dry air results in desert conditions.

## **3** Latitudinal desert

Latitudinal deserts result from global atmospheric circulation. Warm, humid air has a low density and rises at the equator, where it is hot. As it rises, the moisture in the air condenses and falls as rain, drying the air. Also, as the air rises away from Earth's surface, it cools. This cold, dry air has a higher density and sinks at 30°N and 30°S latitudes, resulting in deserts at these latitudes. Notice on the map above how most deserts are centered on these latitudes, not the equator.

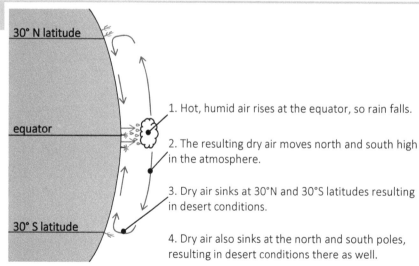

1. Hot, humid air rises at the equator, so rain falls.

2. The resulting dry air moves north and south high in the atmosphere.

3. Dry air sinks at 30°N and 30°S latitudes resulting in desert conditions.

4. Dry air also sinks at the north and south poles, resulting in desert conditions there as well.

## Check

☐ Explain why deserts form where they do around Earth.
☐ Compare and contrast rain shadow deserts and latitudinal deserts in terms of location and cause of formation.

# 16.15 Deserts and the Rock Cycle

**Key Concept:** Eroded sediments are transported and deposited by frequent wind and infrequent water in a desert as part of the rock cycle. Deserts have less water than other environments. Therefore, they are dominated by physical weathering that creates clastic sediments. These are transported and deposited in a variety of environments **1**. Landforms created by the deposition of sediments are mentioned on this page **2** but described in more detail in 16.16.

## **1** Rock cycle processes related to deserts

There is little water and few plants, so wind plays a larger role in deserts in the transportation and deposition of clastic sediments than in other environments. However, water is more effective at carrying sediment than air, so it is still an important factor in desert landscape formation.

**Weathering and Erosion**
Bedrock exposed at the surface is weathered and eroded. Water is needed for chemical weathering, so weathering in deserts is slow and dominated by physical weathering. These processes result in the formation of clastic sediments (see 8.1).

**Transportation**
Infrequent rainfall transports sediments, generally in temporary streams that flow through dry stream valleys. Water is rare, but when it does appear, it can transport a tremendous amount of sediments due to the abundant sediments present and the lack of plants to hold the sediments in place. Wind also transports sand- and mud-sized sediments, either by carrying them or by bouncing them along the ground (see 8.9).

**Deposition**
Water and wind deposit sediments in the desert, after they are transported. In both cases, the sediments are deposited where the water or wind slows down or where the water evaporates. Depositional processes are summarized below, but the characteristics of landforms created are described in the next page.

## **2** Sediments and the desert landscape

Erosion, transportation, and deposition of sediments create the landscapes we identify with deserts.

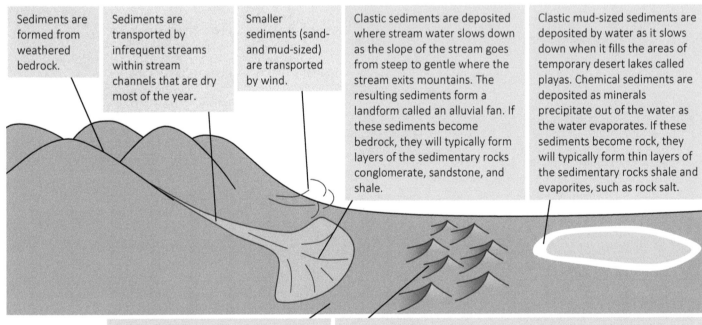

Sediments are formed from weathered bedrock.

Sediments are transported by infrequent streams within stream channels that are dry most of the year.

Smaller sediments (sand- and mud-sized) are transported by wind.

Clastic sediments are deposited where stream water slows down as the slope of the stream goes from steep to gentle where the stream exits mountains. The resulting sediments form a landform called an alluvial fan. If these sediments become bedrock, they will typically form layers of the sedimentary rocks conglomerate, sandstone, and shale.

Clastic mud-sized sediments are deposited by water as it slows down when it fills the areas of temporary desert lakes called playas. Chemical sediments are deposited as minerals precipitate out of the water as the water evaporates. If these sediments become rock, they will typically form thin layers of the sedimentary rocks shale and evaporites, such as rock salt.

Large sediments previously deposited and not transported away by wind form a flat gravel surface called desert pavement.

Clastic sand-sized sediments are deposited when wind slows down, forming sand dunes. If these sediments become rock, they will typically form the sedimentary rock sandstone with cross-bedding (see 8.12).

## Check
- ☐ Explain how deserts fit into the rock cycle, in terms of erosion, transportation, and deposition.
- ☐ Describe four landforms that result when sediments are deposited in a desert.

# 16.16 Desert Landforms

**Key Concept:** Many landforms are unique to desert environments. As discussed previously, sediments are eroded, transported, and deposited in deserts, by both wind and flowing water. Wind transports sand-sized sediments and deposits them forming sand dunes **1**. Wind also transports away small sediments, leaving behind larger sediments called desert pavement **2**. Where streams slow down as they leave mountains, they deposit sediments in a fan shape landform called an alluvial fan **3**. Slow-moving water in temporary lakes deposits mud and evaporates to form a landform called a playa **4**.

## 1 Sand dunes

Wind transports and deposits sand to form sand dunes. Dunes shift locations as wind continually transports and deposits the sand. The shape of these sand dunes in Death Valley, California can be used by geologists to determine information such as the dominant wind direction.

### Sediments
The sand sediments in dunes are well-rounded, because their jagged edges have been smoothed by the sand rubbing together. The sediments are well-sorted to be nearly the same size, the size the wind can transport. Deposited sand within dunes creates cross-bedding (see 8.12).

## 2 Desert pavement

Desert pavement forms where the sand- and mud-sized clastic sediments are transported away by the wind, leaving behind larger sediments. This desert pavement has a rock hammer for scale.

### Sediments
The larger gravel- and boulder- sized sediments are left behind, forming a mosaic of rocks that protect the ground from additional erosion.

## 3 Alluvial fans

alluvial fan          dry stream

Alluvial fans form where sediments are deposited as a stream valley exits mountains. Water slows down as it flows onto the flatter slopes, and it deposits many of the sediments it is carrying. This alluvial fan in Death Valley, California has a road going across it for scale.

### Sediments
Large gravel sediments are deposited first, and smaller sand-sized sediments are deposited further down the alluvial fan. In addition, debris flows through the stream valleys can deposit all sizes of sediments on the alluvial fan, adding to it. Alluvial fans create gentle slopes from the mountains as they build up over time. They are frequently shaped similar to deltas in water (see 8.15), but the sediments do not travel as far, so the sediments tend to be poorly-sorted and angular. Alluvial fans are sometimes quarried for gravel construction material because of their abundance of large-sized, loose sediments.

## 4 Playas

salty water          salt

Playas form where a temporary lake in a desert evaporates, leaving behind deposited sediments. Where valleys do not drain into the ocean, flowing surface water carrying mud-sized sediments and dissolved ions accumulates after infrequent, large rain storms. Water exits the lake by evaporating, leaving behind mud and precipitated salt minerals, as pictured.

### Sediments
Mud-sized sediments are deposited in the still lake water, and dissolved ions are precipitated out of the water to form evaporite minerals (e.g. the salt mineral halite) as the lake water evaporates (see 8.7). Periodic rainstorms result in repeated flat layers. Playas are frequently quarried for salts.

## Check
☐ Explain how sand dunes, desert pavement, alluvial fans, and playas form.
☐ Describe the characteristics of sediments in sand dunes, desert pavement, alluvial fans, and playas.

## End of Chapter Questions: Student Debates

For each of the following questions, determine which student you agree with and explain why.

**1. Two students are discussing the age of Earth's surface.**

**Student 1:** The surface is the outermost rock of Earth. A new surface can be formed by a variety of surface processes, so most of Earth's surface is younger than Earth itself.

**Student 2:** Earth formed 4.6 billion years ago, so all the atoms that make up Earth are 4.6 billion years old. Therefore, Earth's surface is 4.6 billion years old as well.

**2. Three students are discussing the speed of damaging landslides.**

**Student 1:** Landslides are when the land slides downhill. To slide implies speed, so all landslides are fast and dangerous.

**Student 2:** Landslides can be fast or slow, but only the fast ones cause damage. You can get out of the way of slow ones.

**Student 3:** Although only fast landslides are dangerous to people, slow landslides can damage people's property.

**3. Two students are discussing the motion of shrinking glaciers.**

**Student 1:** When a glacier is shrinking, there is more ice melting from the glacier than what is being added. As a result, the ice moves backwards, which is why the front of the glacier moves backward.

**Student 2:** Glacier ice is always moving downhill even if the glacier is shrinking. The front of the glacier moves backward because the end melts faster than new ice flows down to replace it.

**4. Two students are discussing how glaciers affect bedrock.**

**Student 1:** Glaciers scrape and scratch the bedrock they flow over. The ice and the sediments in the ice carve out U-shaped valleys by removing bedrock.

**Student 2:** Glaciers do scrape and scratch the bedrock, but they also metamorphose it because of their immense weight. The U-shaped valleys form because of the pressure of the glacier.

**5. Two students are discussing the location of deserts.**

**Student 1:** Deserts are located wherever the air is dry enough that it does not rain very much.

**Student 2:** Deserts are located where it is hot and dry, such as along the equator.

**6. Two students are discussing rock types in a desert.**

**Student 1:** Deserts have a lot of sand, which is sediment, so the predominant type of bedrock in a desert is sedimentary rock which then weathers and erodes to form sand.

**Student 2:** The sand in deserts only reflects what the area is like today. The environment was probably very different millions of years ago when the bedrock formed, so it can be any rock type.

## End of Chapter Questions: Short Answer

Using your own words or sketching and labeling a diagram, answer the following questions.

7. Imagine you discover a new planet. Determine five landforms you would look for to determine what processes are changing the planet's surface. Explain how you would identify each landform and what it would tell you about the surface processes happening on the planet.

8. Identify three surface processes that occur or have occurred in the area where you live or go to school. Explain how they are changing or have changed the surface, listing specific locations or observations.

9. Draw a table to compare and contrast at least four separate aspects of how landslides, glaciers, and deserts fit into the rock cycle. Things to consider include weathering, transportation of sediments, deposition of sediments, and resulting future sedimentary rock.

10. A friend says "Glaciers were larger in the past than they are today." Explain five observations of landforms you would make to determine if you agree or disagree.

11. Two towns are built in two different areas. Town A is more frequently and severely damaged by landslides than Town B. Hypothesize at least four distinct explanations why there is a difference.

12. Imagine you took this photo of a landslide. Write two hypotheses explaining why the landslide happened. To test your hypotheses, describe two observations you could make by visiting the landscape or data you could collect by reviewing historic records. Explain what the data or observations would tell you about your two hypotheses.

13. A friend has only seen pictures of deserts with sand dunes. Describe three other features you could find in a desert, and explain how each one formed.

**Hints:** For each question, see the sections listed here for information relevant to answering it.

**1.** (16.1, 16.2) **2.** (16.5) **3.** (16.9, 16.10) **4.** (16.10, 16.12) **5.** (16.13, 16.14) **6.** (16.15) **7.** (16.1, 16.2, 16.3, 16.4, 16.5, 16.8, 16.11, 16.12, 16.13, 16.16) **8.** (16.1, 16.3, 16.5, 16.11, 16.12, 16.16) **9.** (16.4, 16.10, 16.15) **10.** (16.8, 16.10, 16.11, 16.12) **11.** (16.4, 16.5, 16.6, 16.7) **12.** (16.4, 16.5, 16.6) **13.** (16.13, 16.15, 16.16)

**abyssal plain** Deep seafloor that is flat because it is covered by sediment. (Ch 15)

**alluvial fan** A fan-shaped sedimentary landform formed where sediments are deposited when streams leave mountains and flow onto flatter ground. (Ch 16)

**aquifer** Bedrock or sediments that contains enough flowing groundwater to be a useful source of water for people. (Ch 14)

**asthenosphere** The solid rock layer of Earth that moves and deforms because it is ductile (it bends rather than breaks); the asthenosphere is located under the lithosphere and includes part of the mantle. (Ch 3)

**atmosphere** The gases that form a layer above a planet's surface; the atmosphere is also called air on Earth, and is held next to the surface by the planet's gravity. (Ch 2)

**atom** The smallest unit into which elements, such as oxygen, carbon or iron, can be divided while still retaining their basic characteristics; atoms are composed of protons, electrons, and neutrons, and they bond together to form minerals. (Ch 2, 4, 8)

**basalt** Igneous rock that has the combination of a mafic composition and extrusive texture; it is dark-colored with small minerals. (Ch 6)

**beach** A coast where there are sand- or gravel-sized sediments. (Ch 15)

**bedrock** The rock that makes up the solid component of Earth's crust; every place on Earth has bedrock underneath it, sometimes exposed at the surface where you can see it and sometimes deep beneath soil, sediments, and buildings. (Ch 5, 8, 9, 11)

**bedrock structure** The feature in the bedrock, such as a fold or fault, that results from deformation. (Ch 9)

**biochemical sedimentary rock** Sedimentary rock formed from sediments created when organisms remove ions that are dissolved in water and bond them together to form minerals; an example is limestone. (Ch 8)

**bond** The attraction between atoms that holds them together; many bonds are created when an electron is shared or transferred between two atoms. (Ch 4)

**brittle deformation** Deformation that breaks an object under stress, such as shattering a glass. (Ch 2, 9)

**carbon cycle** The geologic model describing how carbon moves between reservoirs, through processes such as volcanic eruptions and breathing. (Ch 12)

**carbon dioxide** A gas, comprised of two oxygen atoms bonded to one carbon atom ($CO_2$), that makes up a very small proportion (0.04%) of Earth's atmosphere. (Ch 5, 12)

**carbon reservoir** Locations on Earth where there is a significant amount of carbon, such as in the ocean, in the air, in organisms, and in rock. (Ch 12)

**chemical sedimentary rock** Sedimentary rock formed when ions that are dissolved in water bond together to form minerals; an example is rock salt. (Ch 8)

**chemical sediments** Minerals that have precipitated out of water. (Ch 8)

**chemical weathering** Processes that break down rock through breaking or rearranging the bonds between atoms in minerals, resulting in dissolved ions or minerals that have a new composition. (Ch 14)

**clastic sedimentary rock** Sedimentary rock formed from clastic sediments that have been compacted and cemented together; examples are sandstone and shale. (Ch 8)

**clastic sediments** Pieces of rock created by the weathering of bedrock. (Ch 8)

**climate** The long-term average of daily weather conditions of an area. (Ch 12)

**coast** Land near the ocean. (Ch 15)

**compression stress** Stress caused by bedrock being pushed together. (Ch 9)

**contact metamorphism** Metamorphism that occurs when the temperature of the parent rock increases due to contact with nearby magma. (Ch 9)

**continental margin** The relatively shallow ocean floor near the coast where ocean water covers continental crust instead of oceanic crust. (Ch 15)

**continental shelf** Part of the continental margin next to the continent. (Ch 15)

**convergent plate boundary** A plate boundary where two tectonic plates are moving towards each other (converging); subduction occurs at convergent plate boundaries. (Ch 3)

**crystallize** The process of atoms bonding together in a specific, orderly pattern to form minerals that make up rock. (Ch 4, 5)

**debris** A general term for an accumulation of rock, sediments, soil, and plants; a debris flow is a landslide that occurs when debris flows like a fluid. (Ch 16)

**deformation** A change in shape of rock due to stress. (Ch 9, 10)

**density** The mass per volume, or the amount of something compared to the space it fills. (Ch 2, 3)

**deposit** (definition relating to sediments) When sediments that were being transported are no longer moving and are left in place. (definition relating to volcanoes) Anything that has been erupted from a volcano and left behind, such as pyroclasts and lava, creating a record of the eruption. (Ch 8, 13, 15, 16; Ch 7)

**depositional environment** An environment where sediments are deposited over time, rather than eroded away; different depositional environments have distinctive combinations of sediments and sedimentary structures. (Ch 8)

**desert** An area with little rain fall. (Ch 16)

**desert pavement** A flat surface of gravel formed where wind has blown smaller sediments away. (Ch 16)

**differentiation** The process during planetary formation when gravity pulled heavier elements in the melted interior of Earth and other large planetary objects toward the center, and light elements rose toward the outside because of differences in density; this process formed layers with different densities and compositions. (Ch 2)

**dip** The direction and amount that rock layers or a fault are tilted downward. (Ch 9)

**directional pressure** Pressure on rock that pushes more in one direction than another; often the direction of greatest pressure is caused by two tectonic plates moving towards each other. (Ch 9)

**discharge** The amount of water that flows past a particular point in a stream per second; it is often measured in cubic feet per second. (Ch 13)

**dissolve** The process of separating ions from a solid mineral and surrounding them with water molecules by breaking the bonds between atoms. (Ch 8)

**divergent plate boundary** A plate boundary where two tectonic plates are moving apart (diverging). (Ch 3)

**downstream** The direction in which the water is flowing in a stream. (Ch 13)

**ductile deformation** Deformation that changes the shape of an object under stress but does not break it, such as squeezing playdoh. (Ch 2, 9)

**earthquake** The shaking felt when the bedrock making up Earth's crust on either side of a fault suddenly moves and releases energy. (Ch 3, 10)

**ecosystem** The living organisms in a given area and their physical environment, which is influenced by the climate. (Ch 12)

**era** A division of Earth's history, such as the Paleozoic Era, Mesozoic Era, and Cenozoic Era. (Ch 11)

**erode** To initially move sediments away from the soil or bedrock from which they weathered. (Ch 15, 16)

**erosion** The initial movement of sediments away from the soil or bedrock from which they weathered. (Ch 8, 13)

**evaporation** When a liquid becomes a gas, such as liquid water becoming water vapor. (Ch 13)

**extrusive igneous rock** Erupted lava of any composition that cools quickly to form igneous rock with a texture of small minerals. (Ch 6)

**fault** A broken surface within rock, like a crack, where the two sides have moved relative to one another. (Ch 9, 10)

**felsic composition** The composition of magma, lava, or igneous rock that contains a high amount of silica, approximately 70% silica. (Ch 6, 7)

**flood** When there is too much water for the stream channel and the water spreads onto the floodplain. (Ch 13)

**flood control** Attempts to reduce or limit the negative impacts of floods. (Ch 13)

**floodplain** The flat land made up of deposited sediments that stream water covers when there is too much to contain in the stream channel. (Ch 13)

**fold** A bend or curve in rock that was initially flat. (Ch 9)

**foliated texture** A metamorphic texture in which flat or long minerals in a rock are aligned nearly parallel to each other. (Ch 9)

**formula** The relative amounts of different atoms that are bonded together, such as in the form of a mineral. (Ch 4)

**fossil** The preserved remains or evidence of a prehistoric living organism that died in the geologic past. (Ch 11)

**fossil fuel** Fuel—such as coal, natural gas, and oil—that formed from the remains of ancient organisms, such as plants and single-celled organisms. (Ch 5, 12)

**freeze** The process in which atoms that are not bonded together in a liquid bond together to form a solid which often occurs as temperatures cool, although rock freezes, or crystallizes, when the temperature is still very hot. (Ch 6)

**friction** The resistance of a surface to movement; surfaces that are slippery have a low friction while surfaces that are rough tend to have a higher friction. (Ch 10)

**geologic process** A natural occurrence that causes geologic changes; examples include volcanoes erupting, water moving sand, rock melting, and water flowing underground. (Ch 1)

**geology** The science that studies Earth and how it works—past, present, and future. (Ch 1)

**glacial budget** The balance between the inputs and outputs of ice from a glacier; glaciers grow if there are more inputs than outputs, and shrink if there are more outputs than inputs. (Ch 16)

**glacial till** Sediments deposited directly by glacial ice; characteristics of glacial till is that the sediments are not deposited in layers, have an angular shape, and are poorly-sorted (all sediment sizes). (Ch 16)

**glacier** Ice on land that flows downhill due to gravity; it forms from snow. (Ch 12, 16)

**global climate change** A sustained change in the world's long-term weather conditions. (Ch 12)

**global warming** The current global climate change that is caused by a global increase in temperature due to a more intense greenhouse effect. (Ch 12)

**granite** Igneous rock that has the combination of a felsic composition and intrusive texture; it is light-colored with large minerals. (Ch 6)

**gravity** The force that pulls objects toward each other's centers; for example, it is the force that pulls you toward Earth's center. (Ch 2)

**greenhouse effect** The absorption of infrared radiation by greenhouse gases in a planet's atmosphere; the absorption causes the planet's average surface temperature to be higher than it would be without greenhouse gases in the atmosphere. (Ch 12)

**greenhouse gas** A gas that traps infrared radiation (felt as heat) in the atmosphere, such as carbon dioxide and methane. (Ch 12)

**groundwater** Water that resides underground in pore spaces within bedrock or overlying sediments. (Ch 14)

**half-life** The number of years it takes for half of the unstable atoms to radioactively decay into stable atoms. (Ch 11)

**hardness** Referring to minerals, hardness is a physical property that describes how easily a mineral is scratched or how easily a mineral scratches something else; for example, a hard mineral scratches most other things while a soft mineral is scratched by most other things. (Ch 4)

**hazard** A potential event that has the possibility to negatively impact people; volcanic hazards generally involve lava, volcanic gases, and pyroclasts erupting out of a volcano. (Ch 7, 10)

**heavier elements** Elements are made up of one type of atom; atoms of heavier elements, such as oxygen (O), carbon (C), silicon (Si) and iron (Fe), have many protons. (Ch 2)

**high-energy stream** The stream's energy is its ability to transport sediments, with high-energy streams often being quicker, more turbulent, and more able to transport sediments. (Ch 13)

**high pressure metamorphism** Metamorphism that occurs at particularly high pressure relative to the temperature; it occurs in the subducting plate at a convergent plate boundary with subduction. (Ch 9)

**hotspot volcanoes** Areas unrelated to plate boundaries where magma erupts and volcanoes form. (Ch 3)

**ice age** A period in Earth's history when the average temperature is a few degrees cooler than normal, resulting in extensive glaciers covering large parts of Earth's surface; the most recent Ice Age began about 2 million years ago and continues through today, although we are in a warm period within it. (Ch 12, 16)

**igneous rock** The rock type that forms from magma or lava that cools and solidifies (crystallizes) into solid rock. (Ch 5, 6)

**infiltration** Water soaking into the ground from the surface. (Ch 13, 14)

**infrared radiation** Wavelengths of light energy that people cannot see but which we can feel the effects of as heat energy. (Ch 12)

**intensity** The measurement of the impact of an earthquake based on the amount of damage caused. (Ch 10)

**intermediate composition** The composition of magma, lava, or igneous rock that contains an intermediate amount of silica, between felsic and mafic compositions. (Ch 6, 7)

**intrusive igneous rock** Magma of any composition that cools slowly beneath the surface to form igneous rock with a texture of large minerals. (Ch 6)

**ion** An atom that has gained or lost negatively charged electrons, resulting in a negative or positive charge on the atom. (Ch 4, 9)

**iron-free silicate mineral** Minerals with primarily silicon and oxygen atoms that do not contain iron and magnesium atoms; they are generally light colored, and examples include quartz and potassium feldspar. (Ch 6)

**iron-rich silicate mineral** Minerals with primarily silicon and oxygen atoms that also contain iron and magnesium atoms; they are generally dark colored, and examples include pyroxene and olivine. (Ch 6)

**karst landscape** An area with landforms such as abundant sinkholes and few streams that forms as a result of groundwater chemically weathering limestone bedrock. (Ch 14)

**lahar** A volcanic mudflow created when ash and other pyroclasts mix with water from sources such as rivers, melted glaciers, or rain. (Ch 7)

**landforms** Natural features with a distinctive shape on Earth's surface, such as mountains, volcanoes, valleys, ridges, and trenches. (Ch 3, 15, 16)

**landscape** Shape of Earth's surface made up of bedrock and sediments. (Ch 16)

**landslide** All types of movement of bedrock, soil, or sediment downhill, including sliding land, flowing mud, and falling rocks. (Ch 16)

**landslide scar** The mark on the ground's surface resulting from a landslide, both the location where the land started moving and the path along which it traveled. (Ch 16)

**lava** Molten rock that has erupted on Earth's surface. (Ch 6)

**light elements** Elements are made up of one type of atom; atoms of light elements, such as hydrogen (H) and helium (He), have few protons. (Ch 2)

**light energy** Energy that may be radiated in a broad spectrum with different wavelengths. (Ch 12)

**lithosphere** The solid, rigid outer layer of Earth based on how layers behave under stress, made up of the crust and the top of the mantle; tectonic plates are composed of lithosphere. (Ch 2, 3)

**longshore current** Movement of the water along the coast, parallel to it. (Ch 15)

**low-energy stream** The stream's energy is its ability to transport sediments, with low-energy streams often being slower, less turbulent, and less able to transport sediments. (Ch 13)

**luster** A physical property of minerals describing how a mineral reflects light; many minerals have a glassy luster, meaning they reflect light and are shiny like glass; other minerals may have an earthy luster, meaning the mineral is dull, like dirt, or a metallic luster, meaning the mineral reflects light like a metal. (Ch 4)

**mafic composition** The composition of magma, lava, or igneous rock that contains a low amount of silica, approximately 50% silica. (Ch 6, 7)

**magma** Molten rock that is below Earth's surface. (Ch 3, 6, 7)

**magnetic field** This force, similar to a large magnet inside Earth, causes sensitive magnets to point north, like a compass; the magnetic field flips in opposite directions every several hundred thousand years. (Ch 3)

**magnitude** The measurement of the amount of energy released by an earthquake; the magnitude is the number most commonly heard in relaying the severity of an earthquake (such as magnitude 7.5). (Ch 10)

**mass extinction** The extinction of a large percentage of living organisms within a relatively short length of geologic time; most mass extinctions took fewer than 100,000 years to occur. (Ch 11)

**melt** The process of breaking bonds between atoms in a solid to form a liquid in which the atoms are not bonded together; melting is the opposite of freezing. (Ch 6)

**metamorphic grade** The amount rock has metamorphosed; low grade metamorphic rock has been slightly metamorphosed while high grade metamorphic rock has undergone significant metamorphism due to high pressures and temperatures. (Ch 9)

**metamorphic rock** The rock type that forms from a preexisting rock when its minerals change shape or composition, generally under high pressure and temperature. (Ch 5, 9)

**metamorphism** The processes that cause bedrock to transform into metamorphic rock, which involve changing the minerals or the texture, usually due to high pressure and temperature. (Ch 9)

**mineral** A solid with unique physical properties made up of a particular combination of atoms that bond together in a specific, orderly pattern and form through geologic processes; they are the components of rocks; examples include quartz and pyrite. (Ch 4, 5, 6)

**moraine** The landform made up of glacial till, often deposited at the end or sides of a glacier. (Ch 16)

**nebula** In space, a cloud made of mostly hydrogen and helium atoms with some space dust that may eventually collapse to form new stars. (Ch 2)

**nonfoliated texture** A metamorphic texture in which minerals in rock are not aligned parallel with each other. (Ch 9)

**numerical age** The age of a rock or event as a number (e.g., this igneous rock is 65 million years old); commonly determined by using radiometric dating. (Ch 11)

**ocean floor** Also called the seafloor, it is the bottom of the ocean. (Ch 15)

**ocean ridge** A range of undersea mountains; ocean ridges form in oceans at divergent plate boundaries. (Ch 3, 15)

**ocean trench** A long, deep depression on the ocean floor; ocean trenches form at convergent plate boundaries where subduction occurs. (Ch 3, 15)

**oceanic crust** Crust made up of the igneous rock basalt that is thinner and denser than continental crust. (Ch 15)

**offset** The distance the two sides of a fault move relative to each other. (Ch 10)

**Pangaea** The most recent of many "super" continents made up of all Earth's continents together as one; it formed when continents came together at convergent plate boundaries, and it broke apart due to divergent plate boundaries. (Ch 11)

**parent rock** The original rock before it was metamorphosed. (Ch 9)

**permeability** How well water flows through the pore spaces in rock; a rock with a high permeability allows water to flow through quickly. (Ch 14)

**physical property** Something you can observe with your senses, by seeing, feeling, tasting, or smelling. (Ch 4)

**planetary objects** Objects in the solar system that revolve around the Sun, including planets, their moons, and asteroids. (Ch 2)

**planetesimals** Objects roughly the size of a mountain range that once orbited the Sun and collided to form the planets. (Ch 2)

**plate boundary** The edge of tectonic plates where two plates touch each other; there are three types—convergent, divergent, and transform—defined by the motion of the two tectonic plates on either side of the boundary, each resulting in key geologic processes. (Ch 3, 5)

**plate tectonics theory** The scientific theory that describes the movement and interaction of segments of Earth's outer layers, called tectonic plates; this scientific theory explains many seemingly unrelated aspects of Earth's characteristics and processes, such as the locations of volcanoes, earthquakes, and mountains. (Ch 1, 3)

**playa** The area of a dry, temporary lake in a desert that repeatedly fills with water that evaporates away. (Ch 16)

**pore spaces** The empty spaces in rock or sediments; they are generally very small spaces between sediments or in cracks in rock. (Ch 14)

**porosity** The percentage of pore spaces that are in rock or sediments; higher porosity means more pore spaces. (Ch 14)

**positive feedback** A change in one thing that causes a change in something else, which increases the original change, resulting in continually amplifying the initial change; positive refers to the amplification, not that it is good or beneficial. (Ch 12)

**precipitate** When ions that are mixed with water molecules bond together with other ions and become large enough that they are no longer dissolved in water and separate from the water molecules as solid minerals; "undissolve." (Ch 4, 8)

**precipitation** Rain and snow. (Ch 13)

**process of science** The guidelines scientists use to do science; they include asking scientific questions; collecting, analyzing, and interpreting data to test scientific hypotheses; reaching consensus; and sharing results; the process of science is flexible and generally requires collaboration and creativity. (Ch 1)

**pyroclast** A fragment of lava and rock that erupts out of volcanoes. (Ch 7)

**radiometric dating** Determining the numerical age of a rock by using unstable atoms and their half-lives. (Ch 11)

**radioactive decay** To change or convert from an unstable atom to a stable atom through the process of releasing energy and/or particles. (Ch 11)

**recharge** The process of water infiltrating and becoming groundwater. (Ch 14)

**recrystallize** To break the bonds between atoms making up minerals and bond them again into a specific, orderly pattern, forming new minerals without melting. (Ch 9)

**regional metamorphism** Metamorphism that occurs across a broad region due to an increase in temperature and pressure, which happens at convergent plate boundaries. (Ch 9)

**relative age** The age of a rock or event compared to something else (e.g., this igneous rock is older than that sedimentary rock). It is determined by using relative dating. (Ch 11)

**relative dating** Determining the relative ages of bedrock and the sequence of events by using guiding principles of relationships between rocks and knowledge of how they form. (Ch 11)

**resource** Something that benefits people, such as materials and energy; many resources people currently use may eventually run out because they take millions of years to form. (Ch 5)

**river** Another word for a large stream. (Ch 13)

**rock** A geologic solid made up of minerals; the three rock types—igneous, sedimentary, and metamorphic—are categorized based on the way the rock formed. (Ch 4, 5)

**rock record** History of geologic events recorded in rock. (Ch 11)

**rocky inner planets** The planets closest to the Sun that have a surface made up of rock, as opposed to those further away from the Sun that have a "surface" made of gas. (Ch 2)

**rounding** A description of the shape of the sediment, where angular sediments have pointy or jagged edges or corners, and well-rounded sediments are more shaped like a sphere with rounded edges. (Ch 8)

**sand dune** A hill of sand that is transported and deposited by wind. (Ch 16)

**science** The process of answering questions about the natural world using specific guidelines that are often called the process of science or scientific method. (Ch 1)

**scientific hypothesis** A proposed explanation to a scientific question based on current knowledge of how nature works. (Ch 1)

**scientific question** A question that is answerable by science because it is testable with evidence, is logical, and can be used to make predictions. It is different than a philosophical or spiritual question. (Ch 1)

**scientific theory** An exceptionally well-supported, overarching explanation of how a part of nature works; a scientific theory is so well supported that it is accepted as an accurate explanation, which is unlike the way "theory" is used in everyday language. (Ch 1, 3)

**sea ice** Ice floating in the ocean formed from freezing ocean water. (Ch 12)

**sedimentary rock** The rock type that forms from sediments that form together into a new rock; sediments are pieces resulting from weathering of preexisting rock, either pieces of broken rock or pieces that form when dissolved ions bonds together. (Ch 5)

**sedimentary structures** Structures and shapes in sedimentary rocks that give clues to the environments in which they were deposited. (Ch 8)

**sediments** Pieces resulting from weathering of preexisting rock, either pieces of broken rock or pieces that form when dissolved ions bonds together. (Ch 13)

**seismic wave** Waves of energy created when an earthquake occurs; they can travel through Earth's interior as body waves (P waves and S waves) or along its surface as surface waves. (Ch 10)

**shear stress** Stress caused by bedrock sliding sideways or being skewed. (Ch 9)

**shield volcano** A large, flat volcano made from layers of lava flows that have a mafic composition and low viscosity. (Ch 7)

**silica** Silicon bonded with oxygen ($SiO_2$); silica is the primary ingredient of magma or lava and bonds together upon cooling to form minerals in igneous rock; the amount of silica varies with composition. (Ch 6)

**silicate mineral** A mineral with both silicon and oxygen in the chemical formula. (Ch 4)

**sorting** A description of the variety of sediment sizes in one location; poorly-sorted sediments have a wide range of sediment sizes, whereas well-sorted sediments are all the same size (e.g., all sand). (Ch 8, 16)

**stratovolcano** A medium-sized, steep-sided volcano made of layers of lava flows and pyroclasts of felsic or intermediate composition. (Ch 7)

**stream** Surface water flowing through a stream channel; the entire stream system includes the stream channel and the floodplain. (Ch 13)

**stream channel** A long, narrow low area where water flows downhill due to gravity. (Ch 13)

**stress** Pressure exerted on rock that may cause metamorphism on the atomic scale or deformation on the large scale; the different stress directions are compression, tension, and shear. (Ch 10)

**subduction** The process by which ocean lithosphere descends into the solid but slowly moving mantle beneath the lithosphere at a convergent plate boundary. (Ch 3)

**subduction-zone earthquake** An earthquake formed at a convergent plate boundary with subduction where ocean lithosphere descends into the asthenosphere; these plate boundaries tend to form the largest magnitude earthquakes which in turn often cause tsunami. (Ch 10)

**subsidence** The shifting downward of the ground surface due to the compaction of underground pore spaces. (Ch 14)

**surface process** The way that the surface of a planet is changed, such as lava flowing, impacts forming, or sediment being moved by wind or water; different surface processes create unique landforms, such as lava flows or impact craters. (Ch 2, 16)

**tectonic plate** A large segment of Earth's lithosphere that slowly moves as one large piece; each tectonic plate touches other plates at its edges, called plate boundaries. (Ch 3)

**tension stress** Stress caused by bedrock being pulled apart or stretched. (Ch 9)

**texture** The size, shape, and orientation of minerals in a rock; it does not describe how a rock feels when you touch it. (Ch 9)

**transform plate boundary** A plate boundary where two tectonic plates on either side slide past each other. (Ch 3)

**transport** The movement of sediments. (Ch 8, 13, 15, 16)

**tsunami** A series of large, broad ocean waves created by an underwater earthquake, volcanic explosion, or landslide. (Ch 10)

**turbine** A device, often a wheel or cylinder with blades around its edges, that converts energy from moving water, steam, or air into mechanical energy by spinning; the spinning motion is then converted into electricity. (Ch 5)

**unconformity** An erosion surface that is preserved in the rock record indicating there is time missing from the rock record. (Ch 11)

**uniform pressure** Pressure on rock that pushes equally in all directions. (Ch 9)

**unstable atom** An atom that does not last forever because its nucleus is not stable, so it converts, or radioactively decays, into a stable atom; for example the unstable atom uranium-235 radioactively decays into the stable atom lead-207. (Ch 11)

**vertebrate** Animal with a backbone, spinal cord, and head, such as fish, amphibians, reptiles, birds, and mammals. (Ch 11)

**viscosity** The resistance of a liquid to flowing, or the opposite of how runny something is; lava with a high viscosity does not flow well, while lava with a low viscosity flows quickly and far. (Ch 6, 7)

**visible radiation** Wavelengths of light energy that our eyes detect and we see as light. (Ch 12)

**volcanic gas** The gases erupted from a volcano, such as water vapor, carbon dioxide, and sulfur gases. (Ch 7)

**volcano** The location from which lava, pyroclasts, and gases erupt and accumulate; the resulting mountain-like formation from the buildup of lava and pyroclasts is also called a volcano. (Ch 3, 7)

**water reservoir** Locations on Earth where there is a significant amount of water, such as in the ocean, in the air, and in the ground. (Ch 13)

**water table** An underground boundary that separates pore spaces completely filled with water below it and pore spaces containing air above it. (Ch 14)

**weathering** The process by which rock is broken down at Earth's surface. (Ch 8)

**well** A hole dug in the ground to remove water from an aquifer. (Ch 14)

# Focus on Geology
## Kortz and Smay

Index

Printed in the USA
CPSIA information can be obtained
at www.ICGtesting.com
LVHW080249011223
765386LV00017B/345